EDINBURGH UNIVERSITY PUBLICATIONS

SCIENCE AND MATHEMATICS TEXTS 4

AN INTRODUCTION
TO THE PHYSICS OF
VIBRATIONS AND WAVES

NORMAN FEATHER FRS

EDINBURGH
At the University Press

© EDINBURGH UNIVERSITY PRESS 1961
One George Square Edinburgh 9

U.S. and Canadian Agent
ALDINE PUBLISHING CO.
64 East Van Buren Street, Chicago

Reprinted 1963

Printed in Great Britain
by T and A. CONSTABLE LTD., Hopetoun Street,
Printers to the University of Edinburgh

PREFACE

This book is intended as a sequel to *An Introduction to the Physics of Mass, Length and Time* (Edinburgh University Press, 1959). Much of its content could indeed have been included under that general title, for much of it deals essentially with matter in motion. A knowledge of the conditions determining the simple harmonic motions of particles is basic for many of the discussions, and the various theorems relating to the composition and resolution of such motions of necessity find wide application. The general concept of inertia is required, and, of the specific properties of bulk matter, those of elasticity (of solids, liquids and gases) and surface tension (of liquids) are all-important at various stages of the argument. All these topics were treated in the former book.

The decision not to include any systematic discussion of vibrations and waves was taken, when that book was written, after full consideration. Three reasons may be given for it. In the first place, to do justice to the new topics it was considered that they should be accorded wider scope than the previous title allowed. Secondly, whereas it was possible, and I still believe that it was desirable, to present the subject-matter of *Mass, Length and Time* without formal use of the calculus, to accept the same limitation in relation to *Vibrations and Waves* did not appear to be equally profitable—or equally possible. The third reason is of a different order. In modern sub-atomic physics the classical concepts of particle and wave, derived from our accumulated experience of physical phenomena at the macroscopic level, are seen to be related in a fundamental aspect of complementarity. In *Mass, Length and Time*, the classical concept of particles was formulated and elaborated. It was considered appropriate that the sequel, *Vibrations and Waves*, should be devoted to the formulation and elaboration of the classical concept of waves. It is clearly important that the beginning specialist in physics should have every opportunity of familiarising himself with these two concepts, in all their ramifications, as early as possible in his undergraduate career.

Mass, Length and Time was written largely as a record of lectures given, for many years, to first-year students of the University of Edinburgh, in the first term of their course in physics. The present book has no such pedigree. It was written without the prior experience of presenting the subject, in the flesh, to a living class. True, a course of lectures has emerged from the writing of it, but that is not the same thing as the other, in terms of practical experience. Indeed, I am acutely conscious of the presumption of offering, in print, a text which has not been fully tested in the lecture room. Only the first half of the course has in fact been delivered—for the first time, in the first term of the current session. The lectures were given to would-be honours students in the second year of their four-year curriculum. These students were the surviving members of a class which, twelve months previously, took its first steps in physics at the university with *Mass, Length and Time* as its guide. I feel that I owe the class both gratitude and an apology: an apology that I should have asked them, this year, to follow my unorthodox approach to the subject without the background security that a printed text automatically affords—and gratitude that they did so, and so fortified my own conviction that in this case unorthodoxy is not without its rewards.

Now, when the book has been written, when it is soon to be in print, I have other debts to acknowledge. Many friends and colleagues have read parts of it, in its formative stages. Their interest and criticism has been of the greatest value. Dr. M. A. S. Ross, Mr. R. M. Sillitto, and Mr. A. G. A. Rae are my chief creditors in this respect: I offer them my best thanks. I must also thank Miss D. E. Brewster. Over this volume, as over its predecessor, she has spent very many laborious hours, producing a fair typescript from a heavily over-written holograph.

NORMAN FEATHER

4 January 1961

attract anyone's attention is to throw a stone at him. . . . Another way is to poke him with a stick and this has quite a different character, because there is no transfer of matter from me to him —a small motion that I produce in the wood at my end turns into a small motion at his end' (*New Conceptions of Matter*, p. 29). In the fourth century BC, Aristotle had maintained that force cannot be communicated from one body to another except by impact or pressure. In a sense, then, Darwin's dichotomy, although it was not put forward as rigorously all-inclusive, was Aristotelian. But it is Aristotelian with this difference—that the modern view, that the 'small motion' takes time to travel along the stick from one end to the other, has complicated the picture. The final result of the poking may be a 'pressure' exerted through the stick, but the initial phase involves the propagation of a 'pulse' or 'wave' of displacement along its length. For many purposes even the modern physicist finds it convenient to ignore this phase and to use idealised concepts, thus in certain circumstances he treats his real bodies as 'rigid' bodies (see *M L & T*, pp. 7, 154): in this connection, however, he cannot afford that approximation—his real bodies are 'elastic' (see *M L & T*, chap. 16); if he did not recognise that fact he would be left with only the transmitted pressure, as the Greeks supposed.

The notion of wave processes transmitted through solid bodies did not, as we have seen, occur to the scientists of ancient Greece, but the ordinary Athenian—and the artisans of the Pharaohs, a thousand years earlier, in the valley of the Nile—were accustomed to observe waves on the surface of water ruffled by the passing of a boat, the dropping of a stone, or by the wind. By the agency of water waves force is communicated from one body to another without transfer of matter. So firmly has this attribute of an expanse of water in bulk become a feature of man's awareness that the familiar ripple-lines communicate their meaning unambiguously whether, as in an Egyptian papyrus, they stand as a 'determinative' modifying another character in the text, or whether, as in the Bayeux tapestry of the eleventh century, they constitute a directly pictorial element in the design. An expanse of water perfectly still, without any aspect of motion, is a formal abstraction; all around us the waters are in perpetual agitation, the most quiescent of them dappled with patterns of waves, ever breaking out afresh, spreading and dying through a long summer day.

CHAPTER 1

INTRODUCTION

In chapter 1 of *An Introduction to the Physics of Mass, Length and Time* (hereinafter referred to as *M L & T*) the attempt was made 'to set down some of the rules of the game' as they apply to the physicist. Here it is necessary to repeat only the first of these rules: 'Accepting the regularity of happenings in the inanimate external world, the physicist is prepared to find that every event in that world has some relation with—is partially determined by, or partially determines—every other event.' The common-sense experience of early man was the ground on which this expectation was originally based, and the more systematic investigations of professional physicists during the last four centuries have provided its overall justification. Countless situations have been recognised in which the physical behaviour of one piece of inanimate matter may be correlated with the behaviour of another piece of matter, allowing for a suitable lapse of time—short or long according to the circumstances of the case. Over the ages the notion of 'cause' or 'influence' naturally arose from these correlations, and the physicist has refined this notion, diminishing its philosophic content, perhaps, whenever he has been able to give it quantitative expression.

Nowadays, he uses the word 'wave' when he has in mind one particular type of process by which an influence reaches out or is transmitted from one body to another. This book is concerned with the physics of wave processes in general, and with the vibrations in which these processes originate, by which they are sustained, or ultimately dissipated. For the present we shall not define these terms more closely; it will be instructive to examine the origins of the concept of waves first, later to consider particular cases in detail, only then to come to generalities.

Writing in 1931, C. G. Darwin, at that time Tait professor of natural philosophy in the University of Edinburgh, pointed the distinction as follows: 'The most elementary way in which I can

A

CONTENTS

The air, too, is full of sound: a 'still small voice' in the wilderness, or a cacophony of noise in the city—sound born, echoing, dying away in the distance. A Roman architect, a decade or two before the birth of Christ, likened this process to the spreading of ripples on the surface of water. His inspired guess made no impact on his contemporaries: for a millennium and a half it remained a dead letter in a monks' library (see p. 112).

Through these many centuries Aristotle's physics dominated the schoolroom, becoming ever more ineffectual and distorted, circumscribed by the dogmatic metaphysics of the schoolmen. The beginnings of revolt were slow in breaking, and at first made little headway; then, with Galileo, they burst in full flood (see *M L & T*, p. 120). Galileo was an experimenter of genius, and the phenomena of sound occupied him over many years. In the end he was in no doubt: sound, he said, is propagated through the air as a wave process. The analogy with ripples on the surface of water was implicit in his use of language.

With Galileo the thraldom of science to scholasticism was broken: Descartes (1596-1650), thirty-two years his junior, attempted single-handed to construct a speculative philosophy which should replace its metaphysic. History has judged the system which he devised to be a failure, but this was a later verdict: it remained a potent influence on thought for more than a century. It was conceived out of acute dissent from the philosophy of the ancients, but it retained at least one feature of Aristotle's world: force could be communicated only by impact or by pressure. So, empty space became a 'plenum', the locus of mechanical process of great complexity. In so grand a cosmology, light, our only messenger from the heavens, necessarily held a central place; sound, a purely mundane manifestation, raised problems which were too trivial for detailed consideration. Light was conceived as propagated by pressure, instantaneously: the symbol of the stick recurred—the sighted are able to appreciate the pressure which is light, the blind have to feel their way with a stick, by pressure also. The notion of waves does not occur throughout the system as a whole.

In the Cartesian philosophy force is communicated only by impact or by pressure, but the emphasis is heavily on the latter mode. When space is completely filled with matter, albeit of different degrees of tenuity, the simple notion of impact loses its clarity. A contemporary of Descartes, Pierre Gassendi (1592-1655), equally anti-scholastic in his outlook, took the opposite view: for him space was entirely empty except for the unchangeable atoms of matter—there were impacts, but there was no sustained pressure. We recognise in this view the beginnings of the modern approach, but Gassendi could say nothing about light: his was but a partial cosmology, which Newton accepted as a working hypothesis and built upon, but the philosophers largely disregarded it for its obvious limitations. Its ultimate champion was Roger Joseph Boscovich (1711-1787), more than a century later. In Boscovich's world even the unchangeable atoms were de-materialised to become mere centres of force. It is a strange commentary on the fate of fundamental ideas in science that so downright an experimenter as Michael Faraday (1791-1867) should have been sympathetic to this extreme viewpoint, and should have commended it to his readers, in 1844, as still worthy of serious attention.

In his old age Galileo had set down on paper his considered views on the science which had been his life's work. In 1638 his book was published under the title *Dialogues on the New Sciences*. There, for the first time, the propagation of sound was recognised, by a physicist of genius, as involving a wave process in a medium. We have referred already to the break with tradition that Galileo made absolute. After him there was no turning back. The seventeenth century of our era has often been called the century of genius. We may single out four men, two physicists and two philosophers, all of them born within the one decade before Galileo's book was published, who carried his views on wave motion forward, ahead of their time. The physicists were Christiaan Huygens (1629-1695) and Robert Hooke (1635-1703), the philosophers Nicolas de Malebranche (1638-1715) and Ignace Gaston Pardies (1636-1673). The philosophers were Cartesians by discipline and by inclination, but in this matter they renounced the doctrine of their master. To Pardies, the older of the two, the credit of priority probably belongs of maintaining that light is not transmitted instantaneously, but that rather its velocity is finite, and that it is a wave process propagated in a medium. Pardies did not need to renounce Cartesianism to postulate the existence of an all-pervasive medium, or ether: Descartes's plenum provided precedent enough for that.

Of the views of the physicists, Huygens and Hooke, we shall have much to say in the proper place (see, in particular, p. 179). Here we take note of them merely as, first among their scientific fellows, joint proponents of the wave picture in relation to light. Of the philosopher de Malebranche, who was admitted an honorary member of the Académie des Sciences in Paris at the age of sixty-one, it is sufficient to note that in the same year he was the first to point out clearly that in a wave process the amplitude of particle displacement is the physical quantity determining the intensity of the effect produced when the wave is incident on a 'receiver'.

In the seventeenth century Isaac Newton (1642-1727) was, by common consent, the towering genius among men of science in Britain. Newton was the first to obtain, though by intuitive rather than by rigorous methods, an expression for the velocity of propagation of surface waves on shallow water, when the effect of gravity determines the motion (see p. 165). He was likewise the first to obtain an expression for the velocity of elastic waves in a material medium (see p. 114). In view of his contributions to the theory of wave motion in these two particulars, it is at first sight surprising that he should have been so resistant to the view that light, which exhibits so many features in common with sound, is essentially and simply a wave process of some kind, also. It is surprising, at first sight—but the question is a subtle one, and two long chapters of this book (chapters 8 and 9) have been found necessary to treat of its subtleties. In the end, though we cannot justifiably read into Newton's caution any valid foresight of what was to come, we can hardly fail to recognise that his ultimate position in respect of the nature of light was one of dualism, very much as that of the twentieth-century physicist is dualist.

Furnished as they were, through the labours of Newton and Leibnitz (1646-1716), with the tool of the calculus, the mathematicians of the eighteenth century made great advances in the theory of vibrations, but they were less successful with the theory of waves. For the most part, the phenomena of light were described and interpreted in terms of an emission hypothesis, theorists and experimenters alike adopting a point of view more narrowly corpuscular than that which Newton had formulated. Even in relation to the phenomena of sound, doubts arose concerning the adequacy of an explanation in terms of waves. A quotation from a standard text of the mid-century, *Leçons de physique expérimentale* written by l'Abbé Nollet (1700-1770), member of the Académie des Sciences and fellow of the Royal Society, will serve to illustrate these doubts. Nollet wrote (2nd edn., vol. 3, 1750) 'No one has any difficulty in understanding how it is that two bodies, acting as sources of sound, execute their vibrations independently. . . . But how is it that two different notes can be present at the same time in the same air, if the notes themselves are not, in the air, vibrations of a definite frequency, as they are in the sounding bodies; how can the same mass of air reproduce faithfully, at one and the same time, the notes of two strings, one the octave of the other? . . . [It has been thought valid to answer this question] by comparing the motion of the air which transmits these sounds to the circular waves which are produced in still water when stones are thrown in. It is said that the air accepts the different notes together, and transmits them without confusion to the hearer, just as the expanding waves cross one another without loss of identity and spread outwards to the water's edge. But . . . even this comparison is defective, and almost every point of similarity disappears when the character of the respective motions is analysed in detail.' Next follows a passage drawing the distinction between 'gravity' waves on water and elastic waves in a fluid, then Nollet continues, 'Besides, when the water waves cross one another, it cannot be denied that, where the waves meet, the momentum is compounded of the masses and the velocities of the parts that meet, and that a small body placed at this point of intersection necessarily receives this resultant momentum. It is not the same with two sounds . . . each is effective as if it were acting alone.'

In order to explain this imagined difference, Nollet commends, with great power of persuasion, a then recent suggestion of J. J. de Mairan, himself a physicist of considerable renown. 'M. de Mairan', he says, '. . . puts forward a system, so simple but at the same time so happily conceived, that one soon forgets that it is merely an hypothesis, when one applies it to phenomena . . . since the molecules of air are chance assemblages of smaller units, which coalesce and dissociate as the result of innumerable causes, is not one led to believe that they differ from one another in size over an infinite range, rather than to suppose gratuitously that each resembles every other in every particular? This idea, on

which the whole system of M. de Mairan is founded, is the only
feature of it which is merely plausible; all the other features are
such necessary consequences of this assumption (once it is accepted) that they are quite irrefutable. If the molecules of air are
different in size, they must differ also in their degree of resilience.
. . . Consequently, wherever a sounding body may be placed, it
will find in its surroundings some molecules of air whose elasticity
is similar to its own—some molecules capable of receiving,
sustaining and transmitting its vibrations. In this way two strings
of different frequencies may be heard through the same mass
of air. . . .'

If M. de Mairan's ingenious 'system' had still been seriously
entertained by physicists at the turn of the century—which it was
not—the one 'merely plausible' feature of it, the notion of a wide
variation in molecular size, would certainly have been discredited,
and with it the whole system brought into disrepute, by the
experiments of Gay-Lussac, and the hypotheses of Dalton and
Avogadro, which provided their interpretation and laid the
foundation of the new physics of atoms, in the first years of the
century that followed. But the development of physics in the first
years of the nineteenth century did more than provide a refutation
of a speculative hypothesis which never received universal support; in the contributions of Thomas Young (1773-1829) there
was furnished a solution to the problem to which de Mairan's
speculations had been directed—and, incidentally, a complete
exposure of the misconceptions implicit in the posing of the
problem as Nollet posed it.

Young's principle of superposition is described in its own right
in chapter 8 of this book, but it is tacitly assumed in much that
goes before. Indeed, the principle is basic for, and of universal
relevance to, the whole class of wave processes in which isochronous vibrations play a part. Its formulation, as we shall
eventually describe (p. 178), was almost entirely underivative
from the notions that earlier workers had proposed. Daniel
Bernoulli (1700-1782), it is true, had formulated a principle of
superposition in mathematical language, in respect of the vibrations
of strings under tension, in 1755, but he had undeservedly failed
to convince his fellow mathematicians (Euler and Lagrange, in
particular) of the validity of his ideas, and he had certainly not
extended them to the wider realm of wave processes in general.

Young was led to the principle of superposition directly, from common experience, by the intuition of genius.

Having brought our history to this point, it is unnecessary to follow it farther. With the contributions of Young the physicist's ideas of vibrations and waves took on their modern aspect. We are better advised to turn now from the general to the particular, meeting history on the way, but treating each topic systematically, in its relation to the whole. Perhaps, when he has traversed the book, the reader may return with added profit to this introduction, finding in it, also, something of a summary—and a background against which to evaluate the significance of what he has read.

CHAPTER 2

STRETCHED STRINGS

2.1. HISTORICAL

The view has been held, and it is difficult to disprove it, that the origin of the stringed instruments of music is to be traced back to the hunter's bow. The Assyrians and Egyptians of ancient history raised their armies of bowmen, and the earliest musical instruments of which we have direct knowledge have been found in the royal tombs of the valley of the Nile. For the most primitive of these instruments, the nanga, there is abundant evidence of fragments over the period 2000 to 1500 BC, and complete specimens dating from about 1500 BC are to be seen in the British Museum. The frame of the instrument was bow-shaped; it had three strings, or sometimes four; the strings were twanged by the performer using his fingers. The nanga was thus at least as close, in form and function, to the warrior's bow as it is to the modern harp, which, by slow stages of evolution, has developed out of it.

Let us consider, very briefly, this evolutionary history, hypothetical though it may be in its earlier phases. In the use of the hunter's, or the warrior's, bow, the staff is bent as the bow-string is drawn back. At the extremity of this motion, when the barbed head of the shaft is close to the bowman's outstretched hand, there is momentary equilibrium: the tensions in the bow-string at its ends balance the restoring forces of elastic deformation of the staff, and, at the centre of the string, the tensions balance the force of drawing. For a given bow-staff, and a given shaft drawn to the full, the equilibrium situation is well defined. When the shaft is released, the tensions in the string subside after a regular pattern. There is a faint and characteristic sound peculiar to the event. The hunter and the warrior cannot have been insensitive to it. For a bow of another size, or perhaps with a heavier or a lighter string, the sound is similar, but in one respect it is different. The hunter who had known the varied sounds of the forest, with their differences, must eventually have recognised this possibility of difference in the sound of the bow-string—this difference in general 'pitch'. When he and his companions sought to make music for themselves—as the spirit surely led them—one bow with three strings or four provided them with at least a narrow compass of possible 'notes', and a small range of possibility in respect of their combination. In the nanga the strings were of different lengths: this alone opened the compass, and differences of tension could open it wider. In the musical instrument, the bow, its frame, was almost inflexible, the tensions of the strings were not materially altered in the process of playing: the sound of a string was that of a string under effectively constant tension, it was different in primitive 'quality' from the sound of the bow-string.

This is not the place to embark on further technicalities, or to undertake a systematic history of the development of the stringed instruments of the modern age. Suffice to say that in every case we have to do with the vibrations of strings under constant tension, with strings set in vibration by various means—by plucking, or twanging with the fingers or with a plectrum, by bowing, or by being struck with a hammer. It is appropriate, rather, that we should now consider, in the light of our previous knowledge, how such strings may possibly vibrate, leaving on one side, for later consideration, the mechanism of their excitation and the differences which may thereby arise.

2.2. A GENERAL RESULT

Imagine a uniform, flexible string, of total length l and total mass ml, forming a closed loop. In this connection 'uniform' implies constancy of cross-sectional area and homogeneity of material. Suppose this loop to be slightly stretched so as to fit closely around the outer cylindrical surface of a cylinder of radius r ($2\pi r$, the circumference of the right section of the cylinder, being infinitesimally greater than l). In this state let the tension in the string be T. It is required to find the magnitude of the outwards force on a small length Δl of the string in contact with the cylinder ($\Delta l \ll r$). The situation is as represented in fig. 1. Here $\Delta\theta$, the angle subtended at the centre of the circular section of the cylinder by the element of length of string under consideration, is given by $\Delta\theta = \Delta l/r$, and this small portion of the string is assumed to be held in equilibrium by forces T at its extremities and a resultant

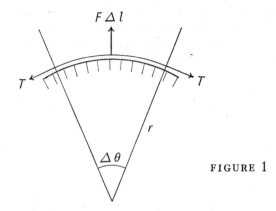

FIGURE 1

outwards force $F\Delta l$ acting radially through its mid-point as shown. Obviously, in this case,

$$F\Delta l = 2T\frac{\Delta\theta}{2},$$

$\Delta\theta$ being a very small angle. If, then, we substitute for $\Delta\theta$, we have

$$F = T/r \qquad (1)$$

The result which we have just obtained is in every way analogous to the result giving the excess pressure due to surface tension inside a spherical soap bubble of radius r (*M L & T*, § 17.2), $p = 4\gamma/r$: in the one case the circular loop of string is in equilibrium when there is a uniformly distributed outwards radial force of magnitude T/r per unit length of string (T being the measure of a force), in the other the spherical soap film is in equilibrium when there is an outwards radial force of magnitude $4\gamma/r$ per unit area of a film (γ being the measure of a force per unit length).

The heading of this section calls for a general result; equation (1), on the other hand, refers to a particular case. Fig. 1, however, is not so limited. It may be taken to represent a small length of a string under tension, the form of the remainder of the string being of no consequence; moreover, the force F may be applied in any way, it is not necessary that it should arise as the normal reaction across the surface of a solid support. From these considerations the required general result emerges without further analysis. It may be expressed in words: if a finite length of string under constant tension T is in equilibrium, any element of length Δl

of the string must be acted on by an external force of magnitude $T\Delta l/r$ directed radially outwards from the centre of curvature of the figure of the string in the neighbourhood of that elementary length, r being the measure of the corresponding radius of curvature. It will be noted that the only concealed condition governing this result is that the string shall be perfectly flexible: it is not necessary that it shall be uniform—moreover, if the string is uniform, the result is independent of the magnitude of m, the mass per unit length.

2.3. THE FUNDAMENTAL MODE

Our immediate object has been defined (p. 10): to 'consider . . . how such strings may possibly vibrate'. Suppose that a uniform string, of length l and total mass ml, is stretched between two fixed supports O and O′ (fig. 2), the tension when the whole string is at rest being T. Let us consider vibrations confined to a plane, and such that the displacement of any element of the string from its equilibrium position is always very small compared with the length of the string. Then we may regard each element of the string as moving in a line at right angles to OO′, and we may assume that the total length of the string remains so nearly constant during the vibrations that the tension remains the same.

Now, for an isolated particle, we accept the view that the basic type of periodic linear motion is simple harmonic motion. The characteristics of this type of motion have been fully treated elsewhere ($M L \& T$, chap. 6). The essential requirement is that the acceleration towards the origin shall be proportional to the displacement, and, when the proportionality constant is given, the important result for our particular purpose is that the periodic time is independent of the amplitude. Such motion is referred to as 'isochronous'. If we are concerned to enquire, therefore, whether the stretched string of our present discussion is capable of executing natural vibrations in which every element of the string oscillates in simple harmonic motion about its position of equilibrium in OO′, the period being the same for all such elements, we have only to enquire whether it is possible so to deform the string initially that, when it is released, the initial acceleration of each element towards its position of equilibrium is proportional to its displacement. If this result is capable of being achieved for an initial small deformation of arbitrary scale-ampli-

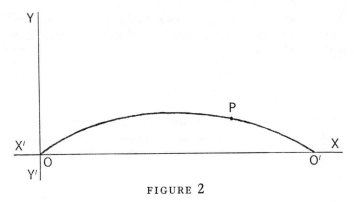

FIGURE 2

tude (see p. 15), it is clear that the string as a whole will continue to vibrate with constant period once it has been deformed in the appropriate manner, and then released. If our enquiry leads to an affirmative answer, it should at the same time provide an analytical expression giving the form of the necessary initial deformation.

Let rectangular axes X'OX, Y'OY be taken, as shown in fig. 2, having the origin at one end of the stretched string. (If the mid-point of the string be taken as origin, the subsequent analysis does not run quite so smoothly!) Consider an element of string of length Δl around an arbitrary point P. Let y_0 be the initial displacement of P, and let the form of the initial deformation of the string be represented by the functional expression $y_0 = f(x)$. Clearly $f(0) = f(l) = 0$. Before release, the element of string in question must be subject to an external force $T\Delta l/r$ (§ 2.2.), r being the measure of the radius of curvature of the figure of the string at this point. When all external constraint is removed, this element of string will experience a resultant force of this amount acting towards the centre of curvature. If $y_0 \ll l$, as we suppose, this restoring force may be regarded as acting in a direction normal to OO'. The initial acceleration of the element of string considered is thus of magnitude $(T\Delta l/r) \div (m\Delta l)$, that is of magnitude T/mr, and it is directed normally towards OO'. The question which we are asking, therefore, is whether a form of the function $f(x)$ can be found such that, for all values of x between 0 and l, T/mr is proportional to y_0.

When all displacements are small, the value of $1/r$ (the curvature of the figure of the string at P) is given by the rate of change of slope of the figure with distance parallel to OO'. In the notation of the calculus, which we shall use as convenient in this book, we have

$$\frac{1}{r} = -\frac{d^2y_0}{dx^2}.$$

Here the minus sign indicates that the centre of curvature lies on the side of the string towards the axis of x. Our immediate question, therefore, is whether a form $y_0 = f(x)$ can be found which satisfies the general requirement

$$\frac{T}{m}\frac{d^2y_0}{dx^2} = -\mu y_0 \tag{2}$$

μ being a constant under the conditions which have been specified.
It will be evident, on trial, that the function

$$y_0 = A \sin\left(\sqrt{\frac{m\mu}{T}}x + \delta\right) \tag{3}$$

meets the condition specified by equation (2), whatever the values of A and δ. It meets the conditions that $y_0 = 0$ when $x = 0$ and also when $x = l$, only if $\delta = 0$ and

$$\sqrt{\frac{m\mu}{T}}\, l = n\pi,$$

where n is an integer.
The second of these results may be written

$$\mu = n^2\pi^2 \frac{T}{ml^2} \tag{4}$$

—and the two results combined lead to the equation

$$y_0 = A \sin n\pi \frac{x}{l} \tag{5}$$

For the present we shall consider only the solution for which $n = 1$, then equation (5) becomes

$$y_0 = A \sin \pi \frac{x}{l} \tag{6}$$

In equation (6) we have found an expression for the simplest form of initial (small) deformation of a string, of length l and arbitrary tension, such that when the string is released it will execute sustained vibrations of constant period whatever the amplitude. Here we use the term 'amplitude' in respect of the vibrations of the whole string (we have used the term 'scale-amplitude' on p. 12), defining it in terms of the linear amplitude of the simple harmonic motion of the mid-point of the string. It is the quantity the measure of which is denoted by A in equation (6). When a stretched string vibrates in this particular way, we say that it is vibrating in the fundamental mode. At this stage we need make only two further observations: first, that none of the methods of excitation of the strings of musical instruments provides an initial deformation of the simple form described by equation (6)—so that the initial vibrations of such strings are not simply in the fundamental mode; secondly, that when we speak of the vibrations as 'sustained' we are speaking of the ideal case. In any actual case there will generally be radiation of energy, and frictional effects, resulting in a gradual decrease in the amplitude of vibration.

An equation describing in full detail the motion of a stretched string vibrating in the fundamental mode may be obtained by a simple extension of the analysis that we have just given in respect of the initial deformation. We denote by y the transverse displacement of P, the arbitrary point distant x from one end of the string (fig. 2), at any time t, and we note that the transverse acceleration of P at that instant is given by

$$\frac{d^2y}{dt^2} = -\mu y$$

(compare equation (2), which is an expression for the acceleration when $t=0$). The motion of P is then according to the equation ($M L \ \& \ T$, § 6.1)

$$y = y_0 \cos \sqrt{\mu}\, t.$$

For a string vibrating in the fundamental mode the values of μ and y_0 are obtained from equations (4) and (5), respectively, writing $n=1$. Making these substitutions, we finally have, for the motion in this mode

$$y = A \sin \frac{\pi x}{l} \cos \frac{\pi}{l} \sqrt{\frac{T}{m}}\, t \tag{7}$$

Within the limits $0 \leqslant x \leqslant l$, $t \geqslant 0$, equation (8) provides a full description of the motion in question. In particular, it shows that f, the characteristic frequency of vibration, is given by

$$f = \frac{1}{2l}\sqrt{\frac{T}{m}} \tag{8}$$

2.4. RESOLUTION INTO WAVES

It is our object, in this section, to approach the problem of the stretched string vibrating in the fundamental mode from another point of view, and to obtain a formal description of the motion different in character from that of equation (7). We shall discover that the concept of wave motion takes shape when our new description has been formulated. Basically, we shall use the procedure of resolution of vectors in deriving the new description from the old.

'In respect of any vector quantity,' the view has been taken ($M\,L\, \&\, T$, p. 76), 'it may be convenient for calculation to resolve that quantity into components. . . . The parallelogram law provides the basis for such resolution . . . and indicates the infinite choice which lies open . . . regarding the precise mode of resolution to be adopted.' We also know ($M\,L\, \&\, T$, § 6.4.2.) that the parallelogram law likewise provides the basis for the composition (and, therefore, in reverse, for the resolution) of collinear simple harmonic motions of common origin and the same period. Here we shall follow out the implications of a particular method of resolving the linear simple harmonic motions which the individual elements of a stretched string execute with common period when the string is vibrating naturally in its fundamental mode.

We begin by noting the fact that, when the string is vibrating in this way, the simple harmonic motions of the individual elements of the string are all in phase, but their amplitudes vary, having all values from 0 to A, the amplitude for any element depending upon the location of the element in accordance with equation (6). We propose to examine the consequences of resolving the simple harmonic motion of each such element into two components, each of amplitude $A/2$, the same for each element. We can do this if the relative phases of the two components vary from element to element along the string so as to provide the actual variation of resultant amplitude to which we have just referred.

Obviously, for each element of the string, the phases of the two component simple harmonic motions must be symmetrically disposed in relation to the phase of the actual motion of that element ($M\,L\,\&\,T$, § 6.4.2.). For the element around P (fig. 2), let one component lead the actual motion by phase angle Δ and the other component lag by the same angle. Then, applying the parallelogram law, we have

$$y_0{}^2 = \left(\frac{A}{2}\right)^2 + \left(\frac{A}{2}\right)^2 + 2\left(\frac{A}{2}\right)^2 \cos 2\Delta,$$

or, if we substitute from equation (6),

$$A^2 \sin^2 \frac{\pi x}{l} = A^2 \cos^2 \Delta.$$

For our purposes the significant solution of this equation is clearly

$$\Delta = \frac{\pi x}{l} - \frac{\pi}{2} \tag{9}$$

As we have already stated, the phases of the actual motions are the same for all elements of the string, thus equation (9) exhibits the relative phases of the 'leading' and 'lagging' components, separately, as each varies smoothly from element to element along the length of the string. At each end, that is when $x=0$, or $x=l$, $|2\Delta| = \pi$, and the two components cancel completely, being out of phase; at the centre, $\Delta=0$, the two components are in phase, and in consequence reinforce completely; generally, the phase angle of the leading component increases linearly and that of the lagging component decreases linearly with x, as x increases.

Suppose now that y_1 represents the instantaneous displacement of P due to the leading component, and y_2 the instantaneous displacement due to the lagging component simple harmonic motion into which the actual motion of P has been resolved in our analysis. Then, because the amplitudes of these component motions are everywhere the same, being equal to $A/2$, and because their phases at $t=0$ vary as represented by equation (9), we have

$$y_1 = \frac{A}{2} \cos \left(\frac{\pi}{l} \sqrt{\frac{T}{m}}\, t + \frac{\pi x}{l} - \frac{\pi}{2} \right)$$

$$y_2 = \frac{A}{2} \cos \left(\frac{\pi}{l} \sqrt{\frac{T}{m}}\, t - \frac{\pi x}{l} + \frac{\pi}{2} \right),$$

B

or
$$y_1 = \frac{A}{2} \sin \frac{\pi}{l} \left(\sqrt{\frac{T}{m}} t + x \right)$$

$$y_2 = -\frac{A}{2} \sin \frac{\pi}{l} \left(\sqrt{\frac{T}{m}} t - x \right)$$

(10)

The analysis which we have just completed has resulted in the
second description which we sought: a description of the motion
of a stretched string vibrating in the fundamental mode that is
equally valid with that of equation (7). Equation (7) is a straightforward description in mathematical terms of the 'actual' motion,
exhibiting the instantaneous displacement of an arbitrary point
on the string as a function of the time reckoned from the instant
at which the string was released from the initial state of deformation itself described by equation (6). The alternative description,
given by equations (10) supplemented by the assumption $y = y_1 + y_2$
which underlies our procedure of resolution, implies that it is
equally valid to assert that the vibrating string is executing two
different motions simultaneously. The mathematical expressions
for these two motions are similar, but they are not identical: it is
necessary to examine them further in order to elicit the physical
character of the motions. We started our analysis by specifying
that the component motions should be such that for each the
amplitude of transverse oscillation is the same for each element
of the string; beyond this the essential physical character of the
component motions is to be seen in the way in which, for each of
them, the phase of an elementary oscillation is propagated from
element to element along the string. On the evidence of equations
(10) we must conclude that for the leading component the condition of constant arbitrary phase (any phase angle between 0 and
2π) is propagated in such a way that the quantity $\left(\sqrt{\frac{T}{m}} t + x \right)$
remains constant; for the lagging component the corresponding
requirement is that $\left(\sqrt{\frac{T}{m}} t - x \right)$ shall be constant. The leading
component, then, is characterised by phase propagation in the
negative direction of x in fig. 2 with velocity $\sqrt{\frac{T}{m}}$, the lagging
component by phase propagation in the positive direction with

the same velocity. Motion of this type, in which an oscillatory process is propagated from point to point in a physical system without transference of matter, is referred to as 'wave motion': here we have analysed the vibration of a uniform stretched string into oppositely travelling waves traversing the string with a velocity uniquely determined by the tension of the string and the mass of unit length of it. In our description of the vibrations as superimposed wave motions we must clearly assume that one of these wave motions is continuously entering the string at O and leaving it at O', whilst the other is continuously entering at O' and leaving at O—or, once the steady state has been established, we may regard the situation as one in which a single wave process is all the time travelling back and forth along the string, being reflected without loss at its fixed ends (see § 2.9). In this mode of description the actual vibration may be said to arise from the 'interference' of the oppositely travelling waves. This notion of interference is discussed more fully in chapter 8.

2.5. VELOCITY, FREQUENCY AND WAVELENGTH

Equations (10) are of the general form

$$y = A \sin 2\pi \left(\frac{t}{\tau} \pm \frac{x}{\lambda} \right) \tag{11}$$

This form is more symmetrical in respect of x and t than the form in which the equations for the component wave motions were first obtained in the last section. It represents, as they do, a wave process of constant displacement amplitude (A in this case), propagated in a one-dimensional system (the x-axis of the mathematical description)—in the negative direction if the positive sign is taken in the equation, or *vice versa*—the velocity of (phase) propagation being λ/τ in the new notation. Our immediate concern is to interpret the parameters λ and τ in this connection.

We note, to begin with, that λ must represent a length, and τ a time, for a phase angle, $2\pi \frac{t}{\tau}$ or $2\pi \frac{x}{\lambda}$, is represented by a pure number. Further, if we regard x as constant in equation (11), considering only the time-variation of displacement at an arbitrary point in the path of the wave, obviously τ is the periodic time of the simple harmonic motion which transmits the wave at that point. If f is the frequency of that motion, $\tau = 1/f$. Similarly, if we regard t as constant, considering only the instantaneous space-variation of displacement, at any arbitrary instant, along the path of the wave, λ is the constant distance between neighbouring points for which the phase of the local simple harmonic motion is the same, and for which, therefore, in the circumstances of the case, the displacement is the same. This constant distance is referred to as the 'wavelength' of the disturbance. If v represents the velocity with which the disturbance is propagated, the results which we have obtained above may be written generally

$$v = f\lambda \qquad (12)$$

—in unit time at each point in the path of the wave the local simple harmonic motion completes f oscillations and the disturbance moves forward through a distance comprising f wavelengths.

There is one further aspect of equation (11) which we should not neglect. In the absence of additional restrictive conditions, this equation represents a wave motion taking place in an infinite one-dimensional system, and extending in time from an infinitely remote past into an unlimited future. Just because of this aspect it is essential to issue the warning that an equation of this ideal form must be used circumspectly when any actual physical process is in question. No such process entirely matches up to this mathematically simple ideal.

2.6. HIGHER HARMONICS

In sections 2.3 and 2.4 we confined attention to the vibration of a stretched string in its fundamental mode. For a uniform string, of length l and total mass ml, under a tension T, the frequency of vibration was found to be $(T/m)^{\frac{1}{2}}/2l$ (equation (8)), and it was shown that the vibrations of the string could be regarded as compounded of two oppositely travelling wave motions, of wavelength $2l$ (compare equations (10) and (11)), of the same amplitude, and common velocity $(T/m)^{\frac{1}{2}}$. These results were obtained by taking $n = 1$ in equations (4) and (5), and disregarding the other possibilities. In this section we take these other possibilities into account.

Considering equation (5) in its general form, we conclude at once that if the initial (small) deformation of the stretched string is as represented by any one of the expressions included in it, namely, any one of

$$y_0 = A \sin n\pi \frac{x}{l} \qquad (13)$$

with n integral, then when the string is released it will execute sustained vibrations of constant period whatever the amplitude of the initial deformation. Brief consideration will show that in all essential respects the character of these vibrations will be the same as that of the vibrations in the fundamental mode $(n=1)$, which we have discussed in detail already. Fig. 3 represents the limits of vibration, schematically, for the cases $n=2$ and $n=3$.

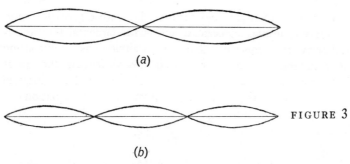

(a)

(b)

FIGURE 3

The whole series of characteristic vibrations of a stretched string $(n=1, 2, 3, \ldots)$ is referred to as a 'harmonic series' of vibrations: colloquially, therefore, vibration in the fundamental mode has come to be the 'first harmonic', that in the next possible mode $(n=2)$ the 'second harmonic', and so on. Alternatively, vibration in the mode of the second harmonic is sometimes referred to as the 'first overtone' of the fundamental vibration, vibration in the mode of the third harmonic as the 'second overtone', and similarly throughout the series. The term 'harmonic' is, of course, derived from the vocabulary of the musician. The whole art and practice of music is based on the fact that certain combinations of notes give pleasure, or at least have emotive significance. The experimental discovery is attributed to Pythagoras, in the sixth century BC, that when the length of a string is halved, the tension remaining constant, the characteristic note of the halved string has a peculiar relation of concord with that of the full ('open') string. This was not an isolated discovery—

Pythagoras indeed found that the lengths of a given string corresponding to all pairs of notes then generally regarded as concordant are in simple integral relation to one another, but the
single result in respect of the simplest such ratio, 2:1, is alone
sufficient to justify the terms first and second harmonic as applied
to the vibration modes of a string of constant length and tension,
when the motion is as specified by the values $n=1$, $n=2$, of our
present analysis. For the figure of a string of length l, vibrating
in the manner represented by fig. 3 (a), is indistinguishable from
the composite figure of two strings, each of length $l/2$, joined
end-to-end, firmly held at their point of junction, and vibrating,
180° out of phase one with the other, each in the fundamental
mode.

It is a matter of traditional history—here we digress to point,
by an early example, an issue which is fundamental for experimental physics generally—that the Babylonians, considering
number in the abstract, formulated the view that the 'most
perfect' proportion capable of generation in terms of two integral
numbers p and q is the proportion expressed by the equation

$$p : \frac{p+q}{2} = \frac{2pq}{p+q} : q.$$

Pythagoras, it is believed, assimilated this semi-mystical point of
view. When he came to experiment on the consonances of the
notes emitted by a vibrating string, 'stopped' to various lengths,
he claimed to have found it exemplified in the physical situation.
If $p=6$, $q=12$, the 'most perfect' proportion of the Babylonians
is given by

$$6 : 9 = 8 : 12.$$

According to Pythagoras, the four lengths, 6, 8, 9 and 12, between
them, provided all the possibilities of consonance which the
Greeks recognised, namely, 2:1, 3:2 and 4:3. The point which
it is here necessary to establish is that no measurement can be
made without possibility of error: we cannot assert, on the basis
of measurements made, that the ratio of the lengths of two strings
vibrating in specified ways is precisely the ratio of integral numbers,
certainly not in the same sense as we can assert that a cube has
12 edges, 8 corners and 6 faces. We may believe that the phenomena of the physical world are such as to be describable in terms

of simple mathematical formulae. Even so, we can do no more than state, on the basis of experiment however refined, that our measurements are consistent with our belief, in respect of a particular mathematical formula: we cannot assert that they establish it absolutely. It is characteristic of the later Pythagoreans that the undeniable fact concerning the elements of the cube, to which we have alluded already, strengthened their confidence in the absolute validity of their empirical 'law' regarding the lengths of strings vibrating in consonance. Today we see no connection between these two fields of knowledge, and we cherish the hope that we have at last outgrown the primitive mysticism of those who vainly imagined that they did, but the experimental physicist must never forget that the essential limitation which informed Pythagoras's deduction informs every deduction which he makes from his own experiments—and the theorist must likewise be on guard continually against the insidious fascination of mathematical analogy, which can lead him to a new clarity or a new confusion with equal ease. These generalities set down for record, let us continue our analysis.

Instead of equation (8), in the general case we have

$$f = \frac{n}{2l}\sqrt{\frac{T}{m}} \qquad (14)$$

—the vibration frequency of the nth harmonic is n times the vibration frequency of the fundamental mode. Equation (14) also shows that for a given string, stopped as in the experiment of Pythagoras, the frequency of the first harmonic (fundamental) of the half string is the same as that of the second harmonic of the full string. Our description of the full string vibrating in its second harmonic, in terms of two juxtaposed and collinear half strings vibrating in opposite phase in the fundamental mode (p. 22), therefore receives added (and necessary) justification: not only is the vibration figure of the full string faithfully reproduced, but the frequency of vibration is correctly given on the basis of this description.

We have now to consider how vibrations in the higher harmonics may be resolved into superposed wave motions, following the procedure of section 2.4. If we start from equation (13), rather than equation (6), and assume, as before, that the component simple harmonic motions of any element of the string are each of the same amplitude, $A/2$, we have, instead of equation (9), for the common phase difference between either component motion and the actual motion of the element,

$$\Delta = \frac{n\pi x}{l} - \frac{\pi}{2} \qquad (15)$$

Finally, instead of equations (10), we obtain

$$y_1 = \frac{A}{2}\sin\frac{n\pi}{l}\left(\sqrt{\frac{T}{m}}\,t + x\right)$$

$$y_2 = -\frac{A}{2}\sin\frac{n\pi}{l}\left(\sqrt{\frac{T}{m}}\,t - x\right) \qquad (16)$$

The important conclusion from these equations is that the component wave motions are again propagated along the stretched string with velocity $\sqrt{\dfrac{T}{m}}$, although the wavelength is now $2l/n$—

n times smaller than the corresponding wavelength when the fundamental mode was in question. We are led to suspect that sinusoidal waves of whatever wavelength, and of whatever amplitude, provided it is small in relation to the wavelength, are propagated along an infinite uniform stretched string with the same velocity. Considerations to be advanced in the next section should confirm this suspicion.

2.7. PROPAGATION OF A PULSE

Let us consider again the situation already discussed in section 2.2: a closed loop of string encircling the right section of a circular cylinder of radius r, the string being under tension T, being uniform, and of total mass $2\pi rm$. Suppose, now, that the cylinder is maintained in rotation about its axis with angular velocity ω. If the string rotates along with the cylinder, and if $F\Delta l$ is the resultant outwards force acting radially from the cylinder on an element of the string of length Δl, extending the previous analysis, we have (see fig. 1)

$$2T\frac{\Delta\theta}{2} - F\Delta l = (m\Delta l)\omega^2 r,$$

or, if we substitute for $\Delta\theta$ as before, and simplify,

$$\frac{T}{r} - F = m\omega^2 r \qquad (17)$$

According to equation (17), as ω increases, F decreases, becoming zero when $\omega^2 r^2 = T/m$. Obviously, if the speed of rotation of the cylinder is increased beyond this stage, there is no longer any normal reaction between the string and the cylinder—and no possibility that the speed of rotation of the circular loop of string can increase further. However rapidly the cylinder rotates, therefore, the encircling loop of string will not rotate more rapidly than is given by the equation $\omega^2 r^2 = T/m$. We note, in this connection, that ωr is the linear velocity of a point on the rotating string, thus we conclude that the limiting situation is that in which the linear velocity of such a point reaches the value $\sqrt{\dfrac{T}{m}}$ —a result which is independent of the radius of the cylinder around which the circular loop of string is held taut. Although, in this situation, we are not concerned with a wave process, we note further that this limiting velocity is the same as the velocity of propagation of a sinusoidal wave along the stretched string (at least under conditions in which the string is straight).

We have just shown that there is no normal reaction between a circular loop of string and the surface of a cylinder, with which it is 'in contact' over a right section, when the speed of rotation of the whole system about the axis of the cylinder is such that the linear velocity of a point on the string is $\sqrt{\dfrac{T}{m}}$. In the ideal case which we have considered, once the system attains this limiting speed, the speed of rotation of the cylinder may be reduced to zero, without the motion of the string being retarded, and there will still be no normal reaction between the string and the stationary cylinder.

FIGURE 4

Suppose, now, that a long uniform string under tension T is threaded through a tube of which the (small) internal diameter is just equal to the diameter of the string. Let the tube be bent so that its axis is an arc of a circle of radius r (fig. 4). The tube being stationary, let the string be in motion through the tube with linear speed $\sqrt{\dfrac{T}{m}}$, m being the mass of unit length of the string as before. Then our previous result implies that there will be no normal reaction between the string and the internal surface of the tube, whatever the value of r. This result being independent of the radius of curvature of the axis of the tube, we next consider a tube of the form shown in fig. 5. The portions AB, CD, are straight and collinear; between B and C the tube is of arbitrary shape—provided only that the axis lies in one plane throughout. Imagine the tube to be threaded over a long uniform string, under tension T as before. If the string is held at rest, and the tube is made to travel along it with velocity $\sqrt{\dfrac{T}{m}}$, we can only conclude that the normal reaction between string and tube will be zero throughout the motion. As a result of the motion of the tube, a 'pulse' of arbitrary shape travels along the stretched string with velocity $\sqrt{\dfrac{T}{m}}$; it travels 'freely', that is without reaction on the guiding tube. We have no option but to conclude that this unique velocity is indeed the velocity of free propagation of a pulse, of whatever form, along a uniform string of which the mass of unit length is m and the tension T. The guiding tube of our argument has served little purpose except to add reality to the hypothetical situation which we have discussed. P. G. Tait (see $M L \, \& \, T$, p. 78) first used this device in this particular context in 1883.

Our discussion has shown that a disturbance of arbitrary form is propagated along a stretched string with a perfectly definite velocity—and without distortion. It is important to stress the last three words of this statement, although their meaning is implicit in the rest of it: when the usual conditions are fulfilled, an arbitrary pulse is in fact propagated without change of form along the stretched string. It is perhaps not surprising that there is an intimate connection between this result and the conclusion to which we were led in the last section (p. 24), that under similar conditions a sinusoidal disturbance of whatever wavelength is

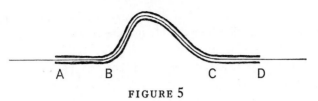

FIGURE 5

propagated along an infinite string with the same velocity. The connection between these two results was first convincingly established by J. B. J. Fourier (see *M L & T*, p. 32) in a memoir submitted to the French Academy in 1811.

Fourier was occupied, at the time, with the general problem of the conduction of heat in solids—in fact the results to which we are to refer were given their final form in his *Théorie analytique de la chaleur*, published in 1822—but the mathematical results themselves are of much wider relevance: they provide a basic method of analysis applicable wherever periodic properties are implicit in physical phenomena. It is interesting to remark that natural philosophers had been groping towards Fourier's theorem for two generations previously, and that, in particular, there had been great activity in this direction over a period of ten years from 1747. At that time the problem of the stretched string had provided the incentive, and J. le R. d'Alembert (1717-1783), L. Euler (1707-1783), D. Bernoulli (1700-1782) and J. L. Lagrange (1736-1813) had joined in the argument without quite clinching the issue. Six years before his death, Euler had come closer than any of the others to the final result, but his memoir on the subject was not published until 1798. Possibly then it did not immediately receive the attention which it deserved. Almost totally blind, as he was, in 1777 Euler had 'engaged to furnish the Academy of St. Petersburg with as many memoirs as would be sufficient to complete its *Acta* for twenty years after his death'. He kept his word, submitting more than seventy such memoirs, 'and left above two hundred more, which were revised and completed by another hand'. The memoir dealing with the subject of Fourier's theorem was but one of this multitude.

2.8. FOURIER'S THEOREM

For our present purpose, Fourier's theorem may be expressed as follows. Let there be a function $\phi(x)$, then, between finite limits, say between $x=0$ and $x=l$, if $\phi(0)=\phi(l)$, it is always possible to represent the function by a doubly infinite series

$$\phi(x) = A_0 + A_1 \cos 2\pi \frac{x}{l} + A_2 \cos 2\pi \frac{2x}{l} + \ldots$$

$$+ B_1 \sin 2\pi \frac{x}{l} + B_2 \sin 2\pi \frac{2x}{l} + \ldots \quad (18)$$

in which the coefficients $A_0, A_1, A_2, \ldots B_1, B_2, \ldots$ are uniquely determinable. Obviously, equation (18) may be re-written

$$\phi(x) = A_0 + C_1 \cos \left(2\pi \frac{x}{l} + \delta_1\right) + C_2 \cos \left(2\pi \frac{2x}{l} + \delta_2\right) \ldots \quad (19)$$

with

$$C_1{}^2 = A_1{}^2 + B_1{}^2, \ldots$$
$$\tan \delta_1 = -B_1/A_1, \ldots.$$

Consider now a stretched string on which arbitrary pulses, such as that of fig. 5, an infinite succession of them, of the same form, but in which the displacements are alternately of opposite sense, are travelling in the same direction. If the pulses are equally spaced along the string, as shown in fig. 6, they will remain so indefinitely: under these conditions they constitute a wave motion of complex wave-form propagated with the characteristic velocity $\sqrt{\dfrac{T}{m}}$. Let A and B be corresponding points on adjacent waves. Then AB is the repetition length of the wave-form, which we shall here denote by λ. Let us apply Fourier's theorem, in the form given by equation (19), to the portion of the wave profile between A and B, taking $\phi(x)$ to represent the displacement. Because this profile is entirely symmetrical with respect to the mean position of the string, we may expect to obtain $A_0=0$. This, indeed, is a general result in such cases. Moreover, the whole profile, from $x=-\infty$ to $x=+\infty$ being made up of contiguous elements identical with that between A and B, our analysis applies over the whole string. We have, in fact, for the instantaneous displacement, y, at any point x,

$$y = \phi(x) = C_1 \cos \left(2\pi \frac{x}{\lambda} + \delta_1\right) + C_2 \cos \left(2\pi \frac{2x}{\lambda} + \delta_2\right) + \ldots.$$

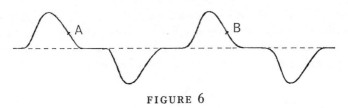

FIGURE 6

In this result we have broken down the complex wave-form of fig. 6 into 'sinusoidal' components, and, because the complex wave-form is propagated without distortion, we have to conclude that all these components are propagated with the same velocity. This is in line with our previous conclusion (p. 24). C_1, C_2, ... are the amplitudes of these component wave motions, and δ_1, δ_2, ... represent their relative phases: we note that their wavelengths are λ, $\lambda/2$, ... and that their frequencies constitute a harmonic series (p. 21).

In 1843 Georg Simon Ohm (1787-1854), discussing the auditory perception of compound notes, put forward a view of the matter which was essentially based on the result which we have just derived. This was probably the first direct application of Fourier's theorem in the realm of acoustics. At various stages in his career (he did not achieve the recognition of a university professorship until he was sixty-two) Ohm showed himself a disciple of Fourier. His work on current electricity, published in 1827, and since commemorated in the name of the practical unit of electrical resistance, was avowedly based on that of Fourier on the conduction of heat (see p. 27).

2.9. REFLECTION OF A PULSE

In the last two sections we have concentrated attention on the propagation of a transverse disturbance, either pulse or sinusoidal wave, along an infinite string. However, we started our present investigation by considering first the vibration of a string of finite length in its fundamental mode (§ 2.3). We showed that, if a stretched string of length l is vibrating in that mode, it can be considered as transmitting two oppositely travelling wave motions, of wavelength $2l$ and the same amplitude, one continuously entering the string at one end, and one at the other, and we gave, without proof, the alternative description in terms of a single sinusoidal wave motion, travelling back and forth along the string and reflected without loss at its fixed ends (pp. 18, 19). Here we consider the phenomenon of reflection at the ends of a string in more detail—and we do this in relation to a pulse of arbitrary form, rather than in relation to a sinusoidal wave.

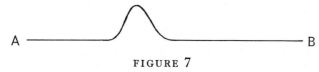

A —————————————————————— B

FIGURE 7

Suppose that a uniform string of length l, stretched between fixed supports at A and B, has an arbitrary initial deformation of the form shown (greatly exaggerated) in fig. 7. Let the initial velocities of the displaced elements of the string be such that at time $t=0$ the whole deformation is moving in the direction from A to B as a single pulse. (The general result of an initial arbitrary deformation, the initial velocities not being specified, is two pulses of the same length moving outwards from the region of original deformation. The shapes and relative sizes of these pulses may be calculated once the initial situation has been given in detail. Here we postulate initial conditions which determine that one of the pulses—that which would travel in the direction from B to A— is entirely suppressed.) Our immediate object is to deduce the sequence of events which must follow the arrival of the leading edge of the pulse at the fixed end of the string at B (fig. 7). This sequence of events is primarily conditioned by the fact that the elements of the string at B, and A, must indeed remain at rest throughout.

We approach the problem by showing that in certain conditions an infinite string will in fact behave as if it were made up of a linear array of equal finite strings, acting in phase but independently. It will appear that we shall attain our object very simply in that way.

Consider an infinite string, of the same mass per unit length, and under the same tension, as the finite string which we are discussing. Let us postulate an initial state of deformation as represented in fig. 8. Between A and B, in the centre of the figure, the deformation is precisely that postulated in fig. 7. Let the points ... A″, A′, A, B, B′, B″ ... divide the string into equal segments each of length l, and let the initial deformation in the segments ... A″ A′, B′ B″ ... be precisely similar, in form and in position

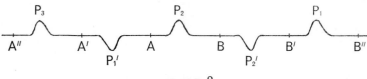

FIGURE 8

within the segment, to the deformation in AB. Further, let the deformations in the segments . . . A′ A, B B′ . . . be obtained from those in the segments . . . A″ A′, A B . . . by geometrical 'reflection', first in the equilibrium axis of the string and then, along the string, in one of the points . . . A′, B . . . respectively (Tait referred (1895) to these deformations as 'the perverse as well as the inverse' of the others). Let the initial velocities of the elements of the string affected by the deformations . . . P_1, P_2, P_3 . . . be such that at $t = 0$ each of these deformations is in motion as a single pulse in the direction AB; similarly, let the initial velocities be such that at the same instant the deformations . . . $P_1′$, $P_2′$ . . . are all moving in the direction BA. On an infinite stretched string we have thus two sets of equally spaced and precisely similar pulses moving in regular succession in opposite directions with the same speed.

Let us confine attention, to begin with, to the situation at B. Obviously, the pulses P_2, $P_2′$ will meet at B. They will affect the element of string around B during the same small interval of time, and at each instant during this interval their effects, being equal and opposite, will cancel completely. (The assumption that small displacements are additive, which was first made in § 2.4—see p. 16—may at this stage be regarded as justified by the general consistency of the results which we have obtained since its adoption.) The same sequence of events will recur when the pulse P_3 arrives at B. Another pulse travelling in the opposite direction will arrive at the same time (this pulse is not shown in fig. 8) and their effects will cancel. The point B, therefore, will remain at rest indefinitely.

Similarly, the point A will remain at rest for as long as the prescribed conditions obtain: the pulse P_3 will cancel with $P_2′$ at A, and so on, continually. The same will indeed be true of the situation at each of the points . . . A″, A′, B′, B″ . . ., and we finally conclude that, if an infinite stretched string is traversed by two oppositely moving sets of equally spaced and precisely

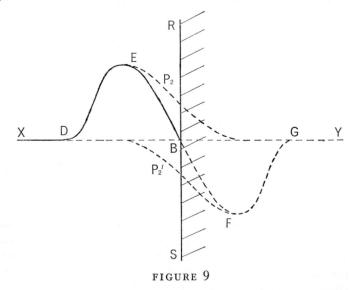

FIGURE 9

similar pulses, the one set being related to the other in the way
that we have described, the string will exhibit a series of 'displacement nodes' . . . A″, A′, A, B, B′, B″ . . . with regular spacing
equal to one-half the distance between the pulses of either set,
and the section of the string between any such node and the next
will behave, as if it were isolated from the remainder, as a finite
string with fixed extremities. In particular, the behaviour of the
section AB of the infinite string, in response to initial conditions
of which fig. 8 indicates the deformations, will be exactly the same
as the behaviour of the finite string AB in response to initial
conditions similarly indicated in fig. 7. This established, we are
at last in a position to discuss the reflection of the pulse at B
(fig. 7) in full detail.

Fig. 9 represents the situation shortly after the arrival of the
leading edge of the pulse at B (fig. 7). RS represents the solid
support to which this end of the string is attached. In the alternative representation, XY would be that part of the infinite string
of fig. 8 in the neighbourhood of the node at B, and the dotted
curves P_2, P_2' would be the instantaneous profiles of the direct
and reverse pulses, partially overlapping in this section of the
string at the instant in question. The profile of resultant displacement of the infinite string would obviously be DEBFG. The

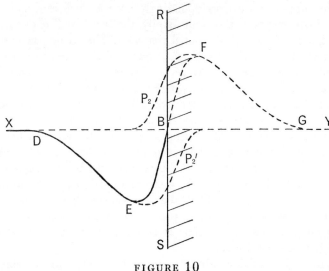

FIGURE 10

portion DEB of this profile, shown solid in the figure, is then the actual profile of instantaneous displacement on the finite string in the region of its extremity. Fig. 10 illustrates the situation at a slightly later stage in the process. A little later again, the reflected pulse is fully clear of B, travelling in the direction of A (fig. 7). A similar process of reflection occurs when the pulse reaches A, and after a time given by $2l\sqrt{\dfrac{m}{T}}$ the whole sequence of events repeats itself at B: the frequency of reflection of the pulse at either end of the string is thus $\dfrac{1}{2l}\sqrt{\dfrac{T}{m}}$. This is the characteristic frequency of vibration of the string in its fundamental mode (see p. 16).

During the process of reflection the solid support experiences a double pulse of sideways force. In the case partially represented by figs. 9 and 10, it should be clear from the figures that a component of force develops at B in the direction BR, grows to a maximum, decreases through zero to increase in the direction BS, reaches a maximum in that direction, and, finally, decreases to zero again, before reflection is complete. Over the same short interval of time, the component of force at B normal to the face

c

of the support varies correspondingly, over a small range.

In instruments of the violin family, the two 'fixed' ends of any string are different in functional character. The string passes over the main bridge at one end, the other end is secured by a peg, being terminated effectively at a subsidiary bridge on the neck, when the string is 'open', or where it is pressed against the finger board when the string is stopped. The belly of the instrument, which is almost the sole source of the emitted sound, makes effective contact with the string only through the main bridge. For an understanding of the behaviour of the instrument, therefore, a knowledge of the forces which act on the bridge is essential. The string and the belly of the instrument are 'coupled' vibrating systems, the bridge providing the physical coupling. We shall be discussing some of the basic properties of such systems in the next chapter: here we confine attention to what happens at the bridge in a special case.

When the initial conditions are as postulated in relation to fig. 7, we have seen that, whatever the shape of the initial deformation, precisely similar pulses are reflected at the bridge as a regular sequence of frequency $\dfrac{1}{2l}\sqrt{\dfrac{T}{m}}$, the characteristic frequency of vibration of the string in its fundamental mode. Suppose now that the initial deformation is centred at a distance d from the bridge, and that, more generally than before, the initial velocities are not specified. Then, when the string is released, two pulses will travel out from the centre of deformation with the same speed, in opposite directions. The result will be that two sets of regularly spaced pulses will be reflected at the bridge. The frequency of either set will be the same as before, but the pulses of the second set will be out of phase with those of the first, and there will be a constant time interval equal to $\tau(l-d)/l$ between each pulse of the first set and the corresponding pulse of the second. Here τ is the periodic time of vibration of the string in its fundamental mode.

2.10. DAMPING

The physical situations discussed in this chapter have hitherto been idealised in certain important particulars. We have disregarded the effects of gravity—assuming the tension in the string to be very large indeed compared with its total weight, we have assumed the string to be indefinitely thin and perfectly uniform, and we have considered it to be completely flexible. In the last respect, at the other extreme, our string becomes a solid rod the vibrations of which are determined predominantly by its elastic properties rather than by the longitudinal tension to which it is subjected. We shall be considering such vibrations in detail in chapter 4. But, finally, we have also assumed, in this chapter, that the motion of the string is uninfluenced by frictional or other effects which might dissipate its energy: equation (7), for example, representing the vibration of a string in its fundamental mode, describes a motion which, once started, continues with un-diminished amplitude indefinitely. In actual physical systems such a situation never obtains. Reference has already been made to the decay of amplitude of pendulum oscillations and torsional oscilla-tions in another place (*M L & T*, pp. 184, 264); here we discuss the matter in a little more detail in respect of oscillating systems in general, and in the context of our present consideration of the vibrations of stretched strings. We shall be concerned specifically only with the case in which the 'damping' effect is small.

Let us first calculate the total energy of vibration, when a string is vibrating in its fundamental mode as described by equation (7). Let us re-write this equation in the form (see § 2.5)

$$y = A \sin 2\pi \frac{x}{\lambda} \cos 2\pi \frac{t}{\tau} \tag{20}$$

Then the instantaneous velocity of the element of the string at x is given by

$$\frac{dy}{dt}(=\dot{y}) = -\frac{2\pi A}{\tau} \sin 2\pi \frac{x}{\lambda} \sin 2\pi \frac{t}{\tau} \tag{21}$$

and, the kinetic energy of this element of string of length dx being $\frac{1}{2}m\dot{y}^2 dx$, the total kinetic energy of the whole string at this instant is

$$\frac{1}{2}m \frac{4\pi^2 A^2}{\tau^2} \sin^2 2\pi \frac{t}{\tau} \int_0^{\lambda/2} \sin^2 2\pi \frac{x}{\lambda} dx,$$

or

$$\frac{m\lambda}{2} \frac{\pi^2 A^2}{\tau^2} \sin^2 2\pi \frac{t}{\tau}.$$

In the last expression, it will be noted, $m\lambda/2$ is the mass of the whole string, and the quantity A/τ is of the dimensions of a velocity as is obviously necessary. Now each element of the string executes simple harmonic motion in which kinetic energy is continuously being transformed into potential energy or *vice versa*, and all these elementary motions are in phase. When the displacement is everywhere zero, as at time $t = \tau/4$ (see equation (20)), the potential energy is likewise zero throughout, and the whole of the energy is kinetic (see $M\,L\,\&\,T$, § 11.3). Writing E for the measure of the total energy of vibration of the whole string, we have, therefore,

$$E = \frac{m\lambda}{2}\frac{\pi^2 A^2}{\tau^2} \qquad (22)$$

An interesting result follows if we substitute for τ and λ in equation (22). We have, in fact,

$$E = \frac{\pi^2}{4}\frac{TA^2}{l} \qquad (23)$$

showing that for a string of length l, vibrating in the fundamental mode, the total energy of vibration is proportional to the tension and to the square of the amplitude of vibration (defined as on p. 15), and independent of the mass of the string.

Consider now the situation in which the motion of each element of the string is resisted by a force proportional to the instantaneous velocity of the element and to its length. This is the situation characteristic of motion through a viscous medium ($M\,L\,\&\,T$, §§ 13.3, 13.4). If R is the measure of the 'viscous' force per unit length of the string at any point, we may write $R = -k\dot{y}$, k being the same for all points on the string. Then the measure of the work done against the viscous force acting over an element of string of length dx, when the displacement of the element increases from y to $y + dy$, is $k\dot{y}\,dx\,dy$, and the rate at which this work is done is $k\dot{y}\,dx\left(\dfrac{dy}{dt}\right)$ or $k\dot{y}^2\,dx$. The total expenditure of energy over this element of string, in one complete vibration period, is consequently

$$k\frac{4\pi^2 A^2}{\tau^2}\sin^2 2\pi\frac{x}{\lambda}\,dx\int_0^\tau \sin^2 2\pi\frac{t}{\tau}\,dt$$

(see equation (21)) or

$$\frac{2\pi^2 A^2 k}{\tau} \sin^2 2\pi \frac{x}{\lambda} dx,$$

and ϵ, the corresponding expenditure over the whole string, is

$$\frac{2\pi^2 A^2 k}{\tau} \int_0^{\lambda/2} \sin^2 2\pi \frac{x}{\lambda} dx,$$

that is
$$\epsilon = \frac{\pi^2 A^2 k \lambda}{2\tau} \qquad (24)$$

It will be observed that in deducing this last result we have made the strictly erroneous assumption that equation (20) correctly describes the motion of the string throughout the whole period τ in question, though the fact of dissipation of energy in overcoming the viscous forces belies this assumption. It is this consideration that invalidates our approximate treatment except in the limiting case of small damping, but that, after all, was a limitation which we accepted at the outset. It may even be held that, sacrificing rigour, we have gained physical insight into the problem by proceeding as we have done.

Combining equations (22) and (24) we have

$$\epsilon = \frac{k\tau}{m} E \qquad (25)$$

from which we conclude that for a given string, under specified tension, the expenditure of energy per complete vibration is a constant fraction of the total energy of vibration at the instant in question. We repeat that this result is strictly correct only when the fraction $k\tau/m$ is very small, and our first concern should be to evaluate the implications of this proviso. The natural comparison to make is that between the maximum values of R and F over the whole string during the course of vibration, R defined as above as the viscous force per unit length of string, and F defined (p. 11) as the restoring force per unit length due to the tension in the string, and operative because of the curvature of the string at the relevant point. The maximum values occur at the centre point of the string, the former when the displacement of that point is zero, the latter when the displacement is A. From equation (21) we have numerically

$$R_{\max} = \frac{2\pi Ak}{\tau},$$

and, from equation (2), $F_{\max} = \mu mA,$

with (see p. 15) $\mu = \dfrac{4\pi^2}{\tau^2}.$

Thus $\dfrac{R_{\max}}{F_{\max}} = \dfrac{1}{2\pi}\dfrac{k\tau}{m}.$

If $k\tau/m$ is to be very small, therefore, $R_{\max}$ must be negligible in the first order, compared with $F_{\max}/2\pi$.

When the condition $2\pi R_{\max} \ll F_{\max}$ is fulfilled, if $E_0, E_1, E_2, \ldots$ denote the total energies of vibration of the string at corresponding instants in successive complete vibrations, we have

$$\frac{E_1}{E_0} = \frac{E_2}{E_1} = \frac{E_3}{E_2} = \ldots = 1 - \frac{k\tau}{m},$$

or, representing the energies by effective instantaneous amplitudes, on the basis of equation (22),

$$\frac{A_1{}^2}{A_0{}^2} = \frac{A_2{}^2}{A_1{}^2} = \frac{A_3{}^2}{A_2{}^2} = \ldots = 1 - \frac{k\tau}{m} \qquad (26)$$

If $k\tau/m \ll 1$, as we have supposed, equation (26) reduces to

$$\frac{A_1}{A_0} = \frac{A_2}{A_1} = \frac{A_3}{A_2} = \ldots = 1 - \frac{k\tau}{2m} \qquad (27)$$

To the same degree of approximation we may write

$$1 - \frac{k\tau}{2m} = e^{-\frac{k\tau}{2m}} \qquad (28)$$

Substitution from (28) in (27) is very convenient mathematically: it allows us to consider the amplitude of the motion as a continuously variable quantity. If, in fact, we replace the basic equation of indefinitely maintained vibration (equation (20)) by

$$y = A_0 e^{-\frac{kt}{2m}} \sin 2\pi \frac{x}{\lambda} \cos 2\pi \frac{t}{\tau} \qquad (29)$$

and regard $A_1, A_2, A_3 \ldots$ as the values of y, at $x = \lambda/4$, at times $t = \tau, 2\tau, 3\tau, \ldots$, respectively, the modified form of equation (27) follows immediately. For our purposes, therefore, we accept equation (29) as the equation of the slightly damped motion of a string vibrating in its fundamental mode. We further conclude that an amplitude damping factor of the same general form as the second factor in (29) similarly applies to any case of resisted harmonic motion in which the resistance varies as the first power of the velocity.

Examination of equation (29) shows that, for the stretched string in its fundamental mode, the amplitude of vibration falls to any specified fraction of its initial value in a time which is proportional to m/k. If the damping is in fact due solely to the viscous drag of the air, then k is independent of a, the diameter of the string (compare $M L \& T$, p. 252). Since m is proportional to a^2, in this case the characteristic decay time of the vibrations is proportional to the square of the diameter of the string, if the material of which the string is made is specified. Neither the length of the string, nor its tension, is significant in this connection.

So far, we have confined attention to the damping of a stretched string vibrating in the fundamental mode. Brief consideration will show, however, that there is nothing specific in the calculations of this section to limit the results to that special case. If the quantities λ and τ of equation (20) are suitably re-interpreted, the ensuing results may be taken over directly as applicable to a string vibrating in any one of its higher harmonics. If the nth harmonic is in question, the string may be regarded as made up of n equal segments each vibrating in the fundamental mode appropriate to its length and tension (p. 22). In what follows equation (20), therefore, if, whenever 'the whole string' is mentioned, we substitute 'a complete segment', and if we replace 'the centre of the string' by 'the centre of the segment', our calculations remain valid for the more general case. Thus the fractional loss of energy per complete vibration is still given by $k\tau/m$ (equation (25)), and is smaller by the factor n than in respect of the fundamental mode, τ being smaller by this factor, but the characteristic decay time remains the same (equation (29))—and essentially for the same reason.

2.11. THE MOST GENERAL VIBRATION

In section 2.8 we showed that an infinite stretched string will transmit a regular succession of positive and negative pulses, constituting a periodic disturbance of arbitrary wave-form, without distortion, and with velocity $v = \sqrt{\dfrac{T}{m}}$. For such a disturbance, propagated in the positive direction of x, we may write (compare equation (11))

$$y = \phi\left(\frac{t}{\tau} - \frac{x}{\lambda}\right),$$

λ being the repetition length of the wave-form and τ the repetition period of the motion of any point in the string. Here $v\tau = \lambda$, and the fact of periodicity may be sufficiently safeguarded by the additional condition

$$\phi(m + \epsilon) = \phi(m - 1 + \epsilon),$$

in which m is any integer, positive or negative, and ϵ is any fractional number between 0 and 1.

Consider now two such disturbances, of precisely similar wave-form, traversing the string in opposite directions, such that one disturbance is the inverse and perverse of the other with respect to the string (compare fig. 8). Then the resultant displacement at any point on the infinite string, at any time, is given by

$$y = \phi\left(\frac{t}{\tau} - \frac{x}{\lambda}\right) - \phi\left(\frac{t}{\tau} + \frac{x}{\lambda}\right) \tag{30}$$

Clearly, the points $x = \ldots - \lambda,\ -\lambda/2,\ 0,\ \lambda/2,\ \lambda \ldots$ are displacement nodes of the resultant disturbance, and the argument which was given fully in section 2.9 may be applied to show that the motion of the infinite string between any two adjacent nodes is a possible motion for a finite string, of length equal to the internodal distance $\lambda/2$, of mass m per unit length, and under tension T. Because we have started from the assumption of an arbitrary wave-form, $\phi\left(\dfrac{x}{\lambda}\right)$, we conclude that equation (30), taken over the range $0 \leqslant x \leqslant \lambda/2$, provides a description of the most general type of sustained motion of which a uniform stretched string of length $\lambda/2$ is capable.

In section 2.8 Fourier's theorem was quoted, showing that it is always possible to resolve an arbitrary wave-form into simple harmonic components, having wavelengths λ, $\lambda/2$, . . ., and individual amplitudes and phases which are uniquely determinable once the wave-form is specified in detail. If we apply this result (p. 28) to equation (30), remembering that a sinusoidal disturbance is propagated along an infinite string with a velocity which is independent of the wavelength, we have

$$y = C_1 \left[\cos \left\{ 2\pi \left(\frac{t}{\tau} - \frac{x}{\lambda} \right) + \delta_1 \right\} - \cos \left\{ 2\pi \left(\frac{t}{\tau} + \frac{x}{\lambda} \right) + \delta_1 \right\} \right]$$

$$+ C_2 \left[\cos \left\{ 2\pi \left(\frac{2t}{\tau} - \frac{2x}{\lambda} \right) + \delta_2 \right\} - \cos \left\{ 2\pi \left(\frac{2t}{\tau} + \frac{2x}{\lambda} \right) + \delta_2 \right\} \right]$$

$$+ \ldots + \ldots,$$

which we may simplify as follows:

$$y = 2C_1 \sin 2\pi \frac{x}{\lambda} \sin \left(2\pi \frac{t}{\tau} + \delta_1 \right) + 2C_2 \sin 2\pi \frac{2x}{\lambda} \sin \left(2\pi \frac{2t}{\tau} + \delta_2 \right)$$

$$+ \ldots + \ldots \qquad (31)$$

Comparison with equations (7) and (13), with $l = \lambda/2$ and $\tau = \lambda \sqrt{\dfrac{m}{T}}$ as is appropriate to the case, shows that equation (31) describes a state of motion of the string which is compounded of its various 'normal modes' excited to arbitrary amplitudes, $2C_1$, $2C_2$, . . ., and having arbitrary phases, δ_1, δ_2 . . . . We conclude, therefore, following Daniel Bernoulli who first reached this conclusion in 1755, that the most general type of motion of which a uniform stretched string is capable is one which is so compounded. In this connection the term 'normal mode' is used generally for any one of the harmonic series of vibrations which we identified in section 2.6. It is characteristic of a normal mode that the form of the displacement profile does not change with time: only the magnitude of the displacement at each point varies periodically. Between adjacent nodes the phase of the motion is constant from point to point along the string. Similar statements are obviously untrue of the general vibratory motion described by equation (31).

The problem of the damping of the general 'compound' vibrations of a stretched string involves no basic principles beyond those which we have discussed in section 2.10, but the analysis is complicated and the matter will not be dealt with further in this chapter.

2.12. SPECTRAL ANALYSIS OF A FINITE DISTURBANCE

In section 2.8 we quoted Fourier's theorem in its simplest form, giving the analysis of an arbitrary function $\phi(x)$ over a limited range of the variable, $0 \leqslant x \leqslant l$—and postulating, as the single condition determining the validity of the analysis, that the range should be such that the value of the function is the same at the limits of the range: $\phi(0) = \phi(l)$. In that section, and again in the last section, we applied this result to the case of a periodic disturbance of unlimited extent and arbitrary form, identifying the parameter l with the repetition length of the wave-form. The analysis thereby effected exhibits such a disturbance as composed of an infinite series of sinusoidal components of wavelengths $l, l/2, l/3, \ldots$. Because this series is infinite, the mathematical analysis, carried out with rigour, involves questions of convergence which are not in fact simple. We cannot here concern ourselves with these niceties, but accepting the fact that they have been adequately resolved by the theorists, as practical physicists we expect to find that, in any actual case of interest, our arbitrary wave-form will be closely represented in terms of a few sinusoidal components of low order. This is generally true.

In this section we wish to consider another problem altogether. We have already drawn attention to the fact (p. 20) that there is no such thing in the real world as a strictly sinusoidal disturbance —unlimited in space and time as such a disturbance must necessarily be, by definition. It is equally true, and equally obvious, that there is no such real thing as a periodic disturbance of given arbitrary wave-form, which is strictly unlimited spatially and in time. In this section, then, we consider a single limited ('finite') disturbance. An extreme case of such a disturbance is a simple pulse, such as that considered in section 2.7. We wish to consider the more general case of a disturbance of arbitrary form $\phi(x)$ which is propagated, without change, with velocity v. We shall express the spatial limitation by saying that, at a given time, the displacement is effectively zero except within limits $x = x_0$ and $x = x_0 + l$. Within these limits the instantaneous displacement varies smoothly with distance, having negative as well as positive values. We might regard this disturbance as a finite wave train.

In another place (p. 173) we shall refer to such a disturbance as a wave group.

Let us take a range of x of length $L(L>l)$ wholly enclosing the disturbance in question. Then, according to our specification, $\phi(x)$ is effectively zero at each extremity of this range, and Fourier's theorem may be applied in the form with which we are familiar (equation (19)). Over the range considered, but not outside this range, our isolated disturbance is faithfully represented in terms of a constant displacement A_0 (see equation (19)) and a series of sinusoidal components, of uniquely determined amplitudes and phases, having wavelengths $L, L/2, L/3, \ldots$. As in our previous discussion, we should expect the amplitudes of the components of very small wavelength to be vanishingly small, and, to the extent that L is greater than l, we should expect that the components of lowest order would be of small amplitude also.

As we have stated, the analysis that we have just outlined fails to represent the isolated disturbance outside the limits of the chosen range. Clearly, to represent the disturbance in its full isolation we must continue the process and extend this range to infinity. If $L=nl$,

$$\frac{L}{n}-\frac{L}{n+1}=\frac{L}{n(n+1)}=\frac{l}{n+1}.$$

Supposing the analysis to be made with a range of this magnitude, we should not expect the amplitudes of the sinusoidal components of order much less than n to be significantly different from zero—and the calculation that we have given shows that, at this order, the wavelength separation of neighbouring orders is $l/(n+1)$. We compare this result with $l/2$, the separation in wavelength of the first- and second-order components which we obtain by making the analysis over the range of the disturbance itself ($L/l\equiv n=1$), and we note that, when $n\gg1$, $l/(n+1)\ll l/2$. In each case analysis gives a series of components constituting a 'line spectrum' of wavelengths. Obviously, as $L\to\infty$ ($n\to\infty$), this line spectrum becomes blurred into a continuum. Formally, the constant term A_0 is outside the continuum: it represents a component of infinite wavelength. In this connection, our physical intuition would lead us to suspect that A_0 must become zero when $L\to\infty$. We have already stated (p. 28) that A_0 is zero, in analysis over a finite range, when the disturbance profile is symmetrical in respect of the 'undisturbed' datum-line. In fact, for any limited disturbance, A_0 indeed tends to zero, when the analysis is made over an infinite range.

We have reached the conclusion that Fourier analysis of a single finite disturbance discloses a continuous spectrum of sinusoidal components, the distribution of amplitude (or intensity) in the spectrum being uniquely determinable in terms of the disturbance profile $\phi(x)$. We have suggested that the intensity is likely to be very small for wavelengths greater than l, where l represents the linear extent of the disturbance, and that it must tend to zero for very short wavelengths. Beyond this we cannot go, if we make no further assumption concerning the form of the disturbance. But there is an important limiting case in which the disturbance is 'nearly homogeneous', of wavelength λ. The instantaneous profile of such a disturbance resembles a series of waves, of very nearly constant crest-to-crest distance, dying away to nothing on either side of a centre. It would be surprising if the Fourier spectrum of such a disturbance was other than sharply peaked about wavelength $\lambda(\lambda \ll l)$. Such, indeed, is the case. Moreover, in general, the spectrum is the more sharply peaked as l/λ is greater—as the actual disturbance approximates more closely to an ideal sinusoidal wave. Expressed in this way, the statement is almost a tautology. But it is an important statement, nevertheless, and it will become relevant many times during our later discussions.

CHAPTER 3

COUPLED VIBRATIONS

3.1. THE LOADED STRING

In the last chapter we considered in detail the vibrations of a light
string under tension, the mass of the string being assumed
uniformly distributed along its length. In this section we take
the other extreme: we assume the string itself to be massless,
and we imagine point masses to be attached to it as required for
the argument. As before, we consider the ideal situation in which
the string is perfectly flexible, all displacements are very small
compared with the length of the string, and gravitational effects
are negligible.

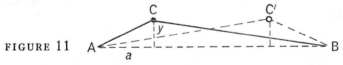

FIGURE 11

Let us consider first the case of a single mass, m, attached, at
C, a distance a from A, one of the fixed ends of a string ACB of
length l under tension T. Let the mass be displaced laterally
through a distance y (fig. 11). Then the equation of motion, for
small amplitudes, is

$$m\frac{d^2y}{dt^2} = -T\left(\frac{1}{a}+\frac{1}{l-a}\right)y,$$

and the motion is simple harmonic, and of period, τ, given by

$$\tau = 2\pi\sqrt{\frac{ma(l-a)}{Tl}}.$$

Obviously, an exactly similar system, having the same characteristic period, would be obtained if, between A and B, a second
string AC′B, under the same tension, had an equal mass m
attached at C′, distant a from B.

Let us now create a composite system by attaching the equal

masses at equal distances a from the ends of a single string stretched from A to B under the same tension T. In this arrangement the motions of the masses at C and C' are 'coupled' through the connecting length of string. We are first concerned to identify the normal modes of the composite system (see p. 41). A little consideration will show that these are two in number. If the instantaneous displacement profile is of either form represented in fig. 12, this form will be maintained throughout the subsequent motion, provided the instantaneous velocities of the masses have the same symmetry as their instantaneous displacements. In respect of these two normal modes, and for small amplitudes, the equations of motion of either mass are

$$m\frac{d^2y}{dt^2} = -T\frac{y}{a}$$

and

$$m\frac{d^2y}{dt^2} = -T\left(\frac{1}{a}+\frac{2}{l-2a}\right)y,$$

respectively, and the corresponding simple harmonic motions have periods

$$\tau_1 = 2\pi\sqrt{\frac{ma}{T}}, \quad \tau_2 = 2\pi\sqrt{\frac{ma(l-2a)}{Tl}}.$$

We note that $\tau_1 > \tau > \tau_2$, and that when $a \ll l$, so that the mechanical coupling of the two motions is slight,

$$\tau_1 = \tau\left(1+\tfrac{1}{2}\frac{a}{l}\right), \quad \tau_2 = \tau\left(1-\tfrac{1}{2}\frac{a}{l}\right) \tag{32}$$

Let us assume that the most general type of motion of the loaded string is a motion compounded of the two normal modes, having arbitrary amplitudes and phases. We verified the corresponding result for the uniform string in the last chapter (§ 2.11) —and the result is, in fact, valid generally for all vibrating systems, though we give no formal proof of it: here we are content to argue by analogy. If y_1 and y_2 are taken to represent instantaneous displacements of the masses at C and C', respectively, motion in the normal modes is described by the equations

$$y_1 = A_1 \cos 2\pi\frac{t}{\tau_1}, \quad y_2 = A_1 \cos 2\pi\frac{t}{\tau_1},$$

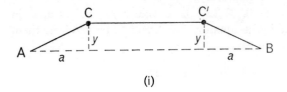

(i)

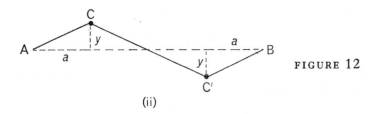

(ii)

FIGURE 12

$$y_1 = A_2 \cos 2\pi \frac{t}{\tau_2}, \quad y_2 = -A_2 \cos 2\pi \frac{t}{\tau_2}.$$

Thus, with essentially the same notation, the most general motion of the system is represented by

$$y_1 = A_1 \cos\left(2\pi\frac{t}{\tau_1} + \delta_1\right) + A_2 \cos\left(2\pi\frac{t}{\tau_2} + \delta_2\right)$$

$$y_2 = A_1 \cos\left(2\pi\frac{t}{\tau_1} + \delta_1\right) - A_2 \cos\left(2\pi\frac{t}{\tau_2} + \delta_2\right)$$

(33)

Here there are four arbitrary constants, A_1, A_2, δ_1, δ_2, to be determined in relation to the four data which describe the initial conditions of motion—the velocities and displacements of the two masses at $t=0$.

For this simple system, the essential features of the most general type of motion can be elicited by determining the four constants of equation (33) in respect of a special case. Suppose lateral forces to be applied to the masses at C and C' in opposite directions, and of magnitudes so adjusted that the former mass is displaced through a distance A whilst the latter remains undisturbed. Imagine the system to be released from this state of initial deformation. Then the initial conditions are given by $y_1 = A$,

$y_2=0$, $\dot{y}_1=\dot{y}_2=0$, $t=0$. When these values are substituted in equations (33) and in the equations for $\dot{y}_1$ and $\dot{y}_2$ derived from them by differentiation, we have

$$A = A_1 \cos \delta_1 + A_2 \cos \delta_2,$$

$$0 = A_1 \cos \delta_1 - A_2 \cos \delta_2,$$

$$0 = \frac{A_1}{\tau_1} \sin \delta_1 + \frac{A_2}{\tau_2} \sin \delta_2,$$

$$0 = \frac{A_1}{\tau_1} \sin \delta_1 - \frac{A_2}{\tau_2} \sin \delta_2,$$

and so obtain $\delta_1=\delta_2=0$, $A_1=A_2=A/2$, as the only effective solution. In this case, then, equations (33) become

$$y_1 = \frac{A}{2} \cos 2\pi \frac{t}{\tau_1} + \frac{A}{2} \cos 2\pi \frac{t}{\tau_2},$$

$$y_2 = \frac{A}{2} \cos 2\pi \frac{t}{\tau_1} - \frac{A}{2} \cos 2\pi \frac{t}{\tau_2}.$$

Remembering that $\tau_1 > \tau_2$, we may rewrite these equations in the form

$$y_1 = A \cos \pi \left(\frac{1}{\tau_1}+\frac{1}{\tau_2}\right) t \cos \pi \left(\frac{1}{\tau_2}-\frac{1}{\tau_1}\right) t$$

$$y_2 = A \sin \pi \left(\frac{1}{\tau_1}+\frac{1}{\tau_2}\right) t \sin \pi \left(\frac{1}{\tau_2}-\frac{1}{\tau_1}\right) t \quad (34)$$

Equations (34) are valid whatever the value of a, the distance of either mass from the end of the string. In the limit, when $a \ll l$ (see equation (32)), they reduce to

$$y_1 = A \cos 2\pi \frac{t}{\tau} \cos \pi \frac{at}{l\tau}$$

$$y_2 = A \sin 2\pi \frac{t}{\tau} \sin \pi \frac{at}{l\tau} \quad (35)$$

In each of these equations, the first of the time-variable factors is periodic in time with periodic time τ, the second such factor is periodic with the much longer periodic time $2l\tau/a$. Effectively, therefore, the motion of either mass is simple harmonic of period

τ (the periodic time of its natural oscillations in the absence of the other mass), and of slowly varying amplitude. The amplitude variations are themselves simple harmonic of period $2l\tau/a$, if sign as well as magnitude is considered—or $l\tau/a$ if magnitude only is taken count of—and the important fact emerges that when the amplitude of the motion of one mass is zero that of the other is a maximum. This maximum value is A, and, indeed, at any stage of the motion the sum of the squares of the effective amplitudes is A^2, as we should expect if the total energy remains constant (see $M L \, \& \, T$, p. 233). The motion of the system as a whole, then, exhibits the phenomenon of 'beats' (see $M L \, \& \, T$, p. 91) energy being transferred back and forth between the coupled components.

In general, when the initial conditions are not as simple as those we have here considered, and when in consequence neither the amplitudes nor the phases of the constituent normal modes are the same, a similar statement is valid: energy is transferred back and forth between the two masses, though it is not completely associated first with one mass and then with the other as equations (35) require.

3.2. COUPLED PENDULUMS

The system considered in the last section was very considerably idealised: any close approximation to it in a large-scale demonstration experiment is almost impossible. In this section we consider a related system much less difficult of realisation, though again we consider the ideal case. We replace the two point masses attached directly to the stretched string, as in fig. 12, by equal masses suspended from the string as simple pendulums of the same length. We retain the assumptions that the stretched string which supports the pendulums, and the pendulum strings themselves, are massless, but, quite obviously, we do not now neglect the effect of gravity—it is all-important for our present considerations.

Because this arrangement is more complicated than the other, it is worth while, before considering it in detail, to state explicitly the properties of stretched strings under tension and in motion, in the ideal case, when the strings are assumed to be massless. Two general results may be noted: first, any section of such a string which is unloaded—by a massive particle or by the attachment of another string under tension—is straight; secondly, when

D

three lengths of massless stretched string are joined in a single point, and are otherwise unloaded, the three lengths are co-planar and are so directed that the tensions which they sustain have zero resultant at the point in question. That these two statements are true is obvious from the fact that if either were invalid a finite force would be acting on a massless element of string, infinite acceleration would result, and the situations could not be maintained.

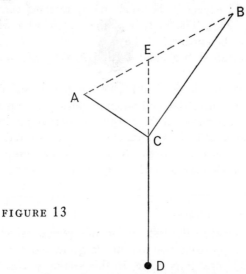

FIGURE 13

These preliminaries having been disposed of, let us consider first a single pendulum supported from a string under tension as illustrated in fig. 13. A and B are fixed supports of a flexible massless string ACB, as before. At C, a similar string CD is attached; at the other end of this string there is a small spherical bob of mass m, as shown. When the system is in equilibrium let E be the point in AB vertically above D. In this situation the tension in CD is mg, g being the acceleration due to gravity, and if T_1, T_2 are the tensions in CA, CB, respectively, if $\angle ACE = \theta_1$, $\angle BCE = \theta_2$,

$$\frac{T_1}{\sin \theta_2} = \frac{T_2}{\sin \theta_1} = \frac{mg}{\sin (\theta_1 + \theta_2)} \tag{36}$$

Obviously, for small oscillations in which D moves in a plane at right angles to the plane of the figure, the system behaves as a

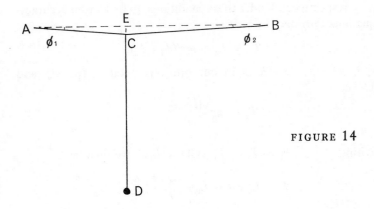

FIGURE 14

simple pendulum of length L, equal to ED. Throughout such oscillations the points A, B, C and D remain co-planar and the strings remain taut. Again, it is clear that, by the application of a suitable force, the bob at D may be held in equilibrium in the plane of the figure, all the strings being taut, provided that CD lies within the angle formed by AC and BC produced. In particular, therefore, the bob may execute simple pendulum oscillations in this plane, of small amplitude, with C as effective point of suspension. In brief, then, the bob is capable of executing simple harmonic oscillations in two planes mutually at right angles, the periodic times of the oscillations being different. If it is arbitrarily displaced from its position of equilibrium and then released, its subsequent motion will be a combination of these two motions, the amplitudes and relative phases being determined by the initial conditions imposed. Considered in this regard, as a practical arrangement for demonstrating the composition of such motions, the system illustrated in fig. 13 is generally referred to as Blackburn's pendulum. It was first devised for this purpose by Hugh Blackburn, Kelvin's undergraduate friend, and later professor of mathematics at Glasgow for thirty years from 1849.

For our present purposes we are interested in Blackburn's pendulum only in relation to its mode of longer period, $2\pi(L/g)^{\frac{1}{2}}$, and only in the limiting case, when the supports A and B are in the same horizontal plane and the angles θ_1 and θ_2 differ very little from right angles. In that case the system has the form shown in fig. 14, the angles ϕ_1, ϕ_2 being the complements of

θ_1, θ_2, respectively. Under these conditions, to first-order accuracy, equations (36) may be written

$$T_1 = T_2 = mg/(\phi_1 + \phi_2),$$

or, if AE $= a$, AB $= l$, as in our previous notation (p. 45), and EC $= d$,

$$T_1 = T_2 = mg \frac{a(l-a)}{dl}.$$

Writing $\qquad T_1 = T_2 = T$, $\quad$ CD $= L_0$, $\quad$ we then have

$$L = L_0 + d = L_0 + \frac{mga}{T} \frac{l-a}{l},$$

and for τ, the period of pendulum oscillations about E, in the plane at right angles to the figure, the mode in which we are interested, when $L \gg d$,

$$\tau = 2\pi (L_0/g)^{\frac{1}{2}} \left(1 + \frac{mga}{2TL_0} \frac{l-a}{l}\right), \qquad (37)$$

Now suppose that, under these conditions, a second exactly similar pendulum is attached to the supporting string at C′ (fig. 15), where BE′ $= a$, and imagine that the tension in the supporting string remains T as before. In the equilibrium configuration let $\angle$BAC $= \angle$ABC′ $= \phi$, EC $=$ E′C′ $= d_1$. Then

$$T = mg/\phi = mga/d_1 \qquad (38)$$

As in the previous case (§ 3.1), the normal modes of transverse motion of this system are those in which the masses concerned execute simple harmonic motions of the same amplitude, transversely to AB, in the one case in phase, in the other 180° out of phase, with one another. For the first normal mode, obviously the six points A, C, D, D′, C′ and B remain co-planar throughout; for the second, G, the mid-point of CC′, remains at rest, the points A, C, D and G remain co-planar, as do G, D′, C′ and B. If FC $=$ F′C′ $= d_2$, if the effective pendulum lengths corresponding to the two modes are L_1 and L_2, and the periodic times are τ_1 and τ_2, then

$$L_1 = L_0 + d_1, \quad \tau_1 = 2\pi (L_1/g)^{\frac{1}{2}},$$
$$L_2 = L_0 + d_2, \quad \tau_2 = 2\pi (L_2/g)^{\frac{1}{2}}.$$

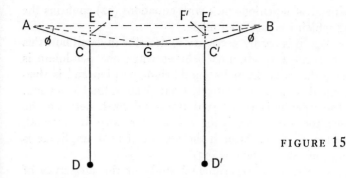

FIGURE 15

Moreover, to a sufficient approximation,

$$d_2 = d_1\, GF/GA,$$
$$= d_1(l-2a)/l,$$

thus
$$\tau_1 = 2\pi(L_0/g)^{\frac{1}{2}}\left(1+\frac{mga}{2TL_0}\right) \tag{39}$$

$$\tau_2 = 2\pi(L_0/g)^{\frac{1}{2}}\left(1+\frac{mga}{2TL_0}\frac{l-2a}{l}\right) \tag{40}$$

The validity of the approximations represented by equations (37), (39) and (40) does not depend upon the condition $a \ll l$, which we had to impose in order to obtain similar first-order approximations in the case of the directly loaded string (§ 3.1), but, this difference having been noted, the final results are of the same general form in the two cases studied: provided that $mga \ll 2TL_0$ (which effectively combines the two conditions previously introduced in treating the present case), we have

$$\tau_1 = \tau\left(1+\frac{mga}{2TL_0}\frac{a}{l}\right), \quad \tau_2 = \tau\left(1-\frac{mga}{2TL_0}\frac{a}{l}\right).$$

These equations may be exhibited in their purely geometrical aspect by substituting for mg/T from equation (38). We then obtain

$$\tau_1 = \tau\left(1+\frac{\phi a^2}{2L_0 l}\right), \quad \tau_2 = \tau\left(1-\frac{\phi a^2}{2L_0 l}\right) \tag{41}$$

or, alternatively,

$$\tau_1 = \tau\left(1+\frac{d_1 a}{2L_0 l}\right), \quad \tau_2 = \left(1-\frac{d_1 a}{2L_0 l}\right) \tag{42}$$

A comparison of equations (42) with equations (32) confirms the statement which has just been made.

At this stage it is hardly necessary to describe in detail how this system of coupled pendulums behaves when one pendulum is transversely displaced from its equilibrium position and is then released: the details have effectively been given in the last section. Briefly, the motion is transferred back and forth between the pendulums, the beat period being $L_0 l\tau/d_1 a$ (or twice this interval, if the change of phase through the instant of zero amplitude is taken count of—see equations (35)).

A very considerable experimental study of the properties of coupled pendulums was carried out during the period 1917-1920 by E. H. Barton, professor of physics at Nottingham from 1906 until his death in 1925; for that reason the system of two pendulums represented in fig. 15 is commonly referred to as an example of Barton's pendulums—indeed it is the simplest example of such an arrangement.

3.3. OTHER COUPLED SYSTEMS

It should be obvious that the results derived in the last two sections may be taken over, with appropriate re-definition of the parameters of the problem, and applied in full to a large variety of situations in which pairs of precisely similar oscillating systems are 'weakly' coupled. Moreover, the coupled systems need not be mechanical systems: they may, for example, be electric circuits having characteristic frequencies for the oscillation of charge— and therefore of electric current, or they may be the nuclei of two hydrogen atoms which are 'coupled' by the back-and-forth motion (in the imagination of the theorist!) of a single electron in their neighbourhood. It would clearly be out of place to follow up these more remote applications here, but two further examples of mechanical systems may be profitably discussed for which the limitations of weak coupling and precise similarity of the oscillators are not invoked.

The first of these systems was introduced, and developed for the purposes of a precise laboratory experiment, by G. F. C. Searle (1864-1954), who taught practical physics in the Cavendish Laboratory, with short interruptions, from 1890 until he finally retired, full of vigour, in 1945. It is illustrated in fig. 16. Three torsion wires AB, CD, EF, are joined as shown to form a vertical

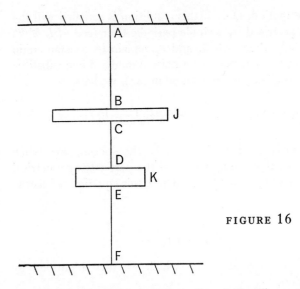

FIGURE 16

suspension for two inertia bars J and K. The ends A and F of the upper and lower wires are firmly secured to rigid supports, and the inertia bars are capable of oscillation in horizontal planes about the common axis of the three wires. We assume, for ease of description, though the limitation is inessential, that in equilibrium the two bars lie with their longitudinal axes parallel and in the plane of the figure. Let us suppose that the moment of inertia of the bar J about the axis of suspension is I_1, and that that of K, about the same axis, is I_2. Let μ_1, μ_2 and μ_3 be the torsional constants of the wires AB, EF and CD respectively. We wish to enquire whether the possible motions of this system include motion in normal modes, and if so to identify them.

Let the instantaneous displacements of J and K, in the positive direction around FA, be θ_1 and θ_2. Then the magnitudes of the restoring couples acting on the two bars are given by

$$G_1 = \mu_1\theta_1 + \mu_3(\theta_1 - \theta_2)$$
$$G_2 = \mu_2\theta_2 + \mu_3(\theta_2 - \theta_1)$$

(43)

The condition that the motion of the system shall be in a normal mode is that

$$\frac{G_1}{I_1\theta_1} = \frac{G_2}{I_2\theta_2}$$

(44)

throughout the motion. Only if this condition is satisfied will the motion be characterised by a single periodic time (see *M L & T*, p. 181), and only then will θ_1 and θ_2 remain in constant ratio throughout. Let $\theta_2 = \kappa\theta_1$ for such a normal mode. Then substituting in equations (43), and from these in (44), we have

$$\{\mu_1 + \mu_3(1-\kappa)\}I_2 = \left\{\mu_2 + \mu_3\left(1-\frac{1}{\kappa}\right)\right\}I_1 \qquad (45)$$

Equation (45) is a quadratic in κ. In the special case, when $I_1 = I_2$, $\mu_1 = \mu_2$, so that the system is of the perfectly symmetrical type which we have previously considered, this equation reduces to

$$\kappa^2 = 1.$$

The solutions,

$$\kappa = \pm 1,$$

represent the two normal modes which we then identified by simple inspection.

In the general case equation (45) reduces to

$$\mu_3 I_2 \kappa^2 + \{(\mu_2 + \mu_3)I_1 - (\mu_1 + \mu_3)I_2\}\kappa - \mu_3 I_1 = 0.$$

That this equation always possesses two real roots (the first and last terms being of opposite sign) is sufficient proof that the system is characterised by two normal modes, whatever the values of the mechanical quantities I_1, I_2, μ_1, μ_2 and μ_3. These two roots are necessarily of opposite sign: the normal modes, therefore, involve oscillations of the two inertia bars which are respectively in phase and 180° out of phase with one another. The numerical values of the roots, κ_s and κ_a, determine the relative amplitudes of the component oscillations in the two modes—the 'symmetric' and the 'antisymmetric' modes. In general, this amplitude ratio is different for the two modes. Finally, if τ_s, τ_a are the periodic times characteristic of the normal modes, and f_s, f_a are the corresponding frequencies, it will be seen that the most direct method of deducing these quantities is to substitute κ_s (or, alternatively, κ_a) for θ_2/θ_1 in one of equations (43) and then to evaluate the appropriate term of equation (44). It will be recognised that, when κ_s is so substituted, this evaluation leads directly to the measure of the quantity $4\pi^2 f_s^2$—and correspondingly, when κ_a is employed. Here we have not thought it worth while to carry through these rather laborious, though simple, calculations for the general case, though for reference we give the two values κ_s (positive) and κ_a (negative) in the single expression

$$\kappa_{s,\,a} = \frac{-\{(\mu_2+\mu_3)I_1-(\mu_1+\mu_3)I_2\} \pm [\{(\mu_2+\mu_3)I_1-(\mu_1+\mu_3)I_2\}^2+4\mu_3{}^2I_1I_2]^{\frac{1}{2}}}{2\mu_3I_2}$$

(46)

As for previously considered systems, any arbitrary motion of the coupled inertia bars may be regarded as compounded of their normal modes, the relative amplitudes and phases being determinable once the initial conditions of the motion have been specified.

It is interesting to consider the general motion of the system when it does not possess the full symmetry represented by $I_1=I_2$, $\mu_1=\mu_2$ (see p. 56), but merely the partial symmetry which the condition $\mu_1I_2=\mu_2I_1$ imposes. This latter condition implies that if inertia bar J were suspended solely by torsion wire AB, and K solely by FE, then the periodic times of torsional oscillations of these isolated component systems would be the same. Under this condition, simplification of equation (45) (or (46)) leads to the results

$$\kappa_s = 1, \quad \kappa_a = -I_1/I_2,$$

and, when the procedure of evaluation of equation (44) outlined above has been carried through, to the expressions

$$4\pi^2f_s{}^2 = \mu_1/I_1,$$

$$4\pi^2f_a{}^2 = \left(\mu_1+\frac{I_1+I_2}{I_2}\mu_3\right)\Big/I_1.$$

Now, if f is the common frequency of either component system considered in isolation, as just described, with τ as the corresponding period, then $\mu_1/I_1=\mu_2/I_2=4\pi^2f^2$, and

$$f_s = f$$
$$f_a = f\left(1+\frac{\mu_3}{\mu_1}+\frac{\mu_3}{\mu_2}\right)^{\frac{1}{2}}$$

(47)

Suppose that we are concerned to determine the motion which would result if, inertia bar J having been displaced through an initial angle α, K meanwhile being held undisplaced, the two bars were then released from rest simultaneously. The process of calculation is precisely that followed, in the case of the loaded string, in section 3.1 (p. 47). We have, finally,

$$\theta_1 = \frac{a}{I_1+I_2}(I_1 \cos 2\pi f_s t + I_2 \cos 2\pi f_a t),$$

$$\theta_2 = \frac{aI_1}{I_1+I_2}(\cos 2\pi f_s t - \cos 2\pi f_a t).$$

The implications of this solution can best be seen by writing it in the alternative form

$$\theta_1 = a \cos \pi(f_s+f_a)t \cos \pi(f_a-f_s)t$$
$$+ \frac{I_1-I_2}{I_1+I_2} a \sin \pi(f_s+f_a)t \sin \pi(f_a-f_s)t \qquad (48)$$
$$\theta_2 = \frac{2I_1}{I_1+I_2} a \sin \pi(f_s+f_a)t \sin \pi(f_a-f_s)t.$$

In this form, equations (48) may be compared directly with equations (34)—and, when the coupling is weak, that is when $\mu_3 \ll \mu_1$, μ_2, so that $(f_a-f_s) \ll (f_s+f_a)$, with equations (35). The initial conditions which have been assumed in the two cases are essentially the same, but we note that, whereas in the former case (of full symmetry) the phenomenon of beats is fully developed, in the latter (of only partial symmetry) this is not so. The effective amplitude of oscillation of inertia bar K varies between zero and $2aI_1/(I_1+I_2)$ as the amplitude of oscillation of J varies between a and $a(I_1-I_2)/(I_1+I_2)$. We note that

$$I_1 \cdot (I_1-I_2)^2 + I_2 \cdot (2I_1)^2 = I_1 \cdot (I_1+I_2)^2,$$

as conservation of energy requires, it being granted that, for an inertia bar in simple harmonic motion about a principal axis, the total energy of oscillation is proportional jointly to the square of the amplitude of oscillation and the moment of inertia of the bar about the axis concerned (compare $M L \& T$, p. 233).

On this particular problem there is nothing further to add at this stage (see, however, § 3.4), except the remark—which should indeed be obvious—that if we had postulated initial conditions in which inertia bar K were displaced and J undisplaced, we should have found that the motion of J, not K, would subsequently exhibit periodic phases of zero amplitude.

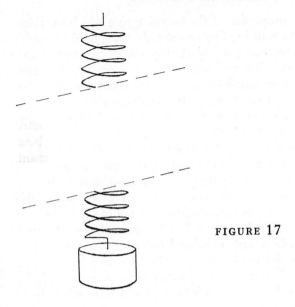

FIGURE 17

The second of the mechanical systems which we shall describe in this section is even more striking in its characteristic behaviour than the system of two inertia bars which we have just been discussing, but it is much more difficult to treat theoretically, and we shall not attempt a full treatment. We consider it here chiefly because it exemplifies a further type of asymmetry: in it we no longer have a system of two separate components executing coupled motions of the same general character, but a single body possessing two dissimilar degrees of freedom of motion which are mechanically coupled. The system was first investigated and described in 1894 by L. R. Wilberforce (1861-1944), who taught in the Cavendish Laboratory with Searle (p. 54) and was professor of physics at Liverpool from 1900 to 1935. It consists of a long, closely wound, helical spring, suspended with its axis vertical, and loaded with a body symmetrical about an axis of revolution which is made to coincide with the axis of the spring. The arrangement is illustrated in fig. 17, in which the load is shown in the form of a solid cylinder of radius somewhat greater than the radius of the flat helix of the spring.

Although we shall not treat the motion of this coupled system in detail, if we are to discuss it at all we must at least consider at some length the properties of the helical spring which provides the coupling. The coiled spring was already being used in mechanisms, and was becoming an object of experimental study, in the seventeenth century: Robert Hooke (*M L & T*, pp. 126, 203) was certainly aware of its possibilities in this connection in 1660. Its use in the spring balance ('spring steelyard') dates from the early years of the following century, but it was not until 1814 that the mode of action of this simple contrivance was properly understood. Even then the work of J. Binet was generally overlooked, until A. J. C. Barre de Saint-Venant gave original credit to his countryman whilst carrying the matter a good deal farther in 1864. Here we separate, for convenience of presentation, the geometrical from the mechanical characteristics of the spring.

Suppose that a uniform wire of length l and radius a is wound as a helix of angle α and cylindrical radius $r(r \gg a)$. Imagine a point to traverse the whole length of the wire, and let z be the distance which this point travels parallel to the axis of the helix in this process, and θ be the angle through which it rotates about this axis. Then

$$l = r\theta \sec \alpha \qquad (49)$$

$$z = r\theta \tan \alpha \qquad (50)$$

and, consequently, $\qquad z = l \sin \alpha \qquad (51)$

In such circumstances the radius of curvature of the axial filament of the wire is constant along its length, its measure, ρ, being given (see p. 293) by

$$\rho = r \sec^2 \alpha \qquad (52)$$

Eliminating α between equations (49) and (52), we have further

$$l^2 = \rho r \theta^2 \qquad (53)$$

Let us consider a change in configuration of the wire in which its form remains helical about the same axis as before, the radius of curvature of the axial filament of the wire remains unchanged, but the length of the helix increases slightly. In equations (49) to (53), therefore, we assume that the values of l and ρ remain constant, whilst the value of z increases. We conclude, from equation (51), that the value of α, the angle of the helix, must necessarily increase, then, from equation (52), that the value of r, the radius of the helix, must decrease, and, finally, since the product $r\theta^2$ (equation (53)) must remain constant, that the value of θ must increase. This last conclusion is important: if the overall length of the helix is increased, under the conditions we have specified, the value of θ, the total angle of coil, must increase proportionately—there must, in fact, be a relative rotation of one end of the helix with respect to the other, about the helical axis, in such a direction as to tend to tighten the coil. Herein, as we shall presently attempt to justify, is the geometrical basis of the mechanical coupling of the axial motion of the load of fig. 17 with its motion of rotation about the axis, shown vertical in the figure.

The physical reason for specifying that the radius of curvature of the axial filament of the helical spring shall remain constant, when its length is steadily increased as we have just supposed, is that to change that radius would require the application of forces providing a bending moment ($M L$ & T, p. 321) about an axis at right angles to the plane of curvature. We are specifically considering a closely wound spring ($\alpha \ll 1$) suspended vertically; in our case, therefore, the plane of curvature is almost horizontal, and the oppositely directed vertical forces, which are sufficient to produce the increase in length, provide no appreciable bending moment about a vertical axis.

Let us consider what in fact the effect of these vertical forces is, at any section of the wire. Here we must specify the mode of application of the forces with greater precision. The arrangement is already illustrated in fig. 17. To each end of the helical wire constituting the spring is attached a rigid member having the shape of an L. One arm of each such member lies symmetrically along the vertical helical axis; the other arm, which is horizontal, lies along a radius of the helix. The total rotation about the axis, guided by the helix, which in imagination would bring the horizontal arm of the upper member into coincidence with the horizontal arm of the lower member is θ. The spring is supported by the upper member, the vertical arm of which is firmly clamped, so that it does not yield. The corresponding arm of the lower member carries the load, being coaxial with it. If W is the weight of the load, the 'stretching' forces constitute an equal and opposite pair, each of magnitude W, acting along the axis of the helical

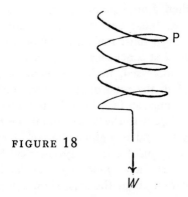

FIGURE 18

spring. The whole situation is symmetrical, top and bottom; that at the lower end of the spring is as illustrated in fig. 18.

Consider now the forces acting across the right section of the coiled wire through P, any point on the spring. The forces acting from the upper part of the spring on the lower part, across this section, must be such as to equilibrate the external force W. Obviously, an upwards force W is required for equilibrium in respect of vertical motion; but, because this force cannot be collinear with the load, having a line of action parallel to the helical axis and at a distance r from that axis, there is also required a couple of moment Wr, the axis of which is horizontal at P, tangential to the cylinder of the helix, and therefore almost collinear with the axis of the wire at P. As P is shown in the figure, this internal couple acting on the lower part of the wire has a clockwise sense of rotation. Now such an internal couple can be brought into play only if the wire is in a state of torsional strain ($M L \& T$, p. 322). We conclude then that one result of the application of an axial load to a closely wound helical spring must be to twist the wire of the spring slightly about its own axis. This conclusion was first reached by Binet in 1814, as indicated above.

The relevance of this conclusion to our discussion of the geometrical characteristics of the spring must now be examined. To do this we consider more closely the original process of winding the helical spring. Imagine that we start with a length of a straight cylindrical wire free from strain. The wire AB (fig. 19) is fixed at one end (A) and makes an angle α with the horizontal plane. It is gradually coiled into the helix A'B', of

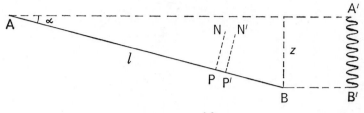

FIGURE 19

radius r and length z, by the continuous process of pure bending, the curvature being maintained uniform along the length of the wire throughout the process and being slowly increased from zero to $(1/r) \cos^2 a$, according to equation (52). This result would be achieved if a rigid arm were fixed securely to the wire at B, at right angles to its length and horizontal, and if a gradually increasing couple were applied through this arm to the free end of the wire, the axis of the couple rotating about the vertical in a cone of semi-vertical angle a as the wire is progressively coiled. To define this procedure fully, we postulate that the arm at B is maintained horizontal throughout the operation.

Consider now two normals to the wire, PN, P'N', through near points, P, P', and suppose that these normals originally lie in the vertical plane through AB (fig. 19). Let $PP' = \Delta l$, and, when the wire is fully coiled, let $\Delta \theta$ be the angle between the radii of the cylindrical helix which pass through these two points, P, P', respectively. Then we have (see equation (49)) $\Delta l = r \Delta \theta \sec a$. If the lines PN, P'N' have remained fixed with respect to the wire during the process of coiling, these lines will no longer be parallel when the wire is fully coiled. Each will be inclined at an angle a to the vertical as before, but the tangent planes to the cylinder of the helix in which they lie will intersect in a vertical line and will be inclined to one another at the angle $\Delta \theta$ already specified. The situation, in respect of directions only, is as shown in fig. 20, PZN and P'ZN' representing the tangent planes that we have mentioned. Here the dotted circle centred at Z is horizontal, $\angle NPZ = \angle N'P'Z' = a$, $\angle NZN' = \Delta \theta$. If $\angle N'PN = \Delta \phi$, $PZ = h$, obviously

$$h \sec a \, \Delta \phi = h \tan a \, \Delta \theta,$$

or $$\Delta \phi = \Delta \theta \sin a.$$

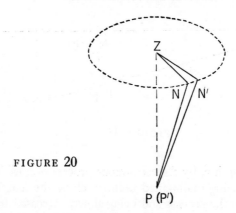

FIGURE 20

P (P')

We conclude that in the process of winding a helical spring, if it is carried out in the manner we have described, the cylindrical wire of which the spring is made is subjected to a total twist ϕ, around its own axis, which is related to the total angle of coil of the spring and to the angle of the helix by the equation

$$\phi = \theta \sin \alpha \qquad (54)$$

We note, in passing, that our requirement that the twisting arm through B (fig. 19) should remain perpendicular to the helical axis throughout the winding process can be achieved only if, in addition to the bending couple already specified, a suitably adjusted twisting couple is concurrently brought into operation about the axis of the wire. Referring to fig. 19 again, we note further that if the initial motion of B in the winding process is 'into the paper', so that the helix A'B' has the character of left-handed screw (see *M L & T*, p. 81), the final twist of the wire is also left-handed, and *vice versa*.

This conclusion having been reached, let us reconsider the change of configuration of a helical spring which we discussed earlier (p. 60). We imposed the condition then that the radius of curvature of the axial filament of the wire, and its total length, should remain constant. Let us add the requirement that a rigid arm attached horizontally, and at right angles to the wire at its lower extremity, should remain horizontal whilst the length of the helix is increased by a small amount, say from z to $z + \Delta z$. Then we conclude, since both α and θ must increase (see above), that ϕ, the total angle of twist, must increase also (equation (54)).

We note that the application of an axial load, as in fig. 18, provides a couple correctly orientated to effect this increase of twist.

In order to relate the increase of twist, $\Delta\phi$, to the increase of length, Δz, we proceed as follows. From equation (54) we have

$$\Delta\phi = \sin\alpha\,\Delta\theta + \theta\cos\alpha\,\Delta\alpha.$$

Similarly, from equations (51), (52) and (53), in turn, we obtain

$$\Delta z = l\cos\alpha\,\Delta\alpha,$$
$$0 = \Delta r + 2r\sec\alpha\sin\alpha\,\Delta\alpha,$$
$$0 = \theta\Delta r + 2r\Delta\theta,$$

l and ρ being constant. Reduction of these equations leads to the result

$$\Delta\phi = \theta\sec^2\alpha\,\frac{\Delta z}{l}.$$

Finally, substituting from equation (49), we have

$$\Delta\phi = \sec\alpha\,\frac{\Delta z}{r} \tag{55}$$

Now ΔG, the measure of the additional couple necessary to produce this increase of total twist in a wire of total length l and radius a, the modulus of rigidity of the material of the wire being n, is given ($M\,L\,\&\,T$, p. 323) by

$$\Delta G = \frac{\pi}{2}\frac{na^4}{l}\,\Delta\phi \tag{56}$$

Suppose that we identify ΔG with the moment, about the axis of the wire, of the axial load of our earlier considerations (see fig. 18). We have already concluded that, when the angle of the helix is small, the main effect of this load is one of uniform torsion about the axis of the wire. Here we neglect any other effect, and, substituting from equation (55) in (56), with this identification, we obtain

$$\Delta G = Wr\cos\alpha$$
$$= \frac{\pi}{2}\frac{na^4}{l}\sec\alpha\,\frac{\Delta z}{r},$$

E

or

$$\Delta z = \frac{2lr^2W}{\pi na^4}\cos^2 \alpha \qquad (57)$$

At this stage we accept equation (57) as giving, at least to a fairly good approximation, an expression for the elongation of a closely wound helical spring under axial load in terms of the dimensions of the spring and the relevant elastic modulus of the material of which it is made.

We have just considered the statical problem of the equilibrium elongation of a helical spring under load: the problem which we set out to discuss was the dynamical problem of the periodic motion of such a load when displaced from its position of equilibrium. We have concluded that in the case which we have considered, when the form of the load is that of a solid of revolution about the vertical axis of the spring, the system has two degrees of freedom: those of linear displacement along the axis and angular displacement around the axis. We have also concluded that the corresponding component motions are mechanically coupled (p. 61). If we consider a displacement of pure axial rotation (l and z constant, θ increasing, according to our previous notation) we have, from equation (51), that α is constant, and then, from equation (49), that the product $r\theta$ is constant during the change. Finally, from equation (53), we conclude that the product $\rho\theta$ remains constant, or that ρ the radius of curvature of the axial filament of the wire decreases as θ increases. To effect such a change in the physical system obviously requires the application of an external couple having its axis along the helical axis of the spring, and the elastic modulus of the material of the spring which determines its deformation by such a couple is Young's modulus, which we denote by Y ($M\,L\,\&\,T$, p. 318).

Combining this last result with that implicit in equation (57), we conclude that, for the general dynamical problem of the motion of the load following upon any arbitrary initial displacement, the dimensions of the spring, and the values of the rigidity modulus, n, and Young's modulus, Y, for its material, are the relevant constants. But, for an isotropic material of which σ is Poisson's ratio, $Y = 2n(1 + \sigma)$ ($M\,L\,\&\,T$, p. 316), thus we should not be surprised to find that the characteristic behaviour of a system of given dimensions can to a large extent be described in terms of σ alone. This is indeed the case. The symmetrically loaded spring is found to have two normal modes in which the linear and rotational component motions have oppositely related phases, and amplitudes in determinate ratios (compare p. 58), and the periods of the normal modes are found to be nearly equal if $\sigma^2 z^2 \ll (1+\sigma)l^2$. We note that, since $0 < 2\sigma < 1$ ($M\,L\,\&\,T$, p. 312), this condition is always satisfied for a closely wound spring. The amplitude ratio is found to be the same for each of the two normal modes, for a closely wound spring, when $k = (1+\sigma)^{\frac{1}{2}}r$, k being the radius of gyration of the load about the vertical axis of the spring. In this case the phenomenon of beats is fully developed: if initially the load is displaced in θ but not in z, and is then released, to begin with the motion is exclusively rotational. Slowly this motion dies down as axial oscillations develop and grow in amplitude. A stage is reached at which instantaneously the load is not rotating, only vibrating up and down; then the reverse sequence ensues. If the load is in the form of a circular cylinder, as shown in fig. 17, its axial rotation is much less conspicuous than its linear motion. From a distance, in the circumstances just described, the load appears to alternate between phases of quiescence and vigorous motion—to the surprise of the casual observer. It was in view of this behaviour that it was stated (p. 59) that the characteristics of this system are 'even more striking' than those of the system of coupled inertia bars previously discussed.

It will be realised that we have merely quoted certain results belonging to the solution of the dynamical problem of Wilberforce's system: we have not derived them from first principles. Moreover, in stating them, we have adopted the assumption that the mass of the spring is negligible compared with the mass of the load. This approximation should be borne in mind in applying the results to actual cases.

3.4. FORCED VIBRATIONS, RESONANCE AND DAMPING

The study of coupled vibrations, in the limiting case, when a massive vibrator is weakly coupled to one much less massive, affords some insight into the phenomena of 'forced vibrations' and 'resonance'. We shall consider these matters here using as example the system of coupled inertia bars already treated in its more general aspects in the last section.

We use the term 'forced vibrations' to describe a situation in which a vibratory system is maintained in steady periodic motion of period considerably different from the natural period characteristic of the system itself. Clearly, this situation will obtain strictly only if the system is subject to a periodic 'external' force of constant amplitude, and in that case the period of the forced vibration of the system will be that of the external force.

In our previous discussion of the system of coupled inertia bars, we obtained (equation (46)) an expression for the ratios of the amplitudes of oscillation of the individual bars in the symmetric and antisymmetric normal modes. This equation refers to the general case. For our present purposes we write $I_2 = \beta I_1$, $\beta \ll 1$, and regard inertia bar J (fig. 16) as the 'driving' component, and bar K as the 'driven' component, of the coupled system. Confining attention to oscillation in a normal mode, let us divide the numerator and denominator of equation (46) by I_1, and re-write it in the form

$$\kappa_s, a_4 = \frac{-b \pm (b^2 + 4\mu_3{}^2\beta)^{\frac{1}{2}}}{2\mu_3\beta} \qquad (58)$$

with
$$b = \mu_2 + \mu_3(1 - \beta) - \mu_1\beta.$$

We are going to assume that the natural frequency of the driving component is varied over a wide range, from a frequency much smaller than, to a frequency considerably greater than, the natural frequency of the driven component. We imagine this variation to be effected by a gradual increase of μ_1, starting from a value for which $\mu_1\beta \ll \mu_2$ and ending with a value such that $\mu_1\beta \gg \mu_2$. During these changes the values of the other mechanical quantities determining the properties of the system remain unaltered. Let us suppose that the coupling is weak, in the sense that $\mu_2 \gg \mu_3$ throughout.

Since κ is the ratio of the amplitude of inertia bar K to the amplitude of J, it may be regarded as measuring the steady 'response' of the driven component to the driving component of the system, in the normal mode. It is convenient to suppose that, in this steady-state motion, energy is passing from the driving component to the driven component at a finite rate and 'leaking back' at the same rate through the coupling element. When the effect of a periodic 'external' force driving an oscillatory system is studied, in the traditional treatment of forced vibrations and resonance, the phenomenon of 'leakage back' is not normally considered: the steady state is rather determined in terms of a dissipation of energy in the driven system as a result of frictional processes. In any actual system—'isolated' or coupled—there will certainly be such effects, but we can disregard them, for present purposes, and still discuss a steady-state situation in our coupled system in the terms which have been stated.

We may begin to understand the implications of equation (58) by working inwards from the two extremes of the range of variation of driving frequency to be considered, and adopting first the limiting conditions (i) $\mu_1\beta \ll \mu_2$, (ii) $\mu_1\beta \gg \mu_2$. If the coupling is weak, as we have supposed, either of these conditions leads to the result $b^2 \gg 4\mu_3^2\beta$, and we then have

$$2\mu_3\beta\kappa_{s,a} = -b \pm |b|\left(1 + \frac{2\mu_3^2\beta}{b^2}\right).$$

A little consideration will show that, taking the positive sign in this equation, we obtain the value of κ_s, and taking the negative sign the value of κ_a, in either case. Results of sufficiently good approximation are as follows:

taking the positive sign,

   (i) when $\qquad \mu_1\beta \ll \mu_2 \; (b>0), \quad \kappa_s = \dfrac{\mu_3}{b},$

   (ii) when $\qquad \mu_1\beta \gg \mu_2 \; (b<0), \quad \kappa_s = \dfrac{|b|}{\mu_3\beta} = -\dfrac{b}{\mu_3\beta},$

taking the negative sign,

   (i) when $\qquad \mu_1\beta \ll \mu_2, \quad \kappa_a = -\dfrac{b}{\mu_3\beta},$

   (ii) when $\qquad \mu_1\beta \gg \mu_2, \quad \kappa_a = -\dfrac{\mu_3}{|b|} = \dfrac{\mu_3}{b}.$

Reviewing these four results together, we see that there are essentially only two independent values of the ratio κ, namely μ_3/b and $-b/\mu_3\beta$, and we note that, over the two ranges of b that we are presently considering, $\mu_3/b \ll 1 \ll b/\mu_3\beta$.

We proceed now to calculate the frequencies of the normal modes to which these values of κ refer. Substituting in equations

(43) and (44) according to the procedure already outlined, after some simplification, we obtain,

when
$$\kappa = \frac{\mu_3}{b},$$

$$4\pi^2 f^2 = \frac{\mu_1 + \mu_3}{I_1},$$

and, when
$$\kappa = -\frac{b}{\mu_3 \beta},$$

$$4\pi^2 f^2 = \frac{\mu_2 + \mu_3}{I_2}.$$

It will be recognised at once that the former of these frequencies is very closely the natural frequency of the driving component (according to our conventional identification), the latter very closely the natural frequency of the driven component of the coupled system. For our present purposes, clearly, only the normal mode having the frequency of the driving component is of interest. We therefore disregard the latter solution altogether.

The result of the analysis that we have just completed has been to give the 'response' of the driven component of our coupled system in terms of the single expression

$$\kappa = \frac{\mu_3}{b} \tag{59}$$

valid over the two extreme ranges in which the frequency of the driving component is (i) very much less than, (ii) very much greater than, the natural frequency of the driven component of the system. We note, first of all, that the phases of the response are different over these two ranges of the variable: when the driving frequency is much less than the natural frequency of the smaller bar, the oscillation of the latter is in phase with that of the larger bar which drives it; when the driving frequency is very much greater than this natural frequency, the oscillations of the two bars are 180° out of phase. The second point of interest in equation (59) concerns the variation of κ with μ_1 which it implies. If we re-write the equation in full, we have

$$\kappa = \frac{\mu_3}{\mu_2 + \mu_3(1-\beta) - \mu_1 \beta} \tag{60}$$

and we see that, whether μ_1 increases in the range for which

$\mu_1\beta \ll \mu_2$, or decreases in the range for which $\mu_1\beta \gg \mu_2$, $|\kappa|$ increases. We conclude that the response of the driven bar (considered without reference to the question of phase) increases as the driving frequency tends towards the natural frequency of driven bar throughout each of these (extreme) ranges.

Throughout the extreme ranges that we have just considered, $|\kappa| \ll 1$. When $\beta \ll 1$, as we have postulated, equation (60) in fact provides a sufficiently close approximation to the truth even when $\mu_1\beta = \mu_2$, as can be verified by direct substitution in equation (58). In this case, to second-order accuracy, $\kappa = 1$. Similarly, when $\mu_1\beta = \mu_2 + 2\mu_3(1 - \beta)$, $\kappa = -1$. When $\mu_1\beta = \mu_2 + \mu_3(1 - \beta)$, that is when $b = 0$, clearly equations (59) and (60) are inadequate. Direct substitution in equation (58) then gives $|\kappa| = 1/\beta^{\frac{1}{2}}$. The condition that we have here identified is the condition of maximum response, or of 'exact' resonance. We note that in these circumstances a_2, the amplitude of oscillation of the driven bar, is considerably greater than a_1, that of the driving bar, the oscillation energies of the two being the same $(I_1a_1{}^2 = I_2a_2{}^2)$. We note further that, in this condition of exact resonance, the amplitude ratios are the same for the symmetric and antisymmetric normal modes of our system: in other words the phase relation as between driving and driven motions in the condition of exact resonance is ambiguous. As the driving frequency is increased through the resonance frequency, then, the phase of the response, in our ideal case, changes discontinuously by 180°.

Fig. 21 summarises the conclusions that we have reached. The full line in the figure shows how κ, taken as a measure of the response (in magnitude and phase), varies with the square of the driving frequency, represented by $\mu_1\beta$. The dotted curve shows the variation, with the same parameter, of $I_2a_2{}^2/I_1a_1{}^2 (\equiv \beta\kappa^2)$, the ratio of the energy of oscillation of the driven to that of the driving bar. Defining w, the peak width of the dotted curve, as its full width at half height, by suitable substitution in equation (45) we obtain $w = (2\beta)^{\frac{1}{2}}\mu_3$; we see, therefore, that the peak width is smaller as the coupling is weaker. This is an invariable feature of the resonance phenomenon: in general resonance is 'sharper' the smaller is the rate at which energy can be lost by the driven system when it is oscillating at a standard amplitude at the resonance frequency. In our coupled system, obviously the strength of the coupling determines this characteristic rate of loss.

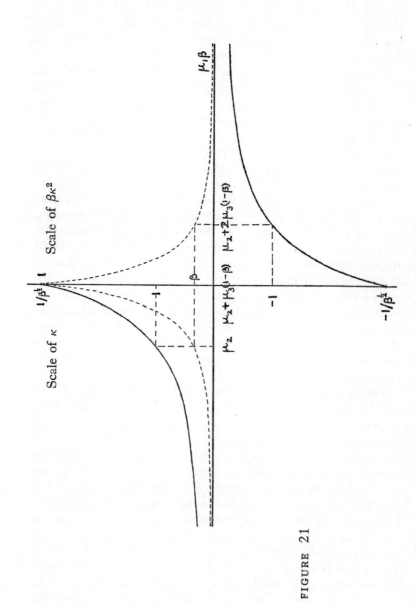

FIGURE 21

Confining attention to the normal mode oscillations of a system of coupled inertia bars of widely different moments of inertia, we have just elicited the more important features of the general phenomena of forced vibrations and resonance. As we have indicated, the traditional mathematical theory of these phenomena is commonly developed from the assumption (almost as commonly not stated explicitly) that the external periodic driving force which it postulates has its origin in a system which is capable of providing an inexhaustible supply of energy. Adopting this assumption, it becomes a formal necessity to postulate frictional dissipation of energy in the driven system (otherwise the amplitude of the system, at exact resonance, would increase linearly with time, without limit). As we have explained, dealing with a finite system of limited energy content, we have been under no such necessity: in any case, in a coupled system, energy may be transmitted from one component to the other in either direction through the coupling element. But we have also admitted that the dissipation of energy, in frictional processes of greater or less importance, is unavoidable in any actual system. Let us, therefore, examine one aspect of this problem, again using the coupled system of two very dissimilar inertia bars for our investigation.

In equations (47) and (48) we obtained a full description of the subsequent motion of such a system, in the special case in which $\mu_1 I_2 = \mu_2 I_1$, when the initial conditions are such that at $t=0$ the whole of the energy of the system is potential energy associated with the displacement of one of the bars (the bar J, to be precise). Let us consider this situation again, under the limitation $\beta \ll 1$, and on the assumption that the coupling is weak $(\mu_1 \gg \mu_2 \gg \mu_3)$. Then the energy given to the system initially is $\frac{1}{2}(\mu_1 + \mu_3)a^2$, and, according to equation (48), the effective amplitude of the driven bar, at any subsequent time t, is given by

$$a_2 = \frac{2a}{1+\beta} \sin \pi(f_a - f_s)t$$

$$= \frac{2a}{1+\beta} \sin \omega t,$$

where, to sufficient accuracy, on the basis of equations (47),

$$\omega = \frac{\pi}{2} \frac{\mu_3(\mu_1 + \mu_2)}{\mu_1 \mu_2} f.$$

If E is the energy of motion of the driven bar, we have

$$E = 2\pi^2 I_2 a_2{}^2 \left(\frac{f_s + f_a}{2} \right)^2.$$

Now let ϵ_1 be the amount of energy transferred from the driving to the driven bar, per oscillation period, at time t. Then

$$\epsilon_1 = \frac{2}{f_s + f_a} \frac{dE}{dt}$$

and

$$\frac{\epsilon_1}{E} = \frac{4}{f_s + f_a} \frac{1}{a_2} \frac{da_2}{dt}$$

$$= \frac{4\omega}{f_s + f_a} \cot \omega t \tag{61}$$

On the basis of equation (61), we see that the first half-cycle of energy transfer, in which, on balance, the driven bar receives energy continuously from the driving bar, lasts from $t = 0$ to $t = \pi/2\omega$; thereafter energy is transferred back to the driving bar, and the motion continues indefinitely as described in detail by equations (47) and (48).

Let us write $\pi/\omega = \tau_0$, and suppose that, at an arbitrary time t within the first half-cycle $(t < \tau_0/2)$, the driven system suddenly becomes subject to a damping couple of magnitude $-k\dot{\theta}_2$ (compare p. 36). If the damping is small, ϵ_2, the amount of energy dissipated in the immediately succeeding oscillation period (τ) of this bar is, to sufficient accuracy,

$$\epsilon_2 = \int_t^{t+\tau} k\dot{\theta}_2{}^2 dt,$$

where

$$\tau = \frac{2}{f_s + f_a}.$$

Thus

$$\epsilon_2 = \frac{4\pi^2}{\tau^2} k a_2{}^2 \int_t^{t+\tau} \cos^2 2\pi \frac{t}{\tau}\, dt,$$

and

$$\frac{\epsilon_2}{E} = \frac{k\tau}{I_2} \tag{62}$$

Combining equations (61) and (62), we have

$$\frac{\epsilon_1}{\epsilon_2} = \frac{2I_2\omega}{k} \cot \omega t$$

$$= \frac{2\pi I_2}{k\tau_0} \cot \pi \frac{t}{\tau_0} \qquad (63)$$

Regarding t in equation (63) as variable, we note that, if the damping of the driven bar is suddenly introduced sufficiently early in the cycle of energy transfer, the rate of loss of energy by dissipation is instantaneously less than the rate of gain of energy from the driving bar. Conversely, however small is the value of the damping constant, there is some time, within the first half-cycle of energy transfer, such that, if the damping is then introduced, instantaneously dissipation will exactly counterbalance gain. This time is given as a solution of the equation

$$\cot \pi \frac{t}{\tau_0} = \frac{k\tau_0}{2\pi I_2},$$

and the amplitude of the driven bar, at the moment in question, is

$$a_2 = \frac{2a}{1+\beta} \frac{1}{(1+\gamma^2)^{\frac{1}{2}}} \qquad (64)$$

where

$$\gamma = \frac{k\tau_0}{2\pi I_2}$$

$$= \frac{k\mu_1\mu_2}{\pi I_2\mu_3(\mu_1+\mu_2)f},$$

or, since $\mu_2/I_2 = 4\pi^2 f^2$,

where

$$\gamma = \frac{4\pi k\mu_1 f}{\mu_3(\mu_1+\mu_2)},$$

indeed, with sufficient accuracy,

where

$$\gamma = \frac{4\pi k f}{\mu_3}.$$

In the calculation just completed we have not solved the problem of the oscillations of a system of coupled inertia bars when the driven bar is subject to damping continuously; we have merely considered the effect of the sudden imposition of damping at an

arbitrary stage of the motion. When damping is operative continuously, obviously there will be a steady drain of energy from
the driving bar, so that eventually the amplitude of each bar will
gradually decrease. In such circumstances it should be clear that
the amplitude of the driven bar can never exceed the critical value
given by equation (64), in which equation a may now be interpreted as the amplitude of the driving bar at any stage in the
steadily decaying motion. We have not solved the general problem,
then, but we have put a limit on the solution, and we can con-
fidently use the form of equation (64), if not the numerical
constants involved, as indicating the manner in which the limitation of amplitude under conditions of near resonance depends
upon the damping and the other dynamical quantities involved.
For the particular system that we have considered, we see that the
maximum amplitude of the driven bar near resonance is the
smaller as the damping is greater, other things being equal, and
further that, for damping of a given intensity, the maximum
amplitude is the smaller as the coupling is weaker. Moreover,
arguing from the equation

$$\gamma = \frac{k\tau_0}{2\pi I_2},$$

we see that, for the effect of damping to be considerable, the
damping constant k must be large enough for the characteristic
time $2\pi I_2/k$ (for γ is a pure number) to be small compared with τ_0.
Now $2I_2/k$ is the time required for the amplitude of the damped
oscillations of the driven bar to decrease to $1/e$ of its initial value,
when this bar is uncoupled from the rest of the system (compare
equation (29)). We conclude, then, that damping is of importance
in respect of the coupled motion, under the conditions we have
specified, only when the characteristic period for damping of the
driven bar is short compared with the period of the back and
forth transfer of energy to that bar from the driving bar. We shall
not pursue the matter farther at this stage.

CHAPTER 4

ELASTIC VIBRATIONS OF RODS

4.1. GENERAL

Throughout the whole of chapter 2 we were concerned with the vibrations of strings under tension, and in sections 1 and 2 of chapter 3 we discussed the vibratory motions of systems of which such strings were essential constituents. In all these considerations we adopted the fiction that the strings were perfectly flexible. This is an idealisation of actuality: any cylindrical filament of isotropic material is 'stiff' in respect of bending to a degree which depends upon the product Yr^4 (see p. 86), Y being the measure of Young's modulus for the material and r being the measure of the cylindrical radius of the filament.

In practice the flexibility of a string is achieved by constituting the string of a large number of independent filaments twisted or plaited together, or by taking a natural fibre which has this general constitution. For we may compare the flexural stiffness of a string constituted of n independent filaments each of radius r (it will be proportional to nr^4) with that of a single cylindrical 'rod', of the same total area of cross-section and made of the same material (which will be proportional to R^4, where $nr^2 = R^2$). We deduce that the stiffness of the rod is n times that of the equally heavy string of n strands. We approach the ideal of the perfectly flexible string, therefore, by constituting our actual strings of a very large number of strands. In common speech (and even in the dictionaries) the word 'flex' has come to signify an electric cable constituted in just this way.

In this chapter, deliberately, we consider the vibrations of single rods; in this connection the elastic properties of the materials of which they are made are all important. We take the word 'rod' to signify a material body greatly elongated in one direction, such that its linear dimensions in directions at right angles to its length are everywhere at least two or three orders of magnitude smaller than that length. We shall, indeed, be dealing exclusively with uniform rods, that is with rods made of homogeneous, isotropic, materials, and such that the figure of the cross-section is everywhere the same and similarly orientated when the rod is straight.

A straight rod, held securely at one end, may be set into flexural vibrations by plucking the free end transversely, or by striking the rod with a light hammer in a direction at right angles to its length. We shall discuss these vibrations. We shall also discuss the less immediately evident, but physically much simpler, vibrations which occur when such a rod, supported in some specified way, suffers a sudden blow in the direction of its length. Vibrations of this latter type have considerable similarity to the vibration of the air enclosed in cylindrical pipes. This will be the topic of our concern in the next chapter.

4.2. BENDING OF A LIGHT CANTILEVER: STATICAL CONSIDERATIONS

When a rod is firmly clamped at one end, so that it protrudes horizontally from the face of its rigid support, the rod is commonly referred to as a cantilever (*M L & T*, p. 317). The depression of the free end of a uniform 'massless' cantilever of rectangular cross-section, and subject to a load applied at its extremity, was considered, in the reference just cited, in terms of a dimensional argument. Appealing to experiment for the empirical result that the depression is proportional to the third power of the free length of the cantilever, other factors remaining unchanged, and to experiment again (or to the results of a detailed calculation which was not given) for the multiplying constant in the final equation, it was accepted that the depression, z, is given in terms of W, the measure of the load, l, the free length of the cantilever, b and d, the (horizontal) breadth and (vertical) depth of its cross-section, and Y, the measure of Young's modulus for its material, by the expression

$$z = \frac{4W}{Y} \frac{l^3}{bd^3} \tag{65}$$

We accepted this expression as a sufficiently close approximation to the truth, having concluded that 'the problem is essentially one of longitudinal extension and compression' of the filaments of the cantilever parallel to its axis, 'the sideways stresses having negligible effect'. However, we did not insist, as it is strictly neces-

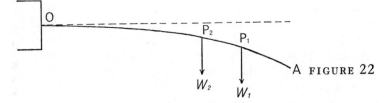

A FIGURE 22

sary to insist, that the approximation is a good one only so long as the depression is small compared with the length of the canti-lever, and only so long as the other linear dimensions of the cantilever are small by the same comparison. Our present defini-tion of 'rod' takes care of the second proviso; here we merely note the necessity of the first ($z \ll l$) for our subsequent discussions. It is our object to treat the problem in more detail than previously, and particularly to derive an expression giving the equilibrium form of the axis of the loaded rod. We first derive a general theorem in this particular context.

Let OA (fig. 22) represent the equilibrium position of the axis of a cantilever subject to vertical loads W_1 and W_2 acting through P_1 and P_2, respectively, any two points along its length. Let the cantilever be clamped at O, and let the depressions of P_1 and P_2 be y_1 and y_2 in this arrangement (hereafter we shall use y rather than z for the depression). Then each of these quantities may be regarded as the sum of two components, namely the depressions which would be produced by the loads W_1, W_2 acting alone ($M L \& T$, p. 309). Moreover, these component depressions, for each point, are directly proportional to the loads. We may there-fore write

$$y_1 = {}_1a_1\,W_1 + {}_2a_1\,W_2,$$
$$y_2 = {}_1a_2\,W_1 + {}_2a_2\,W_2,$$

${}_1a_1$ being the depression of P_1 which would be produced by unit load applied at P_1, ${}_1a_2$ the depression of P_2 which would be produced by unit load applied at P_1, and similarly.

Let us now consider the successive application of the loads, first in the sequence W_1, W_2, then, starting afresh with the bar unloaded, in the sequence W_2, W_1. Since the initial and final states of the system are, respectively, the same in these two cases, we take it as axiomatic that the total work done by the loads, and stored as energy of deformation of the cantilever, is likewise the same whichever sequence is followed. It is only necessary to impose the condition that the application of the loads shall be carried out 'reversibly' (see $M L \mathrel{\&} T$, p. 290); that is, that there shall at no stage be any significant amount of energy associated with the system in the form of kinetic energy, and that the temperature of the system shall remain constant throughout. If the work done in the first sequence is denoted by Q_1, we have

$$Q_1 = \tfrac{1}{2} {}_1a_1 \, W_1{}^2 + \tfrac{1}{2} {}_2a_2 \, W_2{}^2 + W_{1 \, 2}a_1 \, W_2.$$

In this expression the first and second terms represent the amounts of work performed at P_1 and P_2, respectively, as the loads W_1 and W_2 are gradually brought into operation, in succession, through these two points; the third term represents the amount of work performed at P_1 because of the fact that, as the load W_2 is brought into operation at P_2, the load W_1, already fully effective at P_1, moves a further distance ${}_2a_1 \, W_2$ in its own line of action. In the same way, if Q_2 is the amount of work done in the second sequence, we have

$$Q_2 = \tfrac{1}{2} {}_2a_2 \, W_2{}^2 + \tfrac{1}{2} {}_1a_1 \, W_1{}^2 + W_{2 \, 1}a_2 \, W_1.$$

Because $$Q_1 = Q_2,$$

of necessity $${}_2a_1 = {}_1a_2 \tag{66}$$

Stated in words, equation (66) effectively reads 'if two points are arbitrarily chosen in a cantilever, the depression of the first point produced by a given load acting through the second point is the same as the depression of the second point produced by the same load acting through the first'. In the present context this—Rayleigh's* first reciprocal relation—is an important result, of general validity in respect of the elastic deformation of systems of bodies subject to specified constraints.

We now return to the problem of the equilibrium form of the axis of the loaded cantilever of negligible mass. Let the free length of the cantilever be l, and let the depression of any point

* John William Strutt, 3rd baron Rayleigh (1842-1919), famous alike as mathematical physicist and experimenter, spent almost the whole of his active life—except for a period of five years (1879-1884) during which, with some misgivings, he occupied the Cavendish chair of experimental physics at Cambridge—working in his own laboratory at Terling Place, Chelmsford, Essex. He was one of the first to be admitted to the Order of Merit (1902), and received the Nobel prize for physics in 1904.

on its axis, and at a distance x from the fixed end of the cantilever, be y, when a load W is applied at the free end. We write

$$y = \beta \frac{W}{Y} l^s f\left(\frac{x}{l}\right) \qquad (67)$$

the quantity β depending on the transverse dimensions of the cantilever, Y representing, as before, Young's modulus for its material, and s being an unknown exponent. We normalise the function f so that $f(1) = 1$. Our immediate object is to find the form of this function.

According to Rayleigh's reciprocal relation, equation (67) also gives the depression of the free end of the cantilever when a load W is applied at the point x. But we may derive an alternative expression for this quantity as follows. If, in fig. 22, $OP_1 = x$, then, when a load W is applied at P_1, the form of the cantilever, at distances (ξ) from O less than x, is given, in terms of equation (67), as

$$y = \beta \frac{W}{Y} x^s f\left(\frac{\xi}{x}\right) \qquad (68)$$

and the portion P_1A of the cantilever is straight, the cantilever itself being 'massless'. Moreover, all depressions being very small in comparison with the length of the cantilever, the inclination of the axis of the cantilever to the horizontal is given, over the length OP_1, in terms of equation (68), by $\frac{dy}{d\xi}$. Thus the inclination at P_1, and in consequence the inclination of the straight portion P_1A of the axis, is given by

$$\left(\frac{dy}{d\xi}\right)_x = \beta \frac{W}{Y} x^{s-1} f'(1).$$

Equating the two values obtained for the depression of the free end of the cantilever, when the load W is applied at the point x, we therefore have

$$\beta \frac{W}{Y} l^s f\left(\frac{x}{l}\right) = \beta \frac{W}{Y} x^s f(1) + (l-x)\left(\frac{dy}{d\xi}\right)_x$$

or $\qquad l^s f\left(\frac{x}{l}\right) = x^s + (l-x)x^{s-1} f'(1) \qquad (69)$

F

since $f(1)=1$. According to equation (69), in general,

$$f'\left(\frac{x}{l}\right) = s(1-f'(1))\left(\frac{x}{l}\right)^{s-1} + (s-1)f'(1)\left(\frac{x}{l}\right)^{s-2}.$$

Specifically, therefore, when $x=l$,

$$f'(1) = s - f'(1)$$

or

$$f'(1) = \frac{s}{2}.$$

We may now substitute this value for $f'(1)$ in equation (69). We have, finally,

$$f\left(\frac{x}{l}\right) = \left(1-\frac{s}{2}\right)\left(\frac{x}{l}\right)^{s} + \frac{s}{2}\left(\frac{x}{l}\right)^{s-1} \tag{70}$$

With equation (70) we have taken the matter as far as use of the reciprocal relation alone will allow. If we were to accept, as an empirical result, $s=3$, as we did in a previous discussion (see p. 78), we should have, explicitly,

$$f\left(\frac{x}{l}\right) = \frac{3}{2}\left(\frac{x}{l}\right)^{2} - \frac{1}{2}\left(\frac{x}{l}\right)^{3}.$$

Equation (67) would then take the form

$$y = \frac{\beta}{2}\frac{W}{Y}(3lx^2 - x^3) \tag{71}$$

We proceed now to deduce this result from first principles, and in the process to evaluate the quantity β.

Let us suppose that the cross-section of the cantilever has a vertical axis of symmetry, being otherwise of arbitrary form, as represented in fig. 23. We assume that some longitudinal section of the cantilever, originally horizontal, is such that all filaments of the cantilever lying in this section remain unchanged in length when the cantilever is bent under load. Let N'GN be the trace of this 'neutral plane' in fig. 23, Z'GZ being the axis of symmetry of the cross-section represented in the figure. Let R be the radius of curvature of the longitudinal axis of the cantilever through G, in the region of the section in question, the external load W being applied at the free end as before. Then, if two neighbouring

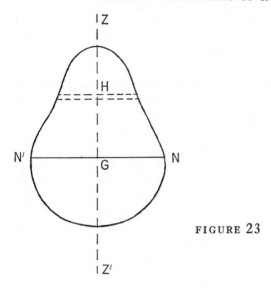

FIGURE 23

sections be considered, parallel and separated by a small distance Δx when the cantilever is unloaded, it will be seen that they will be inclined at an angle $\Delta x/R$ when the load is applied. The segment of the longitudinal axis through G included between these sections will be unchanged in length, but that of the longitudinal axis through H (fig. 23), similarly included, will have lengthened to $\Delta x(R+z)/R$, where GH $=z$. The fractional extension ('elongation') of the longitudinal filament through H, in the region of the section in question, is, therefore, z/R, and we assume that the elongation of all the filaments traversing the section in the elementary strip parallel to N'N, and shown dotted in fig. 23, has this value also. Over this strip, then, the tension is constant and equal to zY/R, Y being the measure of Young's modulus for the material of the cantilever, as previously defined. If a is the area of the strip, the total normal force acting across the strip is zYa/R, and the total normal force across the whole section is

$$\frac{Y}{R}\Sigma az.$$

Now the external forces, acting on that part of the cantilever between the section considered and the free end, comprise only the load W which acts vertically. Therefore the horizontal component of the total normal force across the section is zero, and we have

$$\Sigma az = 0 \tag{72}$$

Equation (72) provides, first of all, formal justification for our assumption that there must be a neutral plane extending longitudinally throughout the loaded rod. For, clearly, negative values of z, as well as positive values, are necessary if this equation is to be satisfied. More precisely, equation (72) shows that N'N, the line of intersection of the neutral plane with an arbitrary cross-section of the cantilever, passes through the centre of area of the section. In this connection we define 'centre of area', by analogy with centre of mass (M L & T, p. 169), locating the centre of area of a plane figure in terms of rectangular co-ordinates given by two equations of the form $\bar{z} = \Sigma az/\Sigma a$. Moreover, because the cross-section of fig. 23 is assumed to be symmetrical about Z'Z, the centre of area of the section is, in fact, at G.

We consider now the turning effort of the normal forces acting across this arbitrary section of the cantilever. The sum of the moments of these forces about N'N is given by

$$M = \frac{Y}{R}\Sigma az^2,$$

or

$$M = \frac{Y}{R}Ak^2 \tag{73}$$

where, by analogy with the definition of moment of inertia, we define Σaz^2 as the moment of area of the section about N'N. Then, A being the total area of the section, k is the radius of gyration of the section about this line. Moreover, the sum of the moments of the forces about any other line, $z = -z_0$, which is parallel to N'N, is given by

$$M_0 = \frac{Y}{R}\Sigma az(z+z_0)$$

$$= \frac{Y}{R}(\Sigma az^2 + z_0\Sigma az),$$

and $\Sigma az = 0$ (equation (72)). Thus

$$M_0 = M.$$

The sum of the moments of the normal forces is the same, therefore, about all lines perpendicular to the plane of bending; these forces thus reduce to a single couple of moment M, the previously defined 'bending moment' ($M L \, \& \, T$, p. 321) effective at the section under consideration. Equation (73) relates the measure of this bending moment to the radius of curvature of the neutral axis in the neighbourhood of the section, the size and shape of the section, and Young's modulus for the material of which the cantilever is made.

Suppose now that the section under consideration is situated at a distance x from the fixed end of the cantilever. Then the portion of the cantilever, of length $(l-x)$, projecting beyond this section is acted on, across the section by the normal forces which we have just discussed, by the load W, and by an internally developed 'shearing force' W acting vertically in the plane of the section equilibrating the load in respect of translatory motion. Obviously, the load and the shearing force together constitute a couple of moment $W(l-x)$, and this must be equilibrated by the couple of the bending moment. We have, therefore,

$$W(l-x) = \frac{Y}{R} Ak^2,$$

an equation giving R, the radius of curvature of the neutral axis of the cantilever, at a distance x from the fixed end, in terms of given quantities. Now, under the conditions which we have imposed throughout (equivalent here to the condition $R \gg l$), we may write

$$\frac{1}{R} = \frac{d^2y}{dx^2},$$

y being the equilibrium depression at distance x, as before. Thus

$$\frac{d^2y}{dx^2} = \frac{W}{YAk^2}(l-x).$$

When $x=0$, obviously $y=0$ and $\frac{dy}{dx}=0$, therefore

$$y = \frac{W}{6YAk^2}(3lx^2 - x^3) \qquad (74)$$

This is precisely equation (71), with $\beta = 1/3Ak^2$.

When $x = l$, equation (74) gives the depression of the free end of the 'massless' cantilever produced by a load applied at that end. For a cantilever of rectangular section (see p. 78), $A = bd$, $k^2 = d^2/12$, and the result previously quoted for this case (equation (65)) is substantiated: when the section is circular, and of radius r, $A = \pi r^2$, $k^2 = r^2/4$, and the 'stiffness' of the cantilever depends upon the product Yr^4 as we have earlier stated (p. 77).

4.3. TRANSVERSE VIBRATIONS OF A LIGHT CANTILEVER

Our problem now is to consider the normal modes of transverse vibration of a cantilever such as we have discussed in the last section. We can no longer consider the cantilever as massless otherwise the question of vibration would not arise (compare p. 49). We postulate, instead, that the cantilever is uniform, and that the mass per unit length is m. We assume, however, that the analysis that we have just given provides a sufficiently accurate description of the deformation of the cantilever, under steady forces externally applied, and within the limits of deformation effective in its vibrations.

Let us re-write equation (67), giving the depression at a distance x from the fixed end of the cantilever, when a steady load W is applied to the free end $(x = l)$, in the form

$$y = aWf\left(\frac{x}{l}\right) \tag{75}$$

with $f(1) = 1$, as before. Let $F\left(\dfrac{x}{l}\right)$, also with $F(1) = 1$, describe the form of the cantilever when it is vibrating in one of its normal modes. A full treatment of our problem should result in explicit expressions for $F\left(\dfrac{x}{l}\right)$ for the various modes. However, this part of the problem is clearly beyond the scope of this book. Let us rather assume that these various forms of the function F are given experimentally: it is not unthinkable that for the lower-order modes, at least, we might obtain such data by photographing the vibrating cantilever. For the first normal mode this was done, as long ago as 1904, by C. A. B. Garrett.

Let η be the depression of the free end of the cantilever, at any instant, when it is vibrating in a normal mode. Then $\eta F\left(\dfrac{x}{l}\right)$

is the depression at a distance x from the fixed end at that instant, and, for the motion to be simply periodic, the upwards force per unit length of the cantilever must be proportional to the depression. If $R(x)$ is the upwards force per unit length around the point x, we have, therefore,

$$R(x) = \phi\eta F\left(\frac{x}{l}\right) \tag{76}$$

where ϕ is a constant. When the cantilever is vibrating, the restoring force acting on any element of length is the resultant of the two shearing forces acting in the neighbouring right sections of the cantilever which enclose that element. These shearing forces arise from the elastic deformation of the rod. The cantilever could be held in equilibrium in its instantaneous state of deformation only if an external "load" were distributed along its length in accordance with equation (76). It should be noted that, depending on the choice of instant, and on the mode considered, $R(x)$ may be negative over the whole range of x, or over part of this range. For that reason we have written ' "load" ', not 'load'. By considering this equilibrium situation we may determine the constant ϕ.

We note that equation (76) specifies the distribution of an external load under the action of which the depression of the free end of the cantilever is η. Let us apply Rayleigh's reciprocal relation to calculate η in terms of this specification. The load acting on an element of length dx at x is $\phi\eta F\left(\frac{x}{l}\right)dx$. The depression of the free end of the cantilever by this element of the distributed load is the same as the depression which would be produced at x, if the element of load were applied at the free end. Thus, the element of load considered contributes to η an elementary component of magnitude (see equation (75))

$$\alpha f\left(\frac{x}{l}\right)\phi\eta F\left(\frac{x}{l}\right)dx,$$

and, integrating over the whole cantilever to obtain the resultant depression, we have

$$\eta = \alpha\phi\eta \int_0^l f\left(\frac{x}{l}\right) F\left(\frac{x}{l}\right) dx,$$

or, writing $x = \gamma l$,

$$1 = a\phi l \int_0^1 f(\gamma)F(\gamma)d\gamma \qquad (77)$$

Equation (77) provides an explicit expression for ϕ, as was required.

Now let τ be the period, and ν the frequency, of vibration of the cantilever in the normal mode to which the form-function F applies. Then, since ϕ is the constant relating restoring force per unit length of cantilever to instantaneous displacement (equation (76)), the constant relating acceleration to displacement is ϕ/m. The period, therefore, is given by

$$\tau = 2\pi\sqrt{\frac{m}{\phi}},$$

and, substituting from equation (77) for ϕ, we have

$$\tau = \frac{1}{\nu} = 2\pi\left\{\int_0^1 f(\gamma)F(\gamma)d\gamma\right\}^{\frac{1}{2}}\sqrt{alm}.$$

If, at this stage, we may apply the results of § 4.2 to the light (but not massless) cantilever of our present considerations, we obtain

$$a = \frac{\beta l^3}{Y} = \frac{l^3}{3YAk^2}$$

(equations (75), (67) and (74)). Further to simplify presentation, we write

$$\int_0^1 f(\gamma)F(\gamma)d\gamma = n^2 \qquad (78)$$

and we note that $m = A\rho$, ρ being the density of the material of the cantilever. We have, finally,

$$\nu = \frac{\sqrt{3}}{2\pi n}\frac{k}{l^2}\sqrt{\frac{Y}{\rho}} \qquad (79)$$

In equation (79), the purely numerical constant n is different for the different normal modes of vibration; the length of the cantilever and the form of its right section enter through the quantity k/l^2, and the properties of the material of which it is made through $(Y/\rho)^{\frac{1}{2}}$. The quantity $(Y/\rho)^{\frac{1}{2}}$ is of the dimensions of a velocity, and, formally at least, the quantity $2\pi n l^2/\sqrt{3}k$ could

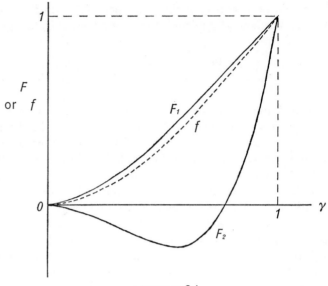

FIGURE 24

be regarded as a wavelength, different for the different modes. The situation has the same formal features as we encountered when we discussed the normal modes of a stretched string in chapter 2. But there is also a very clear point of difference. The frequencies of the normal modes of a stretched string constitute a harmonic series (equation (14)); in the present case it is clear that this is not so. The ratios of the various frequencies of the normal modes of the cantilever are given by

$$\frac{1}{n_1} : \frac{1}{n_2} : \frac{1}{n_3} : \ldots :$$

they may be deduced by inserting the appropriate form-functions

$$F_1(\gamma), F_2(\gamma), F_3(\gamma), \ldots$$

in equation (78). Fig. 24 illustrates, very crudely, the shapes of F_1 and F_2 (full lines), and the shape of f (see equation (71)). It should be obvious that the values of n^2 will not be reducible to a series of integral ratios, let alone to the series

$$1 : \frac{1}{4} : \frac{1}{9} : \ldots$$

which would be necessary if the frequencies of normal vibration were to be harmonically related. Precise evaluation in fact gives

$$\frac{1}{n_1} = 2 \cdot 030, \quad \frac{1}{n_2} = 12 \cdot 73, \quad \frac{1}{n_3} = 35 \cdot 62.$$

We stated above that the quantity $(Y/\rho)^{\frac{1}{2}}$ in equation (79) is of the dimensions of a velocity. As we shall discover in the next section, this quantity is in fact the velocity of propagation of longitudinal elastic waves in a long rod. It is in no real sense a velocity characteristic of the propagation of a transverse disturbance such as we have just been considering. This being granted, the caution of our subsequent statement, 'formally, at least, the quantity $2\pi n l^2/\sqrt{3}k$ could be regarded as a wavelength', is seen to be well founded. This quasi-wavelength is obviously very much greater than the length of the cantilever ($k \ll l$), when the first normal mode is in question, and, for any mode, is very much greater than the inter-nodal distance involved. In no sense, then, is $2\pi n l^2/\sqrt{3}k$ in fact a length characteristic of the displacement profile of the vibrating rod. The identifications that we made established the dimensional homogeneity of equation (79), and provided the basis for a formal comparison with equation (14), but they are of no further significance.

As an example of a practical system to which the considerations of this section have relevance, we may instance a tuning-fork with long parallel prongs. Each prong of such a fork may be regarded, to a good approximation, as a cantilever. In particular, we may note that the frequencies of the normal modes of a standard fork constitute an anharmonic series, the frequency of the second mode being some $2\frac{1}{2}$ octaves higher than that of the 'fundamental'.

4.4. LONGITUDINAL VIBRATIONS

A correct description of the elastic deformation of a rod vibrating as we have described in the last section is that, at any instant, the elongation (p. 83) of any longitudinal filament varies from point to point along the filament, whilst across any section of the rod the elongation varies from filament to filament. The type of vibration which we are now to discuss is simpler, in that, although the elongation still varies from point to point along each filament of the rod, across any section the elongation is instantaneously the same for all filaments.

When a long rod is vibrating longitudinally in one of its normal modes, the elongation characteristic of any right section of the rod will vary periodically with time, the period of such variation will be the same for all sections, and the instantaneous phase will be the same for all: only the amplitude of the oscillation of elongation will vary from section to section. It is our immediate problem to investigate this variation of amplitude along the length of the rod, in respect of the normal modes. Before we embark on that investigation, however, it is well to state explicitly that we are assuming the rod to be free of transverse constraints throughout. On that account, when the elongation characteristic of any right section of the rod is e, the transverse linear dilatation of the rod at that section will instantaneously be $-\sigma e$, where σ is Poisson's ratio for the material of the rod.

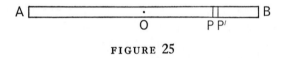

FIGURE 25

We limit our considerations, as before, to uniform rods, as defined in § 4.1. For such rods, once the relations expressing the basic physics of the problem have been derived, the mathematical analysis is exactly analogous to that followed in § 2.3, and in subsequent sections, in respect of the normal vibrations of a stretched string. Let AB (fig. 25) represent a uniform rod, of length l, having its centre at O. Consider an elementary segment of the rod between right sections through the points P and P′, distant, respectively, x and $x + \Delta x$ from O. At any instant, when the rod is vibrating longitudinally in a normal mode, let ξ and $\xi + \Delta \xi$ be the longitudinal displacements of these sections. Then the material of the rod previously occupying a length Δx between P and P′, at that instant occupies a length $\Delta x + \Delta \xi$. Assuming that the amplitude of the displacement is always very small indeed (in any practical case it is so small that the vibrations cannot be seen with the unaided eye), we may proceed to the limit, and write for e, the elongation common to all the longitudinal filaments of the rod in the segment considered—and so, ultimately, for the instantaneous elongation characteristic of the right section of the rod at a distance x from its centre,

$$e = \frac{d\xi}{dx}.$$

If, then, A is the area of cross-section of the rod, the total normal force across the section at x is given by

$$F = AYe = AY\frac{d\xi}{dx} \tag{80}$$

Y being the measure of Young's modulus for the material of the rod.

If F denotes the force across the section through P (fig. 25), the total normal force across the near section through P' may be represented by $F + \Delta F$ (we have already stated that the elongation —and so the force—varies from section to section, at any instant). Instantaneously, then, that portion of the bar between P and A acts on the segment between P and P' with a force F, directed towards O, whilst the portion of the bar between P' and B acts on the segment with a force $F + \Delta F$, oppositely directed. The resultant force on the segment is therefore ΔF, away from O. In the limit, when Δx is very small, we may write

$$\Delta F = \frac{dF}{dx}\Delta x = AY\frac{d^2\xi}{dx^2}\Delta x.$$

The mass of the segment of rod under consideration is $\rho A \Delta x$, ρ denoting the density of the material of which the rod is made. Instantaneously, therefore, the acceleration of this segment, or, in the limit, the acceleration characteristic of the right section of the rod at a distance x from its centre, is given by

$$a = \frac{\Delta F}{\rho A \Delta x} = \frac{Y}{\rho}\frac{d^2\xi}{dx^2}.$$

If the oscillation of displacement of the right section at x is simply periodic, we must have $a = -\mu\xi$, where μ is a constant; furthermore, if the rod is vibrating in a normal mode, μ must be the same for all sections of the rod. For a normal mode, therefore, for all values of x, and at all times,

$$\frac{Y}{\rho}\frac{d^2\xi}{dx^2} = -\mu\xi \tag{81}$$

Equation (81) summarises the basic physics of the problem, in the same way as equation (2) summarised that of the problem of the normal modes of the stretched string: from this point the mathematics is essentially the same, and its interpretation similar, in the two cases. Here, then, we may be brief, relying on the earlier treatment for elaboration.

The general solution of equation (81) is of the form

$$\xi = a \sin\left(\sqrt{\frac{\rho\mu}{Y}}\, x + \delta\right) \tag{82}$$

To proceed farther we must specify the nature of the end constraints of our rod. For the present we shall assume that the rod is under no external constraint at all. This situation could be realised, to a sufficient approximation in practice, if the rod were suspended horizontally by two long flexible strings threaded through small eyelets, one at each end of the rod, and fastened to a rigid support so as to hang parallel to one another. In that case we assume that the normal force acting across each end-section of the rod is zero, and, from equation (80), we have

$$\left(\frac{d\xi}{dx}\right)_{\frac{l}{2}} = \left(\frac{d\xi}{dx}\right)_{-\frac{l}{2}} = 0.$$

Thus

$$\cos\left(\sqrt{\frac{\rho\mu}{Y}}\frac{l}{2} + \delta\right) = \cos\left(\delta - \sqrt{\frac{\rho\mu}{Y}}\frac{l}{2}\right) = 0,$$

giving two solutions, namely,

$$\delta = 0, \qquad \sqrt{\frac{\rho\mu}{Y}}\frac{l}{2} = \frac{2n+1}{2}\,\pi,$$

and

$$\delta = \frac{\pi}{2}, \qquad \sqrt{\frac{\rho\mu}{Y}}\frac{l}{2} = n\pi.$$

Substituting from these solutions in equation (82), we have

$$\xi = a \sin(2n+1)\pi\frac{x}{l} \tag{83}$$

and

$$\xi = a \cos 2n\pi\frac{x}{l} \tag{84}$$

respectively, where, in respect of either equation, n is any integer.

Equation (83) describes a series of normal modes each having a node at the centre of the bar; equation (84) a series of modes for each of which the centre of the bar is an anti-node. For all modes the ends of the bar are anti-nodes. Corresponding to the normal modes of the first set, the vibration frequencies are given by the equations

$$f_o = \frac{1}{2\pi}\sqrt{\mu} = \frac{2n+1}{2l}\sqrt{\frac{Y}{\rho}} \qquad (85)$$

those of the normal modes of the second set are given by

$$f_e = \frac{1}{2\pi}\sqrt{\mu} = \frac{2n}{2l}\sqrt{\frac{Y}{\rho}} \qquad (86)$$

As we have expressed equations (85) and (86)—not cancelling the 2's in the last equation—we see immediately that the frequencies f_o are the 'odd' frequencies, and f_e the 'even' frequencies, of the harmonic series represented by the single equation

$$f = \frac{n}{2l}\sqrt{\frac{Y}{\rho}} \qquad (87)$$

in which n may be any positive integer.

Equation (87) is in every way analogous to equation (14) of § 2.6. In that section, following the procedure of § 2.4, we showed that the vibrations of a stretched string in its nth normal mode can be resolved into oppositely travelling wave trains of the same amplitude, of wavelength $2l/n$, and of velocity $\sqrt{\dfrac{T}{m}}$. In precisely the same way, in our present case, we could show that the vibrations of the unconstrained bar, in its nth normal mode, may be resolved into oppositely travelling trains of longitudinal waves of the same amplitude, of wavelength $2l/n$, and of velocity $\sqrt{\dfrac{Y}{\rho}}$.

As before, we should be justified in concluding, from the fact that the velocity of propagation is the same for each wavelength represented in the harmonic series, that the velocity of propagation of a sinusoidal, longitudinal, elastic wave along an 'infinite' uniform rod is independent of the wavelength (and of the shape and size of the right section of the rod), and is given by the equation

$$v = \sqrt{\frac{Y}{\rho}} \tag{88}$$

Accepting the validity of equation (88), we may further conclude that an arbitrary longitudinal pulse of small intensity is propagated without change of form along an infinite rod. Finally, we may note that we have already quoted equation (88) in our discussion of the transverse vibrations of a cantilever in the last section (see p. 90).

In following the analogy of the unconstrained rod and the stretched string, in our brief survey of the characteristics of the former system, we have overlooked one point of real difference. With the stretched string, the ends of the string are displacement nodes in respect of each normal mode: as we have already remarked, equations (83) and (84) show that the ends of the free rod are displacement anti-nodes for each mode. At the ends of the free rod the total normal force is permanently zero, thus the gradient of displacement, rather than the displacement itself, is zero throughout the vibration (equation (80)). When we consider the vibrations of any normal mode as resulting from the superposition of the oppositely travelling portions of a single wave motion which is transmitted back and forth along the bar, being reflected without loss at its ends, this difference in end conditions shows up as a difference in the circumstances of such reflection.

In § 2.9 we discussed in detail the reflection of an arbitrary pulse of transverse displacement at the fixed end of a finite stretched string. Making reference to that discussion, we can now treat the analogous problem of the reflection of an arbitrary longitudinal pulse, at the free end of a finite rod, more briefly. We cannot in this case use diagrams giving realistic 'pictures' of the instantaneous profile of the rod—for the external appearance of the rod provides no visual evidence of its internal state of strain. If we employ diagrams similar to figs. 8, 9 and 10 of our previous discussion, they must be regarded strictly as two-dimensional displacement-distance curves; it being realised that, in the physical system which they represent, these lengths, displacement and distance, are measured in the same direction.

In § 2.9, fig. 8 represented the regular trains of pulses which, travelling in opposite directions on an infinite stretched string, would reproduce the reflection phenomena of a finite string over an appropriate length (or over successive lengths) of the 'infinite' string. We require now the corresponding diagram for the present case. If the end conditions are to be as specified, namely, that in a normal mode the free ends of the rod shall be displacement anti-nodes, and that $\frac{d\xi}{dx}$ shall be permanently zero there, then obviously the pulses P_1', P_2' of the reverse train must not be 'inverse' pulses with respect to P_3 and P_2, respectively: in Tait's phrase (p. 31) they should merely be the 'perverse' of these pulses as reflected in the points A', B, respectively. This being so, it is almost necessary, to avoid confusion, to represent the direct and reverse trains of pulses separately: this we do in fig. 26. Then, confining attention to the situation at B, to begin with, we note that the pulses P_2 and P_2' will meet there, that at each instant during which they overlap at B, the displacement at this point will be contributed to equally by the two pulses, and that the dis-placement gradient $\frac{d\xi}{dx}$ will indeed remain zero throughout, since at corresponding points on the two pulses the slopes of the pulse profiles are equal and opposite. We note further that at the instant when the pulse P_2 is just clear of the segment AB, the pulse P_2' is completely reconstituted in that segment and is moving clear of B and towards A.

Somewhat later this pulse arrives at A, and we note that the description which we have just given describes the situation at that point during the period in which the pulses P_2' and P_3 overlap there. We recognise that the situation in the segment AB is precisely such as may obtain in an unconstrained rod of length equal to AB. At any instant at which the displacement is zero at each end of the rod there is either a pulse such as P_2 moving from A towards B or a pulse such as P_2' moving from B to A. Because the reflection process (at either end of the rod) results in a returning pulse which is 'perverted' but not 'inverted', we refer to this process as reflection without change of phase. In contradistinction, we refer to reflection such as takes place at the fixed ends of a stretched string—or at the fixed ends of a rod, if, in fact, it is

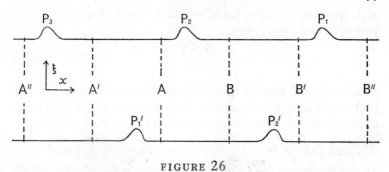

clamped at the ends—as reflection with reversal of phase. These points having been established, it is hardly necessary to reproduce here the diagrams which, for the unconstrained rod, would correspond to figs. 9 and 10 of § 2.9. Their construction can be left as an exercise for the reader.

Throughout this section we have been dealing almost exclusively with the vibrations of an entirely free rod, making reference only incidentally, and in the last paragraph, to those of a rod having its two ends fixed. On the other hand, in § 4.3 we restricted attention to the transverse vibrations of a cantilever—a rod clamped at one end and free at the other, to the exclusion of the other cases which might have been considered. For comparison with the results of that section, we now refer briefly to the normal modes of longitudinal vibration of such a rod. At the fixed end of a cantilever, obviously $\xi = 0$ throughout: this end is a displacement node. In respect of longitudinal vibration, there need be no limitation on the value of $\dfrac{d\xi}{dx}$, or the total normal force across this end, arising from the nature of the support. We note that equation (83), describing the odd modes of an unconstrained rod of total length l, requires that there shall be, in these modes, displacement nodes at the centre of the rod. For such motion, then, the unconstrained rod behaves as if it were constituted of two cantilevers joined at their fixed ends, so that their axes are collinear. Rewriting equation (83) for a cantilever of length l, we therefore have

$$\xi = a \sin (2n+1) \frac{\pi x}{2l} \tag{89}$$

G

and, applying the same transformation to equation (85), for the corresponding frequencies,

$$f = \frac{2n+1}{4l} \sqrt{\frac{Y}{\rho}} \qquad (90)$$

It will be noted that the normal frequencies specified by equation (90) do not constitute a complete harmonic series. Their measures are proportional, successively, to the odd integers, 1, 3, 5, ...

4.5. ORDERS OF MAGNITUDE: REAL WIRES AND RODS

In this section we wish to assess the results obtained, through the discussion of ideal systems in §§ 2.6, 4.3 and 4.4., as regards their relevance to the real systems with which we have to deal in the laboratory. The results of § 2.6 were deduced for the ideal string, assumed to be perfectly flexible. We have already pointed out (§ 4.1) how this ideal may be approached through the use of strings made up of a very large number of fine strands. Here we wish to disregard this possibility, and consider rather a thin wire in its dual aspects of 'string 'and 'rod'. If the radius of a single cylindrical wire is sufficiently small in comparison with its length, it will be possible (see p. 100) to subject it to tension of an amount sufficient for its transverse vibrations to be very closely such as are described in § 2.6. At the same time the wire may undergo longitudinal vibrations as described in § 4.4. Our first object is to compare the frequencies of these two types of vibration of the one wire.

For the transverse (stretched-string) vibrations, we have (equation (14))

$$f_t = \frac{n}{2l} \sqrt{\frac{T}{m}};$$

for the longitudinal vibrations (equation (87) applies equally, whether the rod is unconstrained, or whether it is held at the two ends only),

$$f_l = \frac{n}{2l} \sqrt{\frac{Y}{\rho}}.$$

Thus, for each value of the mode order, n,

$$\left(\frac{f_t}{f_l}\right)^2 = \frac{T}{m}\frac{\rho}{Y}.$$

Now, if e is the longitudinal elongation of the wire under tension T, and A is the measure of its cross-sectional area, $e = T/AY$, $m = A\rho$, thus

$$\left(\frac{f_t}{f_l}\right)^2 = e \tag{91}$$

In practice e is likely to range from 10^{-4} to 10^{-2}—it is unlikely to be very much greater than the latter quantity. Thus $f_l \gg f_t$ in all practical cases. If the frequency of the stretched-string vibrations is in the middle range of audible frequencies, the corresponding frequency of the longitudinal (rod) vibrations is likely to be near or beyond the upper limit of what may be heard.

Next, we wish to compare the frequencies of the transverse and longitudinal vibrations of a cantilever. For the first normal mode, in the former case, we have (equation (79))

$$f_t = \frac{3 \cdot 516}{2\pi} \frac{k}{l^2} \sqrt{\frac{Y}{\rho}};$$

for the first normal mode in the latter case (equation (90)),

$$f_l = \frac{1}{4l} \sqrt{\frac{Y}{\rho}}.$$

In respect of this mode, then,

$$\frac{f_t}{f_l} = \frac{7 \cdot 032}{\pi} \frac{k}{l} \tag{92}$$

Here we are definitely comparing two different types of elastic vibration of the experimental system (the stretched-string vibrations of a wire do not depend upon the elastic properties of the wire, although the ratio of frequencies given by equation (91) is expressed in terms of a parameter describing its elastic behaviour). Equation (92) shows that the frequency of flexural vibrations, in the first normal mode, is very much smaller than that of longitudinal vibrations in the same mode. The ratio k/l, for a rod of circular section of radius r, is $r/2l$; for a rod of any other cross-section, of the same cross-sectional area A, the ratio cannot be greatly in excess of $\left(\frac{A}{\pi}\right)^{\frac{1}{2}} \Big/ 2l$.

In each of the two comparisons that we have just made, we have been concerned with the different types of vibration which are possible for a single system: in a practical, rather than an ideal, case we may have to reckon with situations in which vibrations of more than one possible type are occurring at any one time. We have made these comparisons, however, on the basis of the results which we have derived for the ideal systems. We wish now to amend one of these results to take count of a departure from ideal conditions which we know must occur. We wish to correct equation (14), giving the frequencies of the normal modes of a stretched wire, for the effect of the stiffness of the wire.

Obviously we cannot give the theory of this effect in detail, but it should be clear that, for a disturbance having a given displacement profile, the total potential energy of the displaced wire will be greater, for a specified amplitude, the stiffer the wire. In general, then, frequencies for a wire of finite stiffness will be greater than the corresponding frequencies given by equation (14) on the assumption that the stiffness is zero. If f' is the frequency of the nth normal mode, for a wire of length l and cylindrical radius r (cross-sectional area A), stretched to a tension T, detailed calculation gives

$$f'^2 = f^2 \left(1 + \frac{\pi^2 n^2}{4} \frac{YA}{T} \frac{r^2}{l^2}\right) \tag{93}$$

f being the frequency derived from equation (14), and Y the measure of Young's modulus for the material of the wire. Even to obtain as simple a result as this, it is necessary to assume that the 'correction term' in the bracket is small compared with unity.

In assessing the significance of equation (93), we note that $T/YA = e$, the elongation of the wire under tension T (see p. 99). Then, the equation shows that the sharpening of the pitch of the string by reason of its stiffness is the less as this elongation is the greater. If we accept 10^{-3} as a representative value of e, we see that r/l must be less than 10^{-3}, or thereabouts, if the effect of stiffness is to be significantly less than 1 per cent, as measured by the change of frequency of the first normal mode. And we note that, if the frequency of the first normal mode is raised by 1 per cent, then that of the second normal mode is raised by 4 per cent, and so on—as long as equation (93) gives a sufficiently accurate account of the phenomenon. In any case, when the effect of stiffness is taken count of, it is obvious that we can no longer assert that the normal modes constitute a strictly harmonic series. In fact the modes of higher order fall progressively farther out of step, in respect of this relationship, as the order increases.

4.6. TORSIONAL VIBRATIONS

If a long rod is clamped firmly in a chuck at one end, and if the chuck is very suddenly rotated through a small angle θ, the rod does not turn bodily with the chuck: the motion of the free end of the rod is different from that of the clamped end. Ultimately the rod as a whole takes up a new position of rest, having rotated about its axis, so as to follow the chuck through the angle θ, but not until a pulse of torsional displacement has travelled back and forth down the rod, and has gradually been dissipated by friction and other effects. To imagine otherwise is to entertain the fallacy which, in the last analysis, affects any application of the notion of the 'rigid' body to the real bodies of the physical world (see p. 2).

We shall not, in this chapter, treat the matter of the torsional vibrations of rods in further detail. The mathematical description is precisely analogous to that of the longitudinal vibrations which was given in full in § 4.4: here it is left as an exercise for the reader. In the case of torsional vibrations, the velocity of propagation is $\sqrt{n/\rho}$, where ρ is the density and n is the modulus of rigidity of the material of the rod.

CHAPTER 5

ELASTIC VIBRATIONS OF AIR COLUMNS

5.1. HISTORICAL

In this chapter we shall be dealing specifically with the vibrations of columns of air contained in cylindrical pipes, open or closed at the ends according to circumstance. The modern orchestra contains many instruments the functioning of which depends upon the properties of such columns of air. As with the strings (see § 2.1), so with the wood-wind, the development and differentiation of the various instruments has been continuous throughout recorded history. Each of the civilisations of antiquity contributed its share to this process. Certainly Nature was rich in prototypes; originally man merely took what lay to hand. The bamboos of China and India, or the reeds of the Nile valley, provided him with hollow stems in abundance, closely cylindrical in form, stopped to various lengths by the nodes which are their characteristic features. Later, craftsmen imitated Nature in wood and metal. Thus the primitive flute originated in the säib-it or nay of ancient Egypt—though we probably owe to the Hindus the method of transverse blowing: the nay was blown obliquely across the open end. Similarly, the monaulos, which the Greeks took over from the Egyptians, and improved, was in all essentials a primitive clarinet. In the fourth century BC Aristotle set down precise directions for the boring of the holes—directions as to their position and size—in such an instrument. Empirically, at least, even at this early date its main properties were understood.

The modern organ, too, had its primitive counterparts. In China the yu and the ho—the greater and lesser chengs—had arrays of bamboo pipes blown from a common wind box (nineteen speaking pipes in the larger instrument and thirteen in the smaller —with additional mute pipes, as embellishment, even as some modern instruments have), and the Grecian syrinx (Pan-pipes) consisted generally of a set of ten graded pipes made from the kalamos reed, and blown individually across their open ends, which were arrayed in line for the convenience of the player.

All this is history, but in this chapter we shall not be concerned with it further: indeed we shall not be concerned in any way with the wood-wind instruments of the modern orchestra in their individual peculiarities, only with the basic principles which provide the common background to the understanding of the functioning of any or all of them. We have already adopted the stretched string as the pattern of the simple vibratory system of strictly limited extent; here, working to that pattern, we shall first consider the elastic vibration of a column of air contained in a cylindrical pipe of uniform section and closed at both ends. This is not a system of practical importance, but from its discussion it will be an easy matter to derive the properties of air columns in open-ended pipes—whether pipes open at one end only, or at both ends.

5.2. PIPES CLOSED AT BOTH ENDS

We consider a cylindrical pipe of length l, and, though this assumption will not directly influence our results, of uniform circular cross-section, of area A. We suppose that the pipe is closed by a circular plate at each end, and that it contains a sample of air (or it could equally well be any other gas!) of total mass $Al\rho$. Then, when the column of air in the pipe is not vibrating (and the temperature is the same throughout), the density of the air is the same everywhere in the column and its measure is ρ. Conversely, when the column of air is vibrating, the density in the neighbourhood of any point varies periodically with time, and, at any instant, varies from point to point along the column. Our aim is to identify, and to deduce the frequencies of, the normal modes of longitudinal vibration of the column of air in the pipe, and for this purpose we make certain simplifying assumptions. We assume that the temperature of the material pipe is constant throughout its length and that the effects of air viscosity can be neglected. We assume that the air in the pipe behaves as an ideal gas, and we necessarily assume that the density is at any instant constant over any right section of the cylindrical column. This last assumption is implicit in our decision to confine attention to longitudinal vibrations in which viscous effects are not involved: such vibrations are essentially of a kind wherein the periodic mass movement of the air across any right section of the pipe may be completely specified in terms of the time-dependence of a linear displacement measured parallel to the axis of the pipe.

The situation is in many ways similar to that in a cylindrical rod which is vibrating longitudinally, the characteristics of which we discussed in detail in § 4.4. In broad outline we shall treat the new situation as we did the old, but at the outset a very real difference should be noted. In the earlier treatment (p. 91) we were able to write, with full justification, 'the material of the rod previously occupying a length Δx . . . at that instant occupies a length $\Delta x + \Delta \xi$'. When the vibrating system is a column of air, we cannot, with the same strict justification, use precisely analogous words. Even when such a column of air is not vibrating, we cannot, at a later time, identify that portion of the air which at any instant occupied a particular segment of length of the column. The molecules are perpetually in motion; the greater the lapse of time, the farther any molecule is likely to have wandered from its 'initial' position. We cannot continuously identify any portion of the air in the pipe; we can only say that under steady conditions the macroscopic density remains constant throughout. When treating the vibrations of the rod, to begin with we concentrated attention on the motion of an elementary segment bounded by right sections distant, in the undisturbed state, respectively x and $x + \Delta x$ from O, the centre of the rod (see fig. 25), We defined the quantity ξ as the instantaneous displacement of the end of this segment nearer to O, and $\xi + \Delta \xi$ as the instantaneous displacement of the end father from O. We assumed without question that the same material—the same atoms of matter—composed the segment throughout the vibration, through all the (periodic) changes of position and length of the segment concerned. In treating the vibrations of the column of air, we shall likewise assign to each right section of the air column a measure of instantaneous displacement, which at any instant will vary from section to section of the column, but we shall not be able to claim that any elementary segment of the column (defined, as before, in terms of the instantaneous, displaced, positions of two neighbouring right sections) contains the same molecules indefinitely. We shall only be able to assert that the segment contains the same mass of air at all times—or, effectively, the same number of molecules. From this point of view, our notion of instantaneous displacement loses some measure of concreteness, but it does not lose its formal significance in our calculations. When we are concerned with macroscopic processes in gases, we find it necessary always to distinguish between mass motion and the motions of the individual molecules (compare $M L \& T$, p. 300).

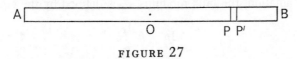

FIGURE 27

Suppose, therefore, that P and P' (fig. 27) are right sections of the column of air enclosed in the uniform circular pipe AB, of length l and area of cross-section A, as described above. When the column of air is not vibrating, let the distances of P and P' from O be x and $x + \Delta x$, respectively. When the column of air is vibrating, let P and P' move so that the net flux of air across either section is zero throughout. Then the two sections will always contain the same mass of air, $A\rho\Delta x$. We shall refer to right sections of the air column which move in this way as 'representative sections'. Let ξ and $\xi + \Delta \xi$ be the instantaneous displacements of these representative sections. Then, if at the arbitrary time in question, the mean density of the air between P and P' is $\rho + \Delta \rho$,

$$A(\rho + \Delta \rho)(\Delta x + \Delta \xi) = A\rho\Delta x,$$

or, when the amplitude of the displacement is very small indeed,

$$\Delta \rho = - \rho \frac{d\xi}{dx} \tag{94}$$

In this form, $\Delta \rho$ is given as the instantaneous value of the excess density of the air in the immediate neighbourhood of any representative section in the region of which, instantaneously, the displacement gradient is $\dfrac{d\xi}{dx}$.

We wish to relate $\Delta \rho$ to the instantaneous value, Δp, of the excess pressure of the air in the immediate neighbourhood of the representative section concerned. We might use the ideal-gas equation of state ($M L \& T$, p. 286) for this purpose, except that we do not know how the temperature of the gas (as distinct from that of the pipe) varies when the column is vibrating. We can avoid, or at least postpone, this difficulty by using instead the equation defining the bulk modulus of the gas. This is a quantity which, for a given gas, has different values according to the precise conditions in relation to change of temperature (or transfer of heat) which obtain in the process concerned ($M\,L$ & T, § 16.3). In our notation, the bulk modulus, k, is defined by the equation

$$\Delta p = k\frac{\Delta \rho}{\rho}$$

(the fractional decrease of volume of any sample of gas is numerically equal to the fractional increase in density in a given change). Substituting from this equation in equation (94) we have

$$\Delta p = -k\frac{d\xi}{dx} \qquad (95)$$

Equation (95) implies that, across the representative section P (fig. 27), when the displacement of that section is ξ, the air in the column to the left of P in the figure exerts a force of magnitude $A\left(p-k\dfrac{d\xi}{dx}\right)$ on the air to the right of P. Here p is the measure of the 'normal' pressure of the air in the pipe, when there are no vibrations. At the same instant, obviously, the air to the right of P' exerts a force, across that section, on the air to the left of P' of magnitude $A\left(p-k\dfrac{d\xi}{dx}-k\dfrac{d^2\xi}{dx^2}\Delta x\right)$, the separation of the sections being such that the change of displacement gradient is small over the distance concerned. These results being accepted, the resultant force acting on the mass of air between P and P', at the instant in question, is $Ak\dfrac{d^2\xi}{dx^2}\Delta x$, in the direction of ξ increasing. By definition, the mass of air between these neighbouring sections remains constant: it is $A\rho\Delta x$. If, therefore, a is the instantaneous acceleration (of mass motion) of this portion of air, we have

$$A\rho\Delta x \cdot a = Ak\frac{d^2\xi}{dx^2}\Delta x,$$

or

$$a = \frac{k}{\rho}\frac{d^2\xi}{dx^2}.$$

In the limit, this expression for the acceleration refers to the mass motion of the air in the immediate neighbourhood of P, the representative section of which ξ is the instantaneous measure of the displacement. When the column of air is vibrating in a normal mode, the motion of P, as of any other representative section of the air column, is simply periodic, and the period is the same for all sections. For a normal mode, therefore, for all values of x from $-\frac{l}{2}$ to $\frac{l}{2}$, and at all times

$$\frac{k}{\rho}\frac{d^2\xi}{dx^2} = -\mu\xi \tag{96}$$

where μ is a constant. The value of this constant will be different for the different modes, and, since the frequency of a normal mode is given by $\sqrt{\mu}/2\pi$, the problem of calculating the frequencies is essentially that of determining the permitted values of μ.

Equation (96) is to be compared with equation (81), and with equation (2). From equation (81) the normal modes of longitudinal vibration of a finite rod were identified, from equation (2) the normal modes of transverse vibration of a stretched string. In each case a solution of the differential equation was sought which satisfied the 'boundary conditions' appropriate to the problem. Equation (96), which is of precisely the same form as each of the other two equations, must be treated similarly. In the vibrating column of air which we are considering it is obviously necessary that the displacement of the representative section shall be permanently zero at each end of the column—the pipe being closed at each end according to our present assumptions. In the present case, therefore, $\xi = 0$ when $x = -\frac{l}{2}$, also when $x = \frac{l}{2}$. With these boundary conditions, the relevant solutions of equation (96) may be written

$$\xi = a \sin 2n\pi\frac{x}{l} \tag{97}$$

and

$$\xi = a \cos (2n+1)\pi\frac{x}{l} \tag{98}$$

where, in either equation, n is an integer, and a is the arbitrary measure of the displacement amplitude at an anti-node. In relation to equation (97), we have

$$\sqrt{\frac{\rho\mu}{k}} = \frac{2n\pi}{l};$$

in relation to equation (98),

$$\sqrt{\frac{\rho\mu}{k}} = \frac{(2n+1)\pi}{l}.$$

It will be recognised that the two equations, with these subsidiary relations, describe the displacement profiles of the 'even' and the 'odd' normal modes of the vibrating air column, respectively, as the corresponding solutions of equation (81) described the displacement profiles of the two sets of normal modes of the vibrating rod. As in that case, also, it will be seen that the frequencies of the two sets together constitute a harmonic series, represented in this instance by the single equation

$$f = \frac{n}{2l}\sqrt{\frac{k}{\rho}} \tag{99}$$

in which n may be any positive integer.

Two comments may be made on the results so far achieved. We should remind ourselves, first of all, that the bulk modulus, k, is not a uniquely specified quantity (see p. 106), so that equation (99), in particular, is not unambiguous in respect of numerical prediction in any case. We shall return to this question later (p. 114). Secondly, we should note that equations (97) and (98) describe the normal modes in terms of the somewhat fictitious parameter ξ, the displacement of a representative section of the vibrating column of air. In our original description of the physical situation we preferred the excess density, $\Delta\rho$, as the descriptive variable. We wrote (p. 103) 'when the column of air is vibrating, the density in the neighbourhood of any point varies periodically with time, and, at any instant, varies from point to point along the column'. This is a more realistic form of description than the other. It is instructive to use equation (94) to transform the less realistic into the more realistic form. From equations (97) and (98), in this way, we obtain

$$\Delta\rho = -\frac{2n\pi}{l}\,a\rho\cos 2n\pi\frac{x}{l}$$

and
$$\Delta\rho = \frac{(2n+1)\pi}{l}\, a\rho \sin(2n+1)\pi\frac{x}{l}$$

respectively. Comparing these results with the original equations, we conclude that displacement nodes are anti-nodes of density variation and *vice versa* for all modes. In particular, we conclude that, the closed ends of the pipe being nodes of displacement, the surfaces of the end plates experience in full the maximum variations of pressure which occur anywhere in the column of gas, when the latter is vibrating in a normal mode. The nodes and anti-nodes of pressure variation coincide, respectively, with the nodes and anti-nodes of density variation, throughout the length of the column, in any case (compare equations (94) and (95)).

Following the development of § 4.4 to the next stage, by an argument which need not here be repeated, we may deduce the velocity of propagation of a sinusoidal, longitudinal wave along an 'infinite' column of air. The result is given by the equation

$$v = \sqrt{\frac{k}{\rho}} \tag{100}$$

and, because the velocity is independent of the wavelength (as in the cases studied previously), we may conclude that an arbitrary longitudinal pulse of small intensity would be propagated with this velocity, without change of form, along such an infinite column of air.

In equation (100) we have a formal expression for the velocity of 'sound' in air contained in a pipe of uniform cross-section. Strictly, this is only an approximate result, for we have neglected any specific effects arising from the presence of the solid wall of the pipe: in particular we have neglected the viscous drag which must occur when a real gas moves, as each segment of the vibrating air column necessarily moves to and fro, over a solid surface. We shall return later (p. 117) to consider the magnitude of the approximation which we have made. Here we are more concerned to note that, in relation to equation (100), reference to a pipe of finite cross-section in our approximate treatment has ultimately had the effect of canalising our thoughts, rather than of limiting the sideways dimensions of the region to which the equation applies. Obviously, equation (100) applies precisely—without any imposed condition except that the disturbance shall be of small amplitude (see § 5.5)—to the case of a boundless gaseous medium traversed by a 'plane wave' of sound. By the term 'plane wave', which we here introduce for the first time in this book—for we have not previously considered a wave disturbance in a three-dimensionally infinite medium, we mean a wave process in which the instantaneous loci of constant phase (and constant displacement) are (two-dimensionally infinite) parallel planes having the direction of wave propagation as common normal.

Quite clearly, the notions of 'infinite medium' and 'plane wave', as here defined, are theoretical abstractions. Neither concept is ever exemplified in its full purity in an actual situation. Each represents an idealisation of actuality. By now the reader will be well aware that it is only through the use of such idealisations— such fictions—that progress is possible in physics, the most 'exact' of the sciences.

5.3. VELOCITY OF PROPAGATION OF SOUND

We have concluded that equation (100) gives precisely—once the situation in respect of the bulk modulus, k, is clarified—the velocity of propagation of a plane wave of sound, of small amplitude, in an ideally infinite homogeneous fluid medium. We have also stated that in no actual case are the exact conditions of validity of this equation satisfied. When sound is transmitted through the free atmosphere, for example, the disturbance spreads outwards from a source of limited extent. Near the source, the wave disturbance is not, even approximately, a plane wave, and the medium is certainly not infinite in the absolute sense. Because of these considerations, it becomes a matter of practical importance to know under what conditions equation (100) is likely to give a 'sufficiently accurate' value for the velocity of propagation. In this connection we have only one 'scale factor' (or 'characteristic length') in terms of which to judge distances as large or small; that is the wavelength of the disturbance itself. Judged by this standard, a wave surface is 'effectively plane' if the radius of curvature of the surface is very large compared with the wavelength—and to say that a portion of the medium is of large extent implies the same standard of comparison. We conclude that equation (100) is likely to give a good value for the velocity when measurements are made, with a source which itself is of linear dimensions not large compared with the wavelength, over a range of distance from the source large by the same standard. The wavelengths of audible sounds in air range from several metres to a millimetre, or thereabouts: our considerations imply, therefore, that, with the shorter wavelengths at least, any practicable measurement in free air is likely to be under conditions for which the equation is a very good approximation to the truth. Exact calculation shows that our dimensional argument has, in fact, erred on the side of caution: under all except extreme conditions equation (100) gives with high accuracy the velocity of propagation of a longitudinal disturbance of small amplitude in a gaseous medium. We need no longer, in general, impose the restriction 'plane wave in an infinite medium' with which we opened this discussion.

It has been stated categorically, first in the last section (p. 109), that equation (100), which we derived as giving the velocity of propagation of a longitudinal wave of density-variation along an infinite column of air, in fact provides a formal expression for the velocity of sound under the conditions specified. Though it would be out of place, in this chapter, to give a detailed description of the experiments which justify this assertion—the assertion that the physical process which affects our sense of hearing, or activates a microphone, is a longitudinal disturbance propagated through the surrounding medium—a brief history of the emergence of this point of view may not be inappropriate. We may discern the first vague formulation of it in the writings of the Greeks. When Aristotle wrote 'Sound takes place when bodies strike the air . . . the air being contracted and expanded and overtaken, and again struck by the impulses of the breath and the strings', he was doing little more, perhaps, than giving expression in general terms to Pythagorean notions (see § 2.6) which had been current in that school nearly two hundred years previously. But in his generalising he seized upon the idea that variations of density are involved in the process of propagation; even if he was in error in supposing that the air as a whole moves forward, 'so that the same voice spreads every way as far as the motion of the air takes place', he had at least contributed this one essential idea which was to find its place in the ultimate synthesis.

The Roman architect Vitruvius, who wrote in the last quarter-century BC, was probably the first to point the analogy between the propagation of sound through the air and the propagation of

ripples on the surface of shallow water. In the literal rather than
the exact sense, therefore, the wave nature of the process of sound
propagation was by him postulated for the first time. But Aristotle's works became standard texts for the schoolmen, whilst
Vitruvius's treatise *De Architectura* achieved no such popular-
ity—thus the two ideas which separately they contained were
never effectively fused until the experimental studies of Galileo
(*M L & T*, p. 121) and others gave them new vitality. Vitruvius's
treatise was lost sight of by the scholars of the Middle Ages; it
was re-discovered in the Swiss monastery of St. Gall by Poggio
Bracciolini, a secretary to the Roman curia, in the second decade
of the fifteenth century. The habit of independent thought was
then re-awakening in Europe: men of learning were at last becoming restive under the incubus of a bookish natural philosophy
which had been sterile for a thousand years, when this work of
the Roman architect again appeared in their libraries. At once it
had a great influence on the practice of the architect, but the
natural philosopher passed it over.

In *Dialogues of the New Sciences* (1638) Galileo wrote : 'Waves
are produced by the vibrations of a sonorous body, which spread
through the air, bringing to the tympanum of the ear a stimulus
which the mind interprets as sound.' The time had passed for a
mere speculative synthesis of the views of Aristotle and Vitruvius:
Galileo's views were given to the world only after a lifetime of careful experiment. Nearly seventy years later Francis Hawksbee was
able to demonstrate, publicly, before the Royal Society of London
(1705), that to extract the air from a vessel in which a bell was ring-
ing was almost to extinguish the sound, but by that time this was no
more than an interesting popular experiment: no one seriously
doubted the truth of Galileo's statement. Indeed Hawksbee was
merely repeating, with improved equipment, as Robert Boyle had
done before him (*M L & T*, p. 278), an experiment first performed by Otto von Guericke (1602-1686), sometime mayor of
Magdeburg, the original inventor of the air-pump, in 1650, or
very shortly afterwards.

To Marin Mersenne (1588-1648), fellow-student with Descartes
at the Jesuit College of La Flèche, who abandoned theology for
scientific pursuits in middle life, is generally attributed the first
experimental determination of the velocity of sound in the
atmosphere. Pierre Gassendi (1592-1655), provost of the cathedral

of Digne, and later for a short time (1645-1648) professor of mathematics at the Collège Royal in Paris, extended these observations. Two years after Gassendi's death, Leopold de' Medici founded the Accademia del Cimento in Florence; in Paris, under the patronage of Louis XIV the Académie des Sciences was established nine years later. Each of these early societies embarked on a further investigation of the propagation of sound. G. A. Borelli (see *M L & T*, p. 215) and Vincenzo Viviani (1622-1703), a protégé of Galileo's old age, carried out the investigation on behalf of the Florentine academy; for the Académie des Sciences, one Frenchman by birth, Jean Picard (1620-1682), one Italian, Giovanni Domenico Cassini (1625-1712), later naturalised in France, Christiaan Huygens (1629-1695), a Dutchman, and a young Danish astronomer, Ole Roemer (1644-1710), collaborated in a truly international undertaking. The results obtained by the two groups were in good agreement: the velocity of sound in air, under ordinary conditions, was 1148 feet per second according to the Italian experiments, 1172 feet per second according to the somewhat later determination in Paris (Mersenne had obtained 1474 feet per second). Of necessity, these were all large-scale experiments: they were all based on the difference in time between the visual observation of the flash of a gun and the arrival of the sound at the place of observation. All involved the assumption that the velocity of light was, by comparison, infinite. By strange coincidence, it fell to Roemer to justify this particular assumption: in 1675 he interpreted his observations on the first satellite of Jupiter as showing that light crosses the orbit of the earth in 22 minutes, or thereabouts. Not all scientists of the time accepted Roemer's interpretation, but his estimate of the velocity was later substantiated as to order of magnitude (it was, in fact, about 25 per cent too small) by other astronomical measurements, and eventually by direct measurement in the laboratory. The velocity of light is, in fact, nearly a million times greater than the velocity of sound in air.

Isaac Newton completed the manuscript of the second Book of the *Principia* in the summer of 1685 (*M L & T*, p. 204). He devoted propositions 43 to 50 of this Book to the theory of periodic vibrations in an elastic medium. Although the concept 'modulus of elasticity' had not then been defined (it was introduced by Thomas Young in 1807), Hooke's law for springs had been

H

formulated (1676), and over the decade 1660 to 1669 Robert Boyle
had published various works 'touching the spring of Air'. This
was enough for Newton to work on: applying his calculations as
he thought to the case most generally familiar, he obtained an
expression for the velocity of sound in air which we may write
in the form

$$v = \sqrt{\frac{p}{\rho}} \qquad (101)$$

This is precisely the result that we should obtain if we used
Boyle's law, as Newton effectively did, to calculate the value of
the bulk modulus, k, as it occurs in equation (100). The isothermal
elasticity of an ideal gas is numerically equal to the pressure
(*M L & T*, p. 326).

When Newton substituted numerical values for the pressure
and density of normal air in equation (101), the 'theoretical' value
for the velocity of sound appeared as 979 feet per second. The
experimental value, obtained by the academicians of Florence
and Paris, was, as we have seen, 1160 feet per second, or thereabouts. The two values, in this case, did not 'answer pretty nearly'
(*M L & T*, p. 202), and the discrepancy was confirmed by a long
series of experiments carried out by Rev. William Derham, rector
of Upminster in Essex, in the years 1704 to 1706. Derham had earlier
corresponded with Newton, and his results were published in
1708. In the following year Roger Cotes (1682-1716) began to
assist in the preparation of the second edition of Newton's
Principia. Derham had concluded that the velocity of sound in
still air is 1142 feet per second. Estimating that 'the diameter of
a particle of air . . . will be to the interval between the particles
as 1 to 8 or 9' (not a grossly erroneous estimate), Newton attempted
to account for the discrepancy on the assumption that the 'solid'
particles transmit sound instantaneously, that in fact equation
(101) gives the velocity in the intervening spaces only. The idea
was unworthy of its author—and it had to be supplemented by
another, equally confused and fallacious, before apparent numerical agreement was reached. Newton supposed that the vapour
present in the air 'will not participate of the motion . . . by which
sound is propagated'. On this supposition he regarded the density,
ρ, as referring to the 'pure air' only (though the pressure, p,
referred to the total pressure!).

To have digressed at this length on one of the rare aberrations of Newton's genius has taken us some way from our course. It may set the matter in correct perspective to remark that as late as 1771, in the third edition of Martin's *Philosophia Britannica* (from which the quotations of the preceding paragraph have been taken), these altogether implausible suggestions still find a place in a systematic account of the subject. With an entire disregard for the elementary rules of evidence, it is there stated 'The truth and accuracy of this noble theory have been sufficiently confirm'd by experiments. . . .' Precisely the opposite was the truth.

Thomas Young, writing in 1807 (*Lectures on Natural Philosophy*, p. 370), had no doubt that Newton's explanation was untenable: 'This difference between calculation and experiment has long occupied the attention of natural philosophers, but the difficulty appears to have been in great measure removed by the happy suggestion of Laplace. . . .' Laplace (*M L & T*, p. 210) did not publish a full account of his 'happy suggestion' until 1816. Qualitatively the matter was simple enough: it was commonly known that sudden compression of a gas results in an increase of temperature, and the great rapidity of the variations of pressure in a sound wave was taken for granted (Mersenne had determined the frequency of a musical note for the first time in 1635). It was a natural conclusion from these premises that the temperature, also, must vary, at any point in a gas through which sound is passing, in phase with the variations of pressure. Equalisation of temperature, by the conduction of heat, takes appreciable time; adequate time for such equalisation might not be available. Clearly Newton's assumption that conditions are isothermal was basically incorrect; it would appear more plausible to assume that the compressions and rarefactions take place adiabatically (*M L & T*, p. 325). This was the 'happy suggestion' of Laplace. What was required to test it was a knowledge of the adiabatic elasticity of air.

By 1816 Laplace had convinced himself that the ratio of the adiabatic and isothermal elasticities of a gas is the same as the ratio of the specific heats at constant pressure and constant volume, but the argument on which he based this conclusion was intuitive rather than logical. The result is true for an ideal gas (*M L & T*, p. 328), but in order to derive it rigorously it is necessary to invoke the principle of the equivalence of heat and work.

This principle was not enunciated unambiguously until 1847, and was not firmly established by experiment for thirty years afterwards (M L & T, §§ 14.2, 14.3). However, in 1819 Clément and Desormes published an account of a direct comparison of the adiabatic and isothermal elasticities of air by a simple experiment, and, for the time being at least, Laplace's 'theoretical' result became superfluous.

The procedure of Clément and Desormes was open to some criticism, in that its success depended too much on the judgment or luck of the observer, but the ratio of the elasticities deduced from it (1·354 for air under ordinary conditions) was very much as Laplace had expected. If the experimental ratio had been 1·41, the calculated value of the velocity of sound would have agreed with the experimental value. In a repetition of the experiment in 1822, Gay-Lussac (M L & T, p. 279) and Welter reduced the discrepancy still further, obtaining a ratio of 1·375 and in 1873 W. K. Röntgen (1845-1923) completed the process of reconciliation. His value, the result of a meticulously careful experiment, was 1·405. Röntgen's discovery of the X-rays, made at the age of fifty, marked the beginning of a new era in physics, but it was in some ways out of character: for the rest of a long life, both before 1895 and afterwards, he was engaged in unpretentious investigations in optics, elasticity and the properties of crystals, of which the investigation just cited is a characteristic example.

For our present purposes we shall assume that Röntgen's experiment clinched the matter: the conditions in a sound wave are adiabatic, the bulk modulus, k, in equation (100) is the measure of the adiabatic elasticity, and for an ideal gas we may write

$$v = \sqrt{\frac{\gamma p}{\rho}} \qquad (102)$$

γ being the ratio of the principal specific heats of the gas.

It is instructive to substitute for p/ρ in equation (102) the expression given by the kinetic theory of gases. For an ideal gas we have $p = \frac{1}{3}\rho c^2$ (M L & T, p. 286), c being the root mean square velocity of the molecules of the gas. Then

$$v = c\sqrt{\frac{\gamma}{3}} \qquad (103)$$

For real gases, the value of γ is never greater than 1·67 and is rarely less than 1·1. The velocity of propagation of sound is, therefore, in all cases less than three-quarters, and generally greater than three-fifths, of the root mean square velocity of the molecules, provided that conditions are such that the ideal gas laws are obeyed. In such circumstances, we may furthersubstitute the kinetic theory result $c^2 = 3RT/M$ (*M L & T*, p. 286) in equation (103), to obtain

$$v = \sqrt{\frac{\gamma RT}{M}} \qquad (104)$$

In equation (104), M is the molecular weight of the gas, R is the universal gas constant, and T is the absolute temperature. For a given gas, the velocity of propagation of sound varies directly as the square root of the absolute temperature; for different gases, at a given temperature, it varies inversely as the square root of M/γ. In the latter connection, differences in respect of molecular weight are obviously greater in general than are differences of γ: the values of the ratio of the principal specific heats may be very closely the same for two gases, as for oxygen and hydrogen, but the molecular weights very different. The velocity of sound in hydrogen is in fact about four times that in oxygen, at the same temperature.

We came to a consideration of the velocity of sound in free air by taking over the result which we had previously obtained, on the basis of certain approximations, for the velocity of propagation of a longitudinal disturbance in a pipe of uniform section. We left over (p. 109) the consideration of those approximations for later discussion. It will be appropriate to discuss them now. The approximation to which we drew particular attention on p. 109 was the neglect of the effects of viscosity, but at an earlier stage (p. 105) we pointed to a possible distinction between the temperature of the wall of the pipe and the temperature of the gas. If these two temperatures are unequal, there is the possibility of the transfer of heat, and this is a dissipative process, in relation to mechanical energy, as the effects of viscosity are also dissipative. We have just concluded that in fact periodic variations of temperature are intrinsic to the process of sound propagation in a gas: we see, therefore, that the neglect of heat transfer is in the same case as the neglect of viscous effects, when the presence of a solid surface (the wall of the pipe) is in question. For simplicity, however, we shall first consider the effect of viscosity in isolation from the other.

If the velocity of sound in a pipe were to depend, to a small degree, on the internal radius of the pipe, we should expect that an empirical relation of the type

$$v' = v\left(1 - \frac{a}{r}\right) \tag{105}$$

would represent the experimental observations, for sound of a given frequency, in a given gas at a specified pressure and temperature, in pipes of the same material but of different internal radii here denoted by r. Under such well-defined conditions, a would be a constant. Obviously, v is the measure of the velocity of sound in the free gas ($r \to \infty$) at the temperature in question. Equally obviously, the constant a is a physical quantity of dimensions L^1. On the assumption that the effect is due to viscosity alone, the quantities involved in the specification of this constant are η, the coefficient of viscosity of the gas, ρ, its density, and f, the frequency of the sound. It is difficult to find physical justification for the inclusion of any other factor. Now, there is only one derived quantity of dimensions L^1 which may be defined in terms of the three quantities mentioned: it is represented by the grouping of symbols $(\eta/\rho f)^{\frac{1}{2}}$ (compare $M\ L\ \&\ T$, p. 260). We conclude, therefore, that equation (105) may be generalised in the form

$$v' = v\left\{1 - \frac{a}{r}\left(\frac{\eta}{\rho f}\right)^{\frac{1}{2}}\right\} \tag{106}$$

—always assuming that we are dealing with viscous effects alone. Equation (106) is a generalisation of equation (105), because, with it, it is no longer necessary, once our main assumption is allowed, to specify the conditions as closely as we did at the previous stage: we should expect equation (106), with a as a unique numerical constant, to apply for all frequencies, and for all gases, contained in cylindrical pipes of whatever material and whatever radius (at least as long as the correcting term remains small compared with unity). An expression essentially of the form of equation (106) was published, without derivation or proof, by Helmholtz ($M\ L\ \&\ T$, p. 274) in 1863.

The situation in respect of transfer of heat is not quite so simple. The coefficient of thermal conductivity of the gas, κ, is obviously involved, together with the density and the specific heat at constant volume (the product ρc_v is the measure of the thermal capacity per unit volume of gas). Moreover, the derived quantity represented by $\kappa/\rho c_v$ has the same dimensions (L^2T^{-1}) as that represented by η/ρ. The first suggestion would therefore be that, when the two effects are considered together, equation (106) should be replaced by

$$v' = v\left\{1 - \frac{a}{r}\left(\frac{\eta}{\rho f}\right)^{\frac{1}{2}} - \frac{\beta}{r}\left(\frac{\kappa}{\rho c_v f}\right)^{\frac{1}{2}}\right\} \tag{107}$$

where β is a second numerical constant which is the same in all cases. A detailed calculation, made by Gustav Robert Kirchhoff (1824-1887) and published in 1868, gave a result of precisely this form. At the age of twenty-six Kirchhoff had been appointed professor at Breslau, and he held in succession chairs at Heidelberg and Berlin.

The difficulty in respect of the second correction term in equation (107) is that it takes no account of the nature of the inner surface of the pipe. It is well known that the rate of loss of heat from a solid body, of which the surface is macroscopically smooth, depends to a marked extent on the degree of polish of the surface. There is nothing in equation (107) to represent this effect.

Very many experiments have been made on the velocity of sound in pipes, since the matter was first studied in detail by Regnault ($M L \,\&\, T$, p. 295) during the years 1862-1866. The results of these experiments have generally been treated in terms of an empirical correction formula of the type

$$v' = v\left(1 - \frac{b}{rf^{\frac{1}{2}}}\right),$$

which is consistent with equation (107). When such a formula is used, b is no longer a dimensionless constant, so that it varies with the gas and with temperature—and there have been many indications that its value also depends on the nature of the inner surface of the pipe. In view of the remarks of the last paragraph, this aspect of the matter need cause no surprise.

5.4. PIPES OPEN AT ONE END, OR AT BOTH ENDS

In the introductory section of this chapter it was stated (p. 103) that we should discuss first the vibrations of a column of air contained in a cylindrical pipe closed at both ends (though this is not a system of practical importance), and on that basis proceed later to consider the properties of pipes open to the surrounding air. Following our digression, in the last section, on the propagation of sound in gases generally, we return now to this problem of open-ended pipes.

Our treatment of the doubly-closed pipe, in § 5.2, followed very closely that of the cylindrical rod which is freely supported, which treatment we gave in § 4.4. At the end of that section (p. 97) we dealt, very briefly, with the normal modes of longitudinal vibration of a rod 'clamped at one end and free at the other'. We then accepted as axiomatic the statement that at the clamped end of such a rod the displacement is zero throughout the motion. We should, perhaps, have been more precise, examining the matter in greater detail. We might have said that, if a cylindrical rod is firmly clamped in a chuck, there will be some transverse section of the rod, not far removed from the face of the chuck, which may be considered as a section of permanently zero displacement. Even this would have been no more than a good approximation to the truth, in the ultimate analysis.

The analogy between the longitudinal vibrations of the air in a doubly-closed pipe and the longitudinal vibrations of a freely supported rod is very close: that which we now wish to pursue, between the vibrations of the air in a pipe open only at one end, and the vibrations in a rod clamped only at one end, is less close. A pipe open at one end is, by definition, open to the atmosphere: the medium in which the vibrations take place extends through the open end of the pipe, effectively 'to infinity'. Suppose that we have a singly-open pipe with an 'infinite' flange, as represented in fig. 28. The medium in which the vibrations take place occupies the whole space to the right of the boundary ABA' in the figure. It will be clear that an arrangement of this type provides the only basis for a reasonable analogy. If the whole of the space to the right of ABA' were a homogeneous solid, then BB' could be regarded as a rod protruding from, and integral with, a 'semi-infinite' block of solid material. The longitudinal vibrations of

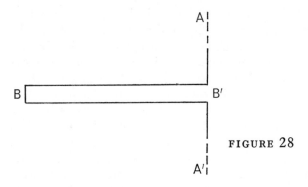

FIGURE 28

such a rod would then be analogous to those of the air in the flanged pipe—though, again, only approximately so because of a fundamental difference between solid and fluid materials which we cannot overlook. A fluid is unable to sustain a shearing stress: the modulus of rigidity has no meaning in respect of it (see § 6.3).

Strictly, the considerations on which we are entering are not without relevance, even in relation to the vibrations of stretched strings. Our brief consideration of the action of the bridge of a stringed instrument, in transmitting energy from the vibrating string to the belly of the instrument, has already given some hint of them (p. 34). With this preamble, therefore, let us consider fig. 28 as representing a singly-open pipe, fitted with an 'infinite' flange, in air.

Whatever is the precise nature of the periodic disturbance in the region of the open end of the pipe at B′, clearly this disturbance constitutes a source of sound in relation to the 'semi-infinite' atmosphere situated to the right of AA′ in the figure. Hemispherical waves must diverge, from this region as centre, spreading into the free air with the characteristic velocity of sound, carrying energy away from the mouth of the pipe. The vibrations of the air in the pipe are the immediate source of this energy. In consequence, unless these vibrations are artificially maintained, they must decrease continuously in intensity. The effect may be referred to as 'radiation damping'. In this section we restrict our considerations to open-ended pipes for which the radiation damping is small.

The theory of radiation damping is beyond the scope of our treatment, but in order to understand our self-imposed limitations we must quote its conclusions. For a singly-open pipe with an 'infinite' flange, and to the first order of approximation, the fractional decrease of energy per complete vibration, in a normal mode for which the wavelength is λ, is $4\pi A/l\lambda$, l and A representing the length and cross-sectional area of the pipe as before. Obviously, for any pipe, the condition of small damping is best satisfied for the fundamental mode (greatest λ). Conversely, for a mode of sufficiently high order, the condition fails altogether. Here we shall confine attention to modes of low order, exclusively. For such modes, in a very rough calculation, we may replace $l\lambda$ by l^2—and, if the pipe is of circular section, we may write $A = \pi r^2$. Then the condition of small damping becomes $4\pi^2 r^2 \ll l^2$, or $r \ll l/2\pi$: the internal radius of the pipe must be small compared with, say, one-tenth of the length. The limitation is, in fact, rather stringent.

If we neglect damping by radiation, we can proceed to discuss the vibration of the air in a singly-open pipe in terms of normal modes of constant amplitude. To be consistent, we should then make the assumption that the excess pressure in the air outside the pipe is permanently zero everywhere, but we are forced to qualify this assumption by the words 'at least for distances from the open end of the pipe greater than a small distance a'. The oscillations, in fact, extend some way into the open. Detailed calculation shows that this distance, a, is the same for all modes, if the radiation damping is small (see below). We assume, therefore, that for each normal mode there is a node of pressure variation at this small distance a beyond the open end of the pipe.

Now, for the doubly-closed pipe discussed in § 5.2, we concluded (p. 108) that the normal modes of odd order are those for which the mid-section of the pipe is a node of pressure-variation. We can adapt equation (99), therefore, to give the frequencies of the normal modes of the singly-open pipe, by replacing n in that equation by $2n + 1$ (giving n successive integral values starting from zero) and l (in reference to the doubly-closed pipe) by $2(l + a)$ (in reference to the present case). We then have, for the singly-open pipe,

$$f = \frac{2n+1}{4(l+a)} \sqrt{\frac{k}{\rho}} \qquad (108)$$

and, for the corresponding wavelengths,

$$\lambda = \frac{4(l+a)}{2n+1}.$$

For a doubly-open pipe, again neglecting damping by radiation, we must obviously assume that a node of pressure variation occurs at the appropriate distance a beyond each open end of the pipe. For a uniform cylindrical pipe of length l, the effective length of the pipe is therefore $l+2a$, and there may be no node of pressure variation within the pipe—or 1, 2, 3, . . . such nodes—according as the vibrations of the air in the pipe are in the fundamental mode, or in a normal mode of higher order. Brief consideration will show that the wavelengths corresponding to these normal modes are given by

$$\lambda = \frac{2(l+2a)}{n},$$

where n may be any positive integer, so that, for the frequencies of the normal modes, we obtain

$$f = \frac{n}{2(l+2a)} \sqrt{\frac{k}{\rho}} \qquad (109)$$

We may now compare the conclusions which equations (108) and (109) represent. We note, first, that the normal modes of a pipe which is open at both ends form a harmonic series, whereas those of a pipe open only at one end do not (the even harmonics are missing). Apart from the effect of the 'end-correction', represented by the added length a in respect of each open end, we note that the effect of closing one end of a doubly-open pipe is to reduce the frequency of the fundamental mode from $(1/2l)(k/\rho)^{\frac{1}{2}}$ to $(1/4l)(k/\rho)^{\frac{1}{2}}$—that is, to depress the fundamental by an octave. Taking count of the end-correction, we conclude that the depression is a little short of this factor.

It has been stated that detailed calculation shows that, provided radiation damping may be neglected, the magnitude of the end-correction a is the same, for a given pipe, for all normal modes. Radiation damping is small, for a cylindrical pipe, when $4\pi^2r^2 \ll \lambda l$ (see above). Strictly, the end-correction approximates to the same value for all modes (that is for the various possible values of λ) when $2\pi r \ll \lambda$. This latter condition is violated more rapidly, as the order of the mode increases (and λ decreases), than is the former. Strictly, then, our original statement is not stringent enough, though it will serve for our present purpose.

The magnitude of the end-correction was first calculated by Helmholtz and Rayleigh, for a pipe with an infinite flange as represented in fig. 28. Since then various theoretical treatments of the same problem have been given, for example by P. J. Daniell (1915) and L. V. King (1936). A. E. Bate (1937) has given reasons why the end-correction for an unflanged pipe should be $1/\sqrt{2}$ of that for a flanged pipe, when damping is negligible. If we accept this conclusion, the theoretical values are

$$\text{for a flanged pipe,} \quad a = 0\!\cdot\!8215r,$$
$$\text{for an unflanged pipe,} \ a = 0\!\cdot\!5809r.$$

The remaining question is only how far these theoretical values apply to a practical case. For narrow cylindrical pipes, and in respect of the normal modes of low order, experiments generally confirm that an end-correction of about $0\!\cdot\!6r$ is appropriate if the pipe is unflanged, and that this is increased by a further $0\!\cdot\!2r$, or thereabouts, when a flange is added. Within these limits, then, the detailed theory applies to the practical situation.

5.5. VIBRATIONS OF LARGE AMPLITUDE

We have now discussed at some length some of the approximations inherent in the simple theory of the vibrations of columns of air enclosed in cylindrical pipes: approximations in relation to the effect of an open end when normal modes of oscillation are in question, and approximations in relation to gaseous viscosity and conduction of heat when the propagation of sound in a long pipe is considered. But there is one further approximation, to which we have made only passing reference hitherto, about which something more should be said. We referred to this matter briefly on p. 109: 'Obviously, equation (100) applies precisely—without any imposed condition except that the disturbance shall be of small amplitude—to the case of a boundless gaseous medium traversed by a plane wave of sound.' The condition 'that the disturbance shall be of small amplitude' is formally an important one, and when it is not fulfilled in an actual situation characteristic results ensue which are not insignificant.

The issue turns on the elastic properties of gases, and the characteristic difference between solids (and liquids) on the one hand and gases on the other, in this respect. When the deformation of a solid body is in question, it is a fact of experience that there is in general a finite range of stress—frequently a considerable range—over which Hooke's law is valid: the observed strain is directly proportional to the applied stress. Empirically, therefore, we can define a modulus of elasticity for the material which has precise significance for practical purposes. This is not strictly the case with gaseous 'bodies'. 'In practical situations, with gases, strains are not always small, in the technical sense, and in general there is no finite range of stress over which strict proportionality between stress and strain obtains. . . . If we were to increase the pressure applied to a gas stepwise, over a finite range from p_1 to p_2, at each step, the pressure having increased further, so likewise would the value of the effective modulus have increased.' (*M L & T*, pp. 324, 326.) Equation (100) purports to give the velocity of propagation of a sinusoidal sound wave in terms of the appropriate bulk modulus of the gas and its density in the undisturbed state. Once it is accepted that no unique value can be assigned to the bulk modulus, it becomes clear that the equation is strictly valid only in the limit, for waves of infinitesimal amplitude.

When the velocity of a wave process is independent of wavelength (and amplitude) then a pulse of arbitrary shape is propagated without change of form (see § 2.8). Within the limits of approximate validity of equation (100), the velocity of sound is in fact independent of the wavelength: within those limits, of very small amplitude, we may therefore expect that an arbitrary pulse would be propagated without distortion. When this statement was made previously (p. 109), the qualification 'of small intensity' was included without comment: now the reason for its inclusion should be obvious.

The theory of the propagation of sound waves of finite amplitude is far from simple—and taken to its logical conclusion leads to the need to question our basic assumption that conditions in the wave are everywhere adiabatic—but a qualitative result may be stated quite plainly. It is that, in the initial stages, the parts of the wave where the excess density is greater gain continuously on those where it is less. The leading fronts of the waves therefore become steeper, at least in the initial stages of the motion. How steep the leading fronts may become is the difficult problem: it is here that the breakdown of essentially adiabatic conditions is probably determinative. Implicitly, we are discussing the matter in relation to plane waves. In reality, however, large amplitudes are more likely to be found near an intense source, in a system of outgoing spherical waves. The operation of the inverse-square law of intensity (inverse-first-power law of amplitude) greatly limits the region, in any such case, in which the finite-amplitude problem is practically important.

Observing at different distances from a source of known energy output, Rayleigh was the first to determine with any accuracy the amplitude of pressure variation in a sound wave at the threshold of audibility. Since that time many workers have carried out extensive investigations of this subject. For our purposes, to quote one general result will be sufficient. Observers in the age group 18-25 are normally found to exhibit maximum sensitivity to sounds of frequency of the order of 4000 per second. At this frequency the limit of audibility occurs when the amplitude of pressure variation is about 10^{-10} atmospheres (say 10^{-4} dyne cm.$^{-2}$). It would be safe to say that in normal air the amplitude of pressure variation could be 10^6 times as large as this without the approximation of 'very small amplitude' being seriously in error.

CHAPTER 6

PLANE WAVES IN AN INFINITE MEDIUM

6.1. INTRODUCTORY

In any actual physical situation, the occurrence of a wave process in a material medium (or, in relation to electromagnetic waves, in 'empty' space) implies the existence of a localised 'source' from which energy is carried by the spreading waves. Logically, the vibrations in the source precede the waves in the medium, and this book, by its title, and by the order of presentation adopted, stresses this logical sequence. The maintained vibrations of a stretched string (chapter 2), of a uniform rod (chapter 4), or of a column of air (chapter 5), may provide the primary source of energy for which sound waves propagated outwards through the atmosphere are the ultimate vehicle. However, our study of the vibrations of a finite system—be it a stretched string, or a metal rod, or an air-column—has revealed a more subtle relation between finite and effectively infinite systems than the asymmetrical relation of source to 'surroundings' to which we have just drawn attention.

We have largely been concerned in earlier chapters to identify the normal modes of vibration of the various finite systems mentioned above; in so doing we have been able to deduce the velocity of propagation of a sinusoidal wave process of arbitrary wavelength in a related infinite system in each case: the velocity of a transverse wave along an infinite string under tension, the velocity of a longitudinal wave along an infinite rod—or in an infinite column of air. This has been possible because we have recognised an alternative description of a normal-mode vibration in these cases: such a localised vibration may be described as the appropriate section of the system of 'standing' waves which would result from the superposition ('interference') of two sinusoidal wave trains, of the same amplitude and wavelength, travelling in opposite directions in the infinite system concerned (see § 2.4). In the three cases with which we have dealt in this way, the infinite system has been effectively one-dimensional, but in respect of the last of them, the infinite column of air enclosed in a pipe, our considerations led naturally to a discussion of the propagation of a plane wave of sound in a three-dimensionally infinite fluid (p. 110). In this chapter we develop another method of dealing with that particular question—and with similar problems—which does not involve the prior consideration of the normal modes of vibration of finite systems. This new approach is that traditionally favoured by the mathematical physicist: its relegation to second place in our considerations is no reflection on the power or generality of the method, but merely of the view that it is one stage more idealised, one step more remote from actuality, than the method we have followed hitherto.

6.2. PLANE WAVES OF SOUND IN FLUID MEDIA

We assume that plane longitudinal waves are propagated along the positive direction of x in an infinite fluid medium, and we adopt the same notation as we previously adopted in discussing the vibrations of an air column (§ 5.2). The essential physics of the problem was already covered in the previous discussion. Two attributes of the medium were seen to be basically involved: its elasticity, represented by the bulk modulus, k, and its inertia, represented by the density, ρ. The measure of the elasticity enters into the relation (equation (95)) between the excess pressure across any representative plane section and the instantaneous gradient of displacement across that section—and the density enters in determining the acceleration of mass motion of the fluid in the immediate neighbourhood of any representative section in terms of the gradient of excess pressure across the section. Following this line of argument, in § 5.2 we obtained the formal result (p. 106)

$$a = -\frac{k}{\rho}\frac{d^2\xi}{dx^2},$$

giving the acceleration of longitudinal mass motion of the medium in terms of k and ρ and the second derivative of the displacement ξ with respect to x. Here, we re-write this result in the form

$$\frac{\partial^2\xi}{\partial t^2} = \frac{k}{\rho}\frac{\partial^2\xi}{\partial x^2} \qquad (110)$$

In § 5.2 we were concerned primarily with the shapes of the instantaneous displacement profiles corresponding to the various normal modes of an enclosed column of air; we were discussing the dependence of ξ upon x, only, for an arbitrary value of t. Now our equation (110) takes count of both the time-dependence and the spatial dependence of the displacement. The equation represents, for any pair of values of x and t, the instantaneous state of affairs in the form of a necessary relation between the measures of the two second derivatives of the displacement appropriate to the values of x and t (position of the representative section and the time) which have been chosen. These second derivatives are written as 'partial' derivatives, according to the normal convention, in equation (110): $\dfrac{\partial^2 \xi}{\partial t^2}$ refers to the dependence of ξ on t, alone, x remaining constant, $\dfrac{\partial^2 \xi}{\partial x^2}$ to the dependence of ξ on x, alone, at a given instant t. Any solution of equation (110) describes a possible disturbance in the medium, restricted in character only by the physical characteristics of the medium itself (as represented by the constants k and ρ), and by the limitations that we have introduced—explicitly, or implicitly—in the course of the mathematics. We have imposed the explicit condition that the displacement shall at any instant be constant over any plane at right angles to the axis of x (the condition for 'plane waves'), and implicit throughout the derivation is the assumption that, as the medium is of infinite extent, so also is the duration of available time infinite. There is nothing in equation (110), or in its solutions, which can describe the beginning or ending of any disturbance in the medium. It is the old story of the physicist idealising his problems in order that they shall be amenable to formal mathematical statement. The mathematics is simple and elegant, but it is several steps removed from actuality.

It should be evident that the general solution of equation (110) can be written down at once. It is

$$\xi = A_1 \phi_1 \left(x - \sqrt{\frac{k}{\rho}}\, t \right) + A_2 \phi_2 \left(x + \sqrt{\frac{k}{\rho}}\, t \right) \qquad (111)$$

Here A_1 and A_2 are arbitrary constants, which we identify immediately as displacement amplitudes, and ϕ_1 and ϕ_2 are arbitrary

I

functions of the variables. Since the amplitudes are arbitrary, either may be zero in a particular case:

$$\xi = A_1\phi_1 \left(x - \sqrt{\frac{k}{\rho}}\, t \right) \qquad (112)$$

represents a possible disturbance in the medium, so also does the solution

$$\xi = A_2\phi_2 \left(x + \sqrt{\frac{k}{\rho}}\, t \right) \qquad (113)$$

Let us examine these two solutions, which are superposed in equation (111). According to equation (112), the position of a plane (at right angles to the axis of x) over which ξ remains constant indefinitely is subject to the condition

$$x - \sqrt{\frac{k}{\rho}}\, t = \text{constant};$$

the corresponding condition for constant displacement, according to equation (113), is

$$x + \sqrt{\frac{k}{\rho}}\, t = \text{constant}.$$

These two conditions lead to the results

$$\frac{dx}{dt} = \sqrt{\frac{k}{\rho}}, \quad \frac{dx}{dt} = -\sqrt{\frac{k}{\rho}},$$

respectively: any plane of constant displacement moves, in the direction of x increasing when equation (112) applies, or in the direction of x decreasing when equation (113) provides the solution, with constant velocity $\sqrt{k/\rho}$. This, then, is the velocity of propagation of plane waves of sound, of arbitrary wave-form, in the infinite medium—as indeed we deduced previously in § 5.2 (equation (100)). To be precise, we may generalise the concept of phase, already familiar when the wave-form is sinusoidal, and assert that, in respect of any arbitrary wave-form the equation

$$v = \sqrt{\frac{k}{\rho}}$$

gives the phase velocity of longitudinal waves of small amplitude (see § 5.5) in a homogeneous fluid medium of which the bulk modulus is k and the density ρ. Having by an entirely independent approach reached this point of agreement with the results of our earlier treatment, it would be superfluous to retrace the steps of that argument, deriving, as we might, the normal modes of vibration of columns of air in pipes of varied specification. Instead we apply our new method to a case which we have not previously considered, that of plane waves of elastic deformation in an infinite solid.

6.3. PLANE LONGITUDINAL WAVES IN AN INFINITE SOLID

Normally, sound is regarded as that agency which affects the human ear. Primarily, therefore, it is a process taking place in the air. By a useful extension of reference, it is a similar process taking place in any gaseous medium—or, for that matter, in water, or in any liquid medium. Physically, the category is that of wave processes in which the displacement is longitudinal. Indeed, there is no reason to restrict the category to wave processes in fluids: to speak of the propagation of sound in solid media is entirely reasonable, if by 'sound' we imply a longitudinal disturbance and nothing more. Thomas Young saw the matter very directly (1807): 'Sound is not simply a vibration or undulation of the air . . . for there are many sounds in which the air is not concerned, as when a tuning fork or any other sounding body is held by the teeth.' In this section we are concerned, then, with the propagation of a plane wave of sound in an infinite solid medium.

In § 4.4 we discussed the longitudinal vibrations of a finite rod, and, as a by-product, obtained an expression (equation (88)) for the velocity of propagation of a longitudinal disturbance—that is, the velocity of propagation of sound—along an infinite rod. In the case of the air column, so closely analogous to the rod in many ways, the velocity of a longitudinal disturbance in an infinite pipe was similarly obtained, and was later identified as the velocity of propagation of a plane wave in a three-dimensionally infinite atmosphere (p. 110). The analogy between the rod and the air column fails, however, at this point. We have already hinted at this failure (p. 121); here we must explain its underlying cause. The velocity of a longitudinal disturbance along an infinite rod is not the same as the velocity of a plane longitudinal wave in a three-dimensionally infinite solid of the same physical constitution: the type of strain involved, and therefore the modulus of elasticity appropriate to the situation, is not the same in the two cases.

In the case of the rod, the outer surface of the rod being free, radial strain is possible. We have already noted that, under these circumstances, 'when the elongation characteristic of any right section of the rod is e, the transverse linear dilatation of the rod at that section will instantaneously be $-\sigma e$, where σ is Poisson's ratio for the material of the rod' (p. 91). In this situation, clearly, Young's modulus is the effective modulus for longitudinal vibrations, and equation (88),

$$v = \sqrt{\frac{Y}{\rho}},$$

gives the characteristic velocity. Let us examine the consequences of assuming that plane longitudinal waves in an infinite medium might involve the same type of strain.

Consider rectangular axes, OX, OY, OZ, so chosen that OX is the direction of plane wave propagation in the solid medium. Let us take as an example of a longitudinal disturbance, a sinusoidal wave, of wavelength λ and period τ. Then the equation

$$\xi = a \sin 2\pi \left(\frac{t}{\tau} - \frac{x}{\lambda}\right) \tag{114}$$

should represent, at least with sufficient accuracy for all practical purposes, the situation at every point in the medium. Here ξ is the instantaneous displacement, parallel to OX, of any particle of the medium whose undisturbed position is in the plane $x = x$. We assume, quite arbitrarily, that equation (114) in fact represents with full precision the motion of particles of the medium lying in OX. We wish to see how nearly it represents the actual motion of particles not in OX, if we accept the assumption that Young's modulus is the appropriate modulus in relation to wave propagation in these circumstances. We argue from the general result (see p. 92)

$$e = \frac{\partial \xi}{\partial x}.$$

On this basis the amplitude of the periodic variations of longitudinal elongation e may be deduced from equation (114): it is
everywhere given by

$$e_0 = \frac{2\pi a}{\lambda}$$

—and the amplitude of transverse motion of a particle of the
medium at a distance r from OX is then given by

$$b = \frac{2\pi \sigma a r}{\lambda} \tag{115}$$

From equation (115) we obtain

$$\frac{b}{a} = \frac{2\pi \sigma r}{\lambda} \tag{116}$$

giving the ratio of the amplitudes of the transverse and longitudinal
vibrations of our representative particle. If this ratio were to be
very small compared with unity for all particles of the medium,
equation (114) would indeed represent fully and 'with sufficient
accuracy' the situation at every point. It needs little consideration
of equation (116) to see, however, that the ratio b/a increases
without limit as r increases. Our assumption that Young's modulus
is the appropriate modulus in respect of longitudinal wave
propagation in an infinite solid medium is thereby shown to be
wholly untenable. We must in due course seek an alternative
assumption, but before doing so we may usefully comment on
equation (116) in another relation—that is in relation to the
infinite rod. We have already (p. 77) defined a finite cylindrical
rod as a cylinder of solid material of which the cylindrical radius
is very small compared with the axial length. In the case of an
infinite rod there is no material length in terms of which to
formulate this definition. Instead we say that the cylindrical radius
must be very small compared with the wavelength of any longitudinal disturbance which the rod may transmit. Indeed, in the
case of a finite rod, and in respect of its normal modes of higher
order, this condition may be more stringent than the other—and
it should in consequence be added to the various limitations by
which the particular results of chapter 4 have already been
qualified.

We return, then, to the problem of longitudinal waves in an

infinite solid medium. Obviously, the assumption that the bulk modulus is effective (as we have shown it to be for longitudinal waves in an infinite fluid) is no more satisfactory than the assumption that we have just considered in detail and found to be valueless, and to consider the rigidity modulus as appropriate would place us in no better case. In truth, all three of the traditional moduli refer to strains having more than one principal component: strictly longitudinal waves in an infinite solid medium imply a one-component strain throughout—transverse particle-motion must be zero, even at infinite distances from any arbitrarily chosen axis of propagation. The problem of longitudinal waves, in these circumstances, is that of identifying the modulus appropriate to such a strain.

After the manner of $M L \And T$, § 16.1, let us consider a cubical specimen of the solid medium subject to tensile stresses p_x, p_y, p_z parallel, respectively, to the three sets of edges of the cube. Let e_x, e_y, e_z be the resultant elongations in these three directions. The modulus appropriate to our investigation is obviously given by p_x/e_x when the magnitudes of the three stresses are so related that $e_y = e_z = 0$.

Now, the elastic properties of a homogeneous isotropic solid substance are completely specified when the values of any two of its elastic constants are given ($M L \And T$, p. 317). Let us therefore choose Young's modulus, Y, and the bulk modulus, k, for specification in the present instance, since these are the two moduli which immediately came to mind when we started our discussion, seeking (as it has proved, false) analogy in the propagation of longitudinal disturbances in solid rods and in infinite fluid media. Having made this choice, we must specify the principal tensile stresses p_x, p_y, p_z correspondingly: as constituted of a single tensile stress p_1 acting along OX, together with a uniform pressure p. Then we may write

$$p_x = p_1 - p,$$
$$p_y = p_z = -p,$$

and we have, simply
$$e_x = \frac{p_1}{Y} - \frac{p}{3k} \tag{117}$$

$$e_y = e_z = -\frac{\sigma p_1}{Y} - \frac{p}{3k} = 0 \tag{118}$$

where σ is Poisson's ratio. From equations (118), we obtain

$$p_x = p_1 - p = p_1\left(1 + \frac{3k\sigma}{Y}\right),$$

and, from equations (117) and (118), similarly,

$$e_x = \frac{p_1}{Y}(1 + \sigma).$$

We conclude that the modulus appropriate to the propagation of a longitudinal disturbance in an infinite isotropic solid medium is given by

$$\frac{p_x}{e_x} = \frac{Y + 3k\sigma}{1 + \sigma} \qquad (119)$$

Using the relations $Y = 3k(1 - 2\sigma) = 2n(1 + \sigma)$ (see *M L & T*, pp. 312, 316), we may derive the alternative forms

$$\frac{p_x}{e_x} = \frac{1 - \sigma}{(1 + \sigma)(1 - 2\sigma)} \, Y,$$

$$\frac{p_x}{e_x} = k + \frac{4}{3} n.$$

The first of these forms shows that for a longitudinal disturbance in an isotropic solid medium the appropriate modulus is greater than Young's modulus; the second shows that it is greater than the bulk modulus and the modulus of rigidity (n). The second form is of immediate significance for our further enquiries (§ 6.4): we shall, therefore, quote only the single expression for the velocity of propagation of plane longitudinal waves in an infinite solid which is based on it, namely

$$v_l = \sqrt{\left(k + \frac{4}{3} n\right) \Big/ \rho} \qquad (120)$$

As we have already insisted (p. 129), the notion of strictly plane waves of constant amplitude in an infinite medium is a highly artificial one: similarly the notion of a spherical pulse spreading from a point source is artificial, though to a lesser degree. The artificiality, in this case, centres largely in the idealisation imposed

on the description of an actual source. Because of its closer
approach to reality, however, it may be more profitable to discuss
the propagation of a spherical pulse in an 'extended' solid body,
than to discuss the propagation of a plane wave in an infinite
medium, in terms of equation (120). Clearly, from the symmetry
of the situation, a distribution of particle motion, in the spherical
shell at any instant occupied by the disturbance, in which back-
and-forth radial motion of particles alone is involved (there being
no motion transverse to the direction of propagation at any point)
is a possible one. The instantaneous strain at any point is, in this
case, a one-component strain, as we have concluded already in
respect of plane longitudinal waves in an infinite medium, and
the velocity specified in terms of equation (120) is the velocity of
propagation of the pulse in question. We may summarise the
conclusions of this section, therefore, most appropriately in the
statement that one of the modes by which energy, from a localised
source in an extended solid body, may be propagated by elastic
waves in the body is that in which the disturbance is a purely
longitudinal disturbance and the velocity of propagation is given
by equation (120).

6.4. TRANSVERSE ELASTIC WAVES IN SOLID MEDIA

If we examine the possibilities in respect of a spherical pulse in an
extended solid further, we shall recognise a second mode of
particle motion by which such a pulse may transmit energy from a
localised source. In this hypothetical mode the instantaneous
particle motion, at any point in a thin spherical shell having the
source at its centre, conforms to the back-and-forth rotation of the
whole shell about an arbitrary diameter. Such particle motion is
transverse to the direction of energy propagation at any point.
We are led, therefore, to an examination of the nature of transverse
elastic waves in a solid medium—and, for mathematical simplicity,
we shall consider the problem in its most severely idealised form.
We shall investigate the propagation of a plane transverse wave
in an infinite solid.

Let us take rectangular axes, X'OX, Y'OY, Z'OZ, in the solid
medium, as before, with X'OX (fig. 29) as the direction of propagation, and Y'OY as the axis parallel to which all (transverse)
particle motion takes place. Consider the situation in PP', a thin
slab of the medium, bounded by plane faces at right angles to OX,

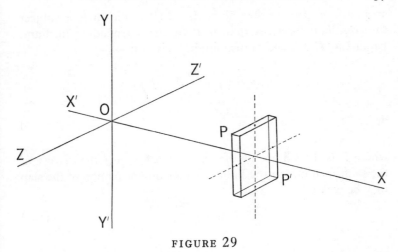

FIGURE 29

and, when the medium is undisturbed, by plane facets at right angles to OY and OZ, respectively. Let η be the measure of the instantaneous displacement of particles situated in the face P. Then, if the thickness of the slab is Δx, the measure of the instantaneous displacement of the particles situated in P', the opposite face of the slab, is given by $\eta + \dfrac{\partial \eta}{\partial x}\, \Delta x$. In general, the form of the slab is no longer as in the undisturbed state: it is sheared, about an axis parallel to Z'OZ, through an angle $\dfrac{\partial \eta}{\partial x}$ (the displacement gradient, as in other similar cases, being assumed to be small). The measure of the equilibrium stress corresponding to this angle of shear is given, in terms of n, the rigidity modulus of the medium, by the expression

$$p = n \frac{\partial \eta}{\partial x} \qquad (121)$$

When the medium in the region of PP' is traversed by a disturbance it is not, however, in equilibrium. We should rather assume that p is the measure of the instantaneous shearing stress appropriate to the face P, and that $p + \dfrac{\partial p}{\partial x}\, \Delta x$ is the corresponding measure appropriate to the face P', at any time. Then, if the area of either face of the slab is A, the slab as a whole is subject to a resultant force, exerted on it by the surrounding medium, parallel to Y'OY, and of magnitude F given by

$$F = A\left(p+\frac{\partial p}{\partial x}\Delta x -p\right),$$

or by

$$F = V\frac{\partial p}{\partial x} \qquad (122)$$

where V is the volume of the whole slab.* If ρ is the density of the solid medium, in the limit, the equation of motion of the slab may be written

$$F = V\rho\frac{\partial^2\eta}{\partial t^2} \qquad (123)$$

Here we have assumed the slab to be indefinitely thin, and we have taken η as the instantaneous displacement of any particle in the slab. From equations (122) and (123), we have

$$\frac{\partial^2\eta}{\partial t^2} = \frac{1}{\rho}\frac{\partial p}{\partial x},$$

and, on substitution from equation (121), we finally obtain

$$\frac{\partial^2\eta}{\partial t^2} = \frac{n}{\rho}\frac{\partial^2\eta}{\partial x^2} \qquad (124)$$

Equation (124) is of precisely the same form as equation (110). We do not need, therefore, to reproduce the mathematical analysis and the discussion applied to that equation in § 6.2. The statements there made have exact counterparts in the present context. We merely note that equation (124) shows that the velocity of propagation of a plane transverse elastic wave, of whatever wavelength, in an infinite solid medium is given by the expression

$$v_t = \sqrt{\frac{n}{\rho}} \qquad (125)$$

* It should be noted that there is no resultant force on the slab parallel to X'OX, although there is tangential stress, of magnitude p, over the facets at right angles to OY.

We are now in a position to make a summarising statement, more complete than that made at the end of § 6.3, and incorporating the results both of that section and of this. We may say that there are two types of wave process by which mechanical energy may be propagated from a localised source in a solid medium. In the one, particle motions are longitudinal; in the other, transverse. The characteristic velocities of propagation are different in the two cases, the velocity of longitudinal waves being greater than that of transverse waves in the ratio $\left(\dfrac{4}{3}+\dfrac{k}{n}\right)^{\frac{1}{2}} : 1$—or $(2-2\sigma)^{\frac{1}{2}}: (1-2\sigma)^{\frac{1}{2}}$, where σ is Poisson's ratio for the medium (see $M\,L\,\&\,T$, equations (137) and (140)). If the disturbance at the surface of any localised source is not strictly of the one type or the other, energy will be radiated as two independent disturbances spreading from the source, the longitudinal disturbance of necessity travelling the faster of the two. The medium, in virtue of its elastic properties, may be regarded as having 'resolved' the original disturbance into these two components, to which it thereafter reacts independently. These conclusions have particular relevance to the earthquake waves which originate in centres of intense local disturbance in the earth's crust, but it would clearly be outside the scope of this book to pursue that subject farther, despite its intrinsic interest and practical importance.

6.5. POLARISATION

In discussing the possible modes of self-propagating particle motion in a spherical pulse spreading from a localised source in an extended solid (pp. 136, 139), we found a basis for the distinction between longitudinal and transverse elastic waves in the medium. In view of our statement regarding the resolution which the nature of the medium imposes on any disturbance originating in such a source, it would indeed be surprising if, in a homogeneous isotropic solid medium which is characterised by only two independent elastic constants, more than two distinct types of wave process were possible. In this section we wish to consider further a fundamental distinction between the two types of process which we have already recognised. Here we merely note, in passing, that in fact wave processes of these two types are the only ones which a homogeneous isotropic solid medium is capable of transmitting.

The distinction between longitudinal and transverse wave processes with which we are concerned is a distinction in respect of symmetry; it is expressed in the statement that an ideal sinusoidal transverse wave is intrinsically 'polarised', whereas a similar longitudinal wave is not. In respect of a sinusoidal transverse wave, in the simplest case, there is a direction of unique significance, other than the direction of propagation (the direction of particle motion in relation to the elastic waves which we are now considering); in respect of a sinusoidal longitudinal wave there is no such unique direction. Referring back to our discussion of the types of hypothetical particle motion in a spherical pulse, we recall that corresponding to the longitudinal wave the motion of particles is purely radial, which motion exhibits full spherical symmetry; corresponding to the transverse wave there is a unique diameter of the sphere about which the particle motion is symmetrical—and such motion does not exhibit full spherical symmetry. We are naturally led to expect that because of this fundamental difference in symmetry character between transverse and longitudinal wave processes generally, there should be physical differences between them which suitable experiments are able to disclose. It should be noted, however, that we have been careful to say that 'in the ideal case' a sinusoidal transverse wave is intrinsically polarised. By this qualification we mean to imply that if in a practical situation such a wave is represented with sufficient accuracy by a displacement equation of the type

$$\eta = A \sin 2\pi \left(\frac{t}{\tau} - \frac{x}{\lambda} \right) \qquad (126)$$

—we have chosen the case of plane waves for formal simplicity—then the wave is by nature a polarised wave. A practical physicist is more likely to make the distinction somewhat differently: he would be inclined to say that an arbitrary transverse disturbance is susceptible of polarisation by appropriate experimental means; a longitudinal disturbance cannot be polarised, whatever means be employed.

The history of the emergence of the concept of wave polarisation in optics has many points of interest in relation to the theory-based statements of the preceding paragraphs. It starts with an observation of Erasmus Bartholinus in 1669. Born in Denmark, Erasmus Bartholinus (1625-1698) was a member of a distinguished family, Swedish by origin, which gave many professors to the university of Copenhagen during a period of almost a century. He himself held successively the chairs of mathematics and medicine; his father, Gaspard (Caspar), had been professor of medicine and later of divinity; his older brother, Thomas, was professor of mathematics for a year before becoming professor of anatomy.

Bartholinus was the first to observe the phenomenon of double refraction of light. In respect of 'ordinary' refraction, some fifty years previously Willebrord Snell (1591-1626) (who followed his father as professor of mathematics at Leyden at the age of twenty-two!) had made the first real advance on the tables of Ptolemy (*M L & T*, p. 107), bringing observation within the compass of a simple mathematical law—but Bartholinus's observations were of a new phenomenon. Some crystals of calcite, found in the Reydar Fjördur, in Iceland, had been brought to Copenhagen, and Bartholinus found that small objects viewed through the crystals appeared double. He concluded that the process of refraction was the effective doubling process, a unidirectional beam of light in the air giving rise to two such beams in the crystal. He concluded further, that one of these refracted beams obeyed Snell's law, whereas the other did not. We are reminded of our conclusion in respect of elastic waves in solids: that the medium, in virtue of its intrinsic properties, may resolve a disturbance into components of which the velocities of propagation are different. That was essentially Huygens's view (*Traité de la Lumière*, written in 1678, published in 1690): 'It is certain that a space occupied by more than one kind of matter may permit the propagation of several kinds of waves, different in velocity.' In this connection it should be emphasised that Huygens recognised, half intuitively, that crystals of 'Iceland spar', though they may be macroscopically homogeneous, are not isotropic (as we should nowadays express the distinction). However, in the twentieth century, we should rather re-write his statement in terms of the basic anisotropy of the crystal structure than accept the suggestion that microscopic inhomogeneity is the root cause of the phenomenon. This more modern view was first adumbrated by Thomas Young in 1809 (see below).

Huygens extended the observations of Bartholinus, examining separately the two beams of light which emerged from a single crystal of spar. He showed that when a second crystal was placed in suitable orientation, and rotated about the general direction of the light incident upon it from the first, two images were obtained which varied in intensity. He found that, whichever beam from the first crystal he used, there was one particular disposition of the second crystal in which one image disappeared entirely—and another disposition in which the other image disappeared. Clearly, he concluded, the light which emerged in either of the two beams from the first crystal had properties different from those of 'ordinary' light. Although the two images produced when ordinary light passed through a single crystal of spar necessarily rotated, as the crystal itself was turned about the direction of the incident light, the intensities of the two images did not vary.

Newton gave his thoughts on the matter first in query 26 of the second edition of the *Opticks* (1717). In query 29 of the third edition (1721), the last published in his lifetime, he wrote 'And are not the Rays of Light very small Bodies. . . . Nothing is more requisite . . . than that they be small Bodies which by their attractive Powers, or some other Force, stir up Vibrations in what they act upon. . . . And lastly, the unusual Refraction of Iceland Crystal looks very much as if it were perform'd by some kind of attractive virtue lodged in certain Sides, both of the Rays, and of the Particles of the Crystal.' It will be noted that Newton maintained the view that light is ultimately corpuscular in nature, but, faced with the phenomenon of double refraction—'the existence of two refractions at the same time, in the same substance, . . . and . . . their interchange with each other, when a ray of light is made to pass through a second piece of spar . . .' (Wollaston's description of the situation, which was still as perplexing in 1802 as it was in 1717), he had to postulate that 'the rays have sides'. No one did better for precisely a century.

William Hyde Wollaston (1766-1828) obtained a fellowship at Caius College, Cambridge, and qualified as a doctor. He attempted to establish himself in practice in London, and to gain a position on the staff of St. George's Hospital. He failed in both attempts, and thereafter devoted himself entirely to scientific research. A few years later, Thomas Young set up his consulting room in Welbeck Street and in due course was appointed to the staff of

St. George's. His great contributions to science were made whilst he still attended conscientiously to the duties of his practice. In 1802 Wollaston published the results of a detailed investigation of double refraction which he had made at Young's request. His observations accorded completely with predictions based on a simple geometrical suggestion of Huygens. This was to the effect that the difference between the two beams in the crystal is essentially the difference between disturbances which from a point source would spread, the one as spherical, the other as ellipsoidal, waves in the anisotropic medium. Young was already becoming convinced that a wave theory of the propagation of light was required to explain other optical effects to which we shall have later to refer (§ 8.2): these observations of Wollaston strengthened this conviction. However, in 1802, Young, like Huygens more than a century earlier, was too obsessed with the analogies between light and sound to think otherwise than in terms of longitudinal vibrations. The phenomenon of double refraction had been brought within bounds of formal mathematical description, but it was not yet understood, 'unless', as Young wrote five years later, 'any person can be satisfied with the name of polarity assigned by Newton to a property which he attributes to the particles of light. . .'.

But there were still distinguished men of science, Laplace among them, who were more satisfied, in 1807, with a corpuscular than with a wave theory of light. Perhaps through a phenomenon which neither theory at the time could well explain lay the way of advance. In any case, in January 1808 the Institut National in Paris announced the subject for the prize to be awarded in physics in 1810: 'To furnish a mathematical theory of double refraction, and to confirm it by experiment.' The eventual winner of the prize was Étienne Louis Malus (1775-1812). Malus had entered the French army as a private, had been commissioned in the corps of engineers, had seen service in Europe and later in Egypt, until in 1801 he was posted to duty in the garrison of Antwerp—then to Strassburg, and finally to Paris. In Paris, in the autumn of 1808, he began experiments on the subject proposed for the prize. One day he happened to turn his crystal of Iceland spar on the light of the sun reflected from the windows of the Luxembourg palace. To his surprise he found, as he rotated the crystal in the familiar way, that the two images of the reflection changed in intensity, much as the pairs of images seen through two crystals of spar changed when the second crystal was rotated. In this chance observation Malus had discovered that rays of light endowed with the property of 'sides' could be produced, not only by double refraction in anisotropic crystals, but also by reflection from isotropic materials such as glass. Malus described this important result in a paper published in January 1809. His prize submission contained an account of much experimental work, extending his original observation in detail and showing that 'polarisation' of light, in some degree at least, was characteristic of the reflection process at the surfaces of separation of all such media from the air, and showing further that the refracted beam was polarised, also, to some extent, whenever the reflected beam was polarised. But, though he obtained the prize, Malus did not in fact 'furnish a (convincing) mathematical theory of double refraction'. Proponents of the corpuscular theory, however, were encouraged to think that the new effect which he had discovered was strengthening their case against the wave-theorists. Malus did not live to see the outcome of the debate: he died of tuberculosis in Paris on 23 February 1812.

For all practical purposes, the debate between the adherents of the corpuscular and the wave theories of the propagation of light was settled (at least for eighty years!) when the Académie des Sciences (then recently reconstituted within the Institut National) awarded the physics prize for 1818 to Augustin Jean Fresnel (1788-1827), for a memoir on 'Diffraction'. That topic will be considered in its own right in a later chapter (p. 224): here we are concerned merely to record that, during the time in which Fresnel was writing his memoir, it first came to be recognised that the phenomenon of polarisation required of any wave theory of light that it should be a theory of transverse waves. This recognition came about through the intervention of Arago and Young.

Dominique François Jean Arago (1786-1853) was two years older than Fresnel. He became secretary to the Observatory of Paris at the age of eighteen and spent an adventurous three years from 1806 to 1809 in the Western Mediterranean. He was officially engaged on a geodetic survey of the Balearic Islands, but he spent much of his time attempting to avoid the hostility of the Spaniards —or, when unsuccessful, languishing in their prisons—or merely

enduring the buffetings of the ill-winds of fortune. The stamina
of his endurance, as well as the thoroughness and accuracy of his
triangulation, earned him the membership of the Académie des
Sciences immediately on his return to Paris. In that capacity he
was appointed a referee of the first communication which Fresnel
submitted to the Academy in 1815. In the following year he
collaborated with Fresnel in experiments on polarised light, and
towards the end of that year he visited Young to discuss with him
the results of this work. The first suggestion that a theory of
transverse waves might provide a general explanation was contained in a letter from Young to Arago dated 12 January 1817. In
September 1817 Young wrote, in an article for the *Encyclopaedia
Britannica*, 'If we assume as a mathematical postulate, on the
undulating theory, without attempting to demonstrate its physical
foundation, that a transverse motion may be propagated in a
direct line, we may derive from this assumption a tolerable illustration of the subdivision of polarised light by reflection. . . .' When
Fresnel's wave theory received the final hallmark of acceptance
in the following year, this assumption, which Young contributed,
became one of its essential features. But, as to the 'physical
foundation', regarding which Young indicated his own misgivings:
this had to await the genius of Maxwell. We shall refer to the
matter again at a later stage (p. 254).

We have stated earlier (p. 139) that in an isotropic homogeneous
elastic medium only two types of wave process are possible:
processes, that is, in which the particle motions are respectively
longitudinal and transverse, in relation to the direction of propagation. In the ideal case, we said, a transverse wave process is
intrinsically polarised. We also referred to the resolution by the
medium of an arbitrary initial disturbance, from a localised
source, into two outgoing component disturbances possessing
these different characteristics. Here we should extend and clarify
these statements. In particular, we should sharpen our previous
definition of polarisation, and generalise it. We should say that
when the particle displacement, in the ideal case, is accurately
represented by equation (126) then the wave is 'plane polarised'.
This statement implies that there is a single plane, containing the
direction of propagation, at right angles to which all particle
displacement takes place. This plane is conventionally referred to
as the plane of polarisation.

K

Now, in respect of displacements in three-dimensional space, there are two independent axes of co-ordinates at right angles to any given direction—in particular, at right angles to any direction of wave propagation in an actual case. Moreover, we are familiar ($M L$ & T, § 6.5) with the procedure of resolution whereby periodic motion in an ellipse, under certain conditions, is shown to be equivalent to the combined effects of two linear simple harmonic motions in directions at right angles, the amplitudes and relative phases of these motions depending upon the constants of the ellipse and the orientation of the rectangular axes of resolution with respect to its principal axes. As a special case, uniform motion in a circle may be resolved into linear simple harmonic motions of the same amplitude, in any two mutually perpendicular directions in the plane of the circle, the difference of phase of the component motions being $\pm \dfrac{\pi}{2}$, depending on the sense of rotation in the circle. It is no real addition, therefore, but merely an obvious expansion of our previous statements, to introduce the notion of elliptically or circularly polarised wave processes. These are transverse wave processes, and indeed it is equally valid to regard them, not as of a distinct character, but as consisting, in the ideal case, of pairs of plane polarised waves of the same frequency travelling together, the planes of polarisation of the paired (super-posed) waves being permanently at right angles. In a similar way ($M L$ & T, p. 97) we may regard a single plane polarised wave, ideally, as a system of two superposed circularly polarised waves of opposite rotation and the same amplitude.

We recognise, then, that a longitudinal wave process is, by its nature, devoid of polarisation, and that a transverse wave process, ideally, is polarised, though it is not necessarily plane polarised with a single plane of polarisation. It remains to consider the possibility that in practice a transverse disturbance may not exhibit any of the characteristic features of asymmetry which might be anticipated in view of our discussion. This situation can only arise (it is, however, the normal situation in respect of light) if conditions in the source change so rapidly that equations of the type of equation (126) are quite inapplicable over sensible durations. In such circumstances effective amplitudes and phases and planes of polarisation do not remain constant over periods of time which are experimentally significant. We have emphasised all along that there is no such thing in the external world as the ideal sinusoidal disturbance, useful though this fiction may be in the hands of the mathematical physicist. A transverse wave process which exhibits none of the features of polarisation asymmetry is referred to as 'unpolarised'.

CHAPTER 7

WATER WAVES

7.1. INTRODUCTORY

Among the natural situations in which wave processes occur, that in which there is a centre of disturbance near the surface of a patch of still water is the most open to casual observation. It is a situation in which the overall features of the process are immediately visible. Early man must often have seen the widening circles of ripples on the pools, as his quarry watered there and he lay in wait. Classical writers, perhaps, did not do justice to this situation: for them the fury of the great waves of the sea provided a more heroic theme. But both effects come within the scope of a general discussion of waves on water, as does the rise and fall of the ocean tide, which seafarers have intuitively accepted as belonging to the natural order of things from the beginning.

We have attributed to Vitruvius (p. 111) the first suggestion of a relation in kind between the spreading of sound from a source and the spreading of ripples on the surface of still water—the first implicit suggestion that the propagation of sound in air is by a 'wave' process. In this chapter we consider the phenomenon, which Vitruvius saw as prototype, in its own right. We have postponed such consideration until now, because the phenomenon is not a simple one: water waves are readily observable both in natural situations and in the laboratory—more readily, perhaps, than waves of any other type—but basically they are of some complexity.

Here a digression on origins is not out of place. In English usage, 'wave' as a verb preceded 'wave' as a noun; the verb 'waver' is older still. The noun was adopted into the language in the sixteenth century; even so, Shakespeare found more use for the verb. We should not be surprised thereby: there is a greater richness of figure awaiting the genius of the poet in the inflections of a verb—the figurative use of the noun is more circumscribed. Thus derive many memorable images:

'Horns whelked and waved like th'enraged sea',
'. . . the waving sedges play with the wind'.

In recalling these images, we recognise—as we might expect—
reflections of the natural order, indeed of the two common situations in which the features of a wave process catch the attentive
eye. It is not necessary here to say more about the first situation—
this chapter deals with its formal aspect in some detail; the second
may be realised in a field of corn ripe for harvest, or, more primit-
ively, in the waste of reeds fringing some shallow pool. But, as
the poet reminds us, it is the play of the wind, on the water or
the sedge-grass, which energises the waves. A twentieth-century
poet reminded us of the same fact, with a shade more sophis-
tication:

'There are waters blown by changing winds to laughter . . .'

We shall not be concerned, in what follows, with this process of
energising, nor shall we be concerned with the waves in the wheat
field: if the problem of water waves is complex, the other problem
is even more difficult to formulate and to discuss in simple
physical terms.

7.2. GENERAL CONSIDERATIONS

Having regard to the scope and standard of other chapters of this
book, our treatment of water waves in this chapter must of necessity be somewhat superficial—illustrative, rather than rigorous.
The essential features of the phenomenon, and its basic com-
plexities, can, however, be exhibited without the use of advanced
mathematics. To begin with we shall make certain simplifications
and approximations with which the discussions of the last chapter
have already made us familiar: we shall treat first the ideal case
of plane waves on an infinite expanse of water. Then we no longer
have an 'infinite' medium in the sense of chapter 6: only the free
surface of the water is effectively infinite in extent. Even the depth
of the water is not 'infinite': it is uniform, but finite; it may be very
large compared with the wavelength of the disturbance we are
considering, or it may be small compared with the wavelength.
We shall find that the physical situations are very different in
these two extreme cases.

It is natural to enquire what must be the basic pattern of periodic motion of the particles of water when it is traversed by the plane wave. Obviously, the particles of water in the layer in immediate contact with the bottom are restricted to periodic motion parallel to this lower boundary (and therefore to the free surface of the undisturbed liquid). We are here ignoring effects due to viscosity, assuming that the liquid behaves as a perfect fluid. Equally obviously, the particles of liquid in the free surface must have a component of periodic motion at right angles to the surface—for the wave process is evident in the surface disturbance. These two statements are simple and unexceptionable. To establish any more general conclusion by simple argument is, however, almost impossible: we must approach the problem, therefore, from a different starting-point.

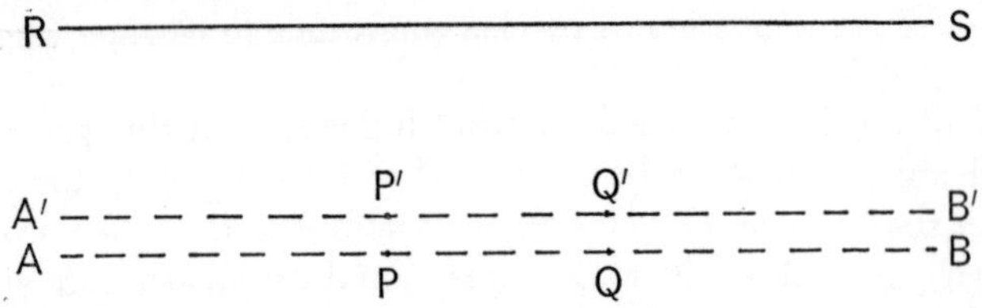

FIGURE 30

Let us consider the situation as represented by a model in two dimensions—a perfectly valid simplification when we are dealing with plane waves. Let the plane of fig. 30 correspond to the vertical plane in which our two-dimensional model liquid has a free upper boundary, one-dimensionally infinite, of which RS is a portion in its undisturbed state. Let the fixed 'bottom' be at a distance h below RS and let AB, A′B′, be horizontal lines distant y and $y + \Delta y$, respectively, from the bottom. Let P and Q, in AB, be distant x and $x + \Delta x$, respectively, from some arbitrary vertical axis in the plane of the figure, the points P′ and Q′ completing an elementary rectangle PQQ′P′ of area $\Delta x \Delta y$. We wish to explore certain consequences of the statement, which is clearly true if the model liquid is incompressible, and the motions of its constituent particles are periodic and 'organised' when a 'boundary' wave is passing, as must be the case in the circumstances of our problem, that the particles which occupy the elementary rectangle PQQ′P′ when the liquid is undisturbed, at any subsequent time occupy an elementary region of equal area.

Suppose, then, that a boundary wave is passing across RS, and let us represent by ξ and η the horizontal and vertical components of instantaneous displacement of the particle whose (arbitrary) undisturbed position is P. In the general case, if the phase velocity of the boundary wave is v (see p. 130), we have

$$\xi = \alpha f_1(x - vt)$$
$$\eta = \beta f_2(x - vt) \tag{127}$$

Also, if, at the same instant, t, the component displacements of the particle whose undisturbed position is Q are $\xi + \Delta \xi$ and $\eta + \Delta \eta$, obviously, to first-order accuracy,

$$\Delta \xi = \alpha f_1'(x - vt)\Delta x,$$
$$\Delta \eta = \beta f_2'(x - vt)\Delta x.$$

Now, it is natural to assume that the phase of the resultant disturbance is instantaneously the same at P′ as it is at P; on the other hand, if we further assume that the component amplitudes are the same at these two points we immediately reach a contradiction. For we find that the particles, which were originally contained within PQQ′P′, at time t occupy a parallelogram of (vertical) base Δy and (horizontal) height $\Delta x + \Delta \xi$. The area of this parallelogram cannot be equal to $\Delta x \Delta y$ at all times, since $\Delta \xi$ is, by assumption, intrinsically finite. So we are forced to conclude that the component displacement amplitudes, α and β, vary with depth below the boundary: our intuition that a 'boundary wave' is essentially a disturbance of which the intensity falls with increasing depth below the geometrical boundary is reinforced, and we proceed to examine the matter further from that point of view.

Let us assume, then, that equations (127) represent the component displacements of an arbitrarily chosen particle whose undisturbed position is in AB (say at P in fig. 30), and that the displacements of the corresponding particle whose undisturbed position is in A′B′ (P′ and P are the undisturbed positions of 'corresponding' particles in this sense) are $\xi(1 + k\Delta y)$ and $\eta(1 + l\Delta y)$, respectively. In the notation of the calculus,

$$k = \frac{1}{\alpha}\frac{d\alpha}{dy}, \quad l = \frac{1}{\beta}\frac{d\beta}{dy} \tag{128}$$

At time t, the co-ordinates of the particles whose undisturbed positions are P, Q, Q' and P' will, in this case, be

$$x+\xi, \qquad\qquad y+\eta$$
$$x+\Delta x+\xi+\Delta\xi, \qquad\qquad y+\eta+\Delta\eta$$
$$x+\Delta x+\xi+\Delta\xi+k\xi\Delta y, \qquad y+\Delta y+\eta+\Delta\eta+l\eta\Delta y$$
$$x+\xi+k\xi\Delta y, \qquad\qquad y+\Delta y+\eta+l\eta\Delta y$$

—at least to the accuracy for which second-order terms are neglected. We note that these four sets of co-ordinates do not determine the corners of a parallelogram; to proceed, therefore, we must use the standard expression giving S, the area of a quadrilateral, in terms of (x_1, y_1), (x_2, y_2), (x_3, y_3), (x_4, y_4), the co-ordinates of its corners taken in (anticlockwise) cyclic order. The expression is

$$S = \tfrac{1}{2}\{(x_3-x_1)(y_4-y_2)-(x_4-x_2)(y_3-y_1)\}.$$

We then obtain the area of the elementary region occupied, at time t, when the disturbance is passing, by the particles originally occupying the elementary rectangle PQQ'P' of fig. 30. We omit the intermediate, purely algebraic, calculation, and state the result. The area is

$$\Delta x\Delta y\left\{\left(1+\frac{\Delta\xi}{\Delta x}\right)(1+l\eta)-k\xi\frac{\Delta\eta}{\Delta x}\right\}.$$

We have imposed the condition that the area in question must remain equal to the undisturbed area $\Delta x\Delta y$, throughout the duration of the disturbance. With this limitation, therefore, we obtain the formal result

$$\frac{\Delta\xi}{\Delta x}+l\eta\frac{\Delta\xi}{\Delta x}-k\xi\frac{\Delta\eta}{\Delta x}+l\eta = 0 \qquad\qquad (129)$$

A little consideration will show that we cannot, in fact, satisfy equation (129) in general: we must examine the relative orders of magnitude of its various terms, and seek a first-order solution. For this purpose it is convenient to particularise, making the assumption that the boundary wave is sinusoidal—thereby introducing a natural reference standard of length, the wavelength λ. This having been done, we further assume that the boundary wave is of small amplitude (being able, for the first time, to give precision to such an assumption in terms of the inequality $B \ll \lambda$). (Here B is the value of β, when $y = h$.) As yet, however, we have no knowledge of the relative phases of the component displacements. We replace equations (127), therefore, by the forms

$$\xi = a \cos \frac{2\pi}{\lambda}(x - vt)$$

$$\eta = \beta \cos \left\{ \frac{2\pi}{\lambda}(x - vt) + \delta \right\}$$

(130)

accepting δ as unknown.

Let us take equation (129) to the limit, writing $\dfrac{\partial \xi}{\partial x}$ for $\dfrac{\Delta \xi}{\Delta x}$

and $\dfrac{\partial \eta}{\partial x}$ for $\dfrac{\Delta \eta}{\Delta x}$; then, on substitution from equation (130), we have,

$$-\frac{2\pi a}{\lambda} \sin \theta - \frac{2\pi a \beta l}{\lambda} \sin \theta \cos(\theta + \delta) + \frac{2\pi a \beta k}{\lambda} \cos \theta \sin(\theta + \delta)$$

$$+ l\beta \cos(\theta + \delta) = 0$$

(131)

Here, for convenience, θ has been written for $\dfrac{2\pi}{\lambda}(x - vt)$. In

equation (131) the relative orders of magnitude of the terms are as $1 : \beta l : \beta k : \dfrac{\beta l \lambda}{2\pi a}$. To assume that $\lambda \gg 2\pi a$ is merely to extend the

meaning attached to our condition that the boundary wave shall be of small amplitude. We therefore make this assumption. If the making of it leads to the conclusion that $\beta l \ll 1$ (and $\beta k \ll 1$), then the second and third terms in the equation can be neglected in comparison with the first and fourth terms. Let us follow this suggestion, considering these latter terms alone. Then equation (131) becomes

$$\frac{2\pi a}{\lambda} \sin \theta = l\beta \cos(\theta + \delta)$$

(132)

We note that this equation admits of a solution which is independent of θ, if $\delta = -\dfrac{\pi}{2}$. The solution is

$$l = \frac{2\pi a}{\beta \lambda}$$

(133)

This solution implies the condition $\beta l \ll 1$, provided that the wave is of small amplitude. Of itself, it implies nothing concerning the magnitude of βk. But we note that any physically acceptable solution of equation (131) must be independent of θ—for our condition of continuity must be valid throughout the duration of the disturbance. Moreover, surface waves constitute an observed phenomenon, therefore such a solution must exist. For this reason alone we must conclude that $\beta k \ll 1$.*

We cannot here pursue the calculation farther. To do so would require that we should work upwards from the region of the bottom, where β must be zero and only α may be finite, and derive a solution which is continuous throughout the whole range of y from zero to h. If this is done, it turns out that when $y \gg \dfrac{\lambda}{2\pi}$, to a high order of accuracy, $\alpha = \beta$ (strictly, $\alpha - \beta$ is always positive) and $k = l$. More precisely, again, $l > \dfrac{2\pi}{\lambda} > k$, throughout. According to equation (133), in the limit when $\alpha = \beta$, $l = \dfrac{2\pi}{\lambda}$; moreover, as long as $\alpha > \beta$, $l > \dfrac{2\pi}{\lambda}$. Our partial solution, then, is entirely consistent with the detailed results.

Let us return to the other conclusion given in terms of our partial treatment: that the component particle displacements differ in phase by 90° at all points in the field of disturbance—more precisely, that the phase angle δ of equations (130) is $-\dfrac{\pi}{2}$. This result implies that in general the periodic motion of the particles is everywhere elliptical, with the major axes of the ellipses horizontal throughout the region of disturbance. Each such ellipse is described with the periodic time characteristic of the sinusoidal wave in question, and in such a way that the corresponding point would describe the appropriate auxiliary circle with constant

---

* An indication that $k < l$ may be seen by re-writing equation (131), with $\delta = -\dfrac{\pi}{2}$, in the form

$$\left(l\beta - \frac{2\pi\alpha}{\lambda} \right) \sin\theta - \frac{2\pi\alpha\beta l}{\lambda} + \frac{2\pi\alpha\beta}{\lambda}(l-k)\cos^2\theta = 0.$$

angular velocity ($M L \& T$, p. 96). Furthermore, the sense of description of the ellipses is everywhere such that when a particle is at the highest point of its path it is travelling in the same direction as the wave is travelling, and *vice versa*. To verify this last statement, we note that, with $\delta = -\dfrac{\pi}{2}$, equations (130) (which represent a wave process travelling in the direction of x increasing) are simultaneously satisfied by $\xi = 0$, $\eta = \beta$, $\dfrac{\partial \xi}{\partial t} = 2\pi a \dfrac{v}{\lambda}$. Here, $\dfrac{\partial \xi}{\partial t}$, the forwards velocity of the particle, is essentially positive, without exception.

Confining attention to our conclusion regarding the phase angle δ, we have just referred to the individual particle motions as elliptical. However, the detailed analysis previously quoted indicates that, except within distances from the bottom of the order of the wavelength or smaller, these motions can hardly be distinguished from circular. Except in shallow water, therefore— except, that is, when $h < \lambda$—we may usefully regard the motion of particles originally near the free surface as circular, and assume that the amplitude (radius) of such motion decreases, as $(h - y)$, the distance below the surface, increases, according to the simple formula

$$a = Ae^{-2\pi(h-y)/\lambda} \qquad (134)$$

This statement is clearly consistent with equation (133), under the conditions which we have postulated. We may note that when $(h - y) = 0 \cdot 73\lambda$ the radius of particle motion is no more than 1 per cent of the vertical amplitude of the boundary wave.

7.3. STANDING WAVES

In the last section we considered in some detail the nature of the periodic motion of the particles of a two-dimensional model liquid, the free upper boundary of which is traversed by a sinusoidal wave. Such a model exhibits all the essential characteristics of the behaviour of an ideal incompressible liquid, of 'infinite' horizontal extent and finite uniform depth, when a plane sinusoidal surface wave is passing. In this section we consider the situation when two such wave processes are travelling in opposite directions over the surface of the liquid, the waves being of the same wavelength and of equal amplitudes.

Let ξ_1, η_1 be the components of instantaneous displacement of a particle whose undisturbed position is at a distance x from a certain vertical plane at right angles to the direction of wave propagation, and at a height y above the bottom—the components, that is, due to the 'direct' wave. Let ξ_2, η_2 be the components of instantaneous displacement of the same particle due to the 'reverse' wave. Making no assumption that the resultant particle motion due to either wave process is circular—only that the two wave processes are identical in character, except for direction of propagation—we have

$$\xi_1 = a \cos 2\pi \left(\frac{x}{\lambda} - \frac{t}{\tau}\right), \quad \xi_2 = a \cos 2\pi \left(\frac{x}{\lambda} + \frac{t}{\tau}\right)$$

$$\eta_1 = \beta \sin 2\pi \left(\frac{x}{\lambda} - \frac{t}{\tau}\right), \quad \eta_2 = \beta \sin 2\pi \left(\frac{x}{\lambda} + \frac{t}{\tau}\right)$$

(here we have merely used the result $\delta = -\dfrac{\pi}{2}$, as obtained in § 7.2).

In the situation which we are considering, when the direct and reverse waves are propagated simultaneously, the actual components of instantaneous displacement of our representative particle are given by $\xi = \xi_1 + \xi_2$, $\eta = \eta_1 + \eta_2$, or

$$\xi = 2a \cos 2\pi \frac{x}{\lambda} \cos 2\pi \frac{t}{\tau}$$

$$\eta = 2\beta \sin 2\pi \frac{x}{\lambda} \cos 2\pi \frac{t}{\tau}$$

(135)

Equations (135) show that the motion of the particle, whose undisturbed position is at (x, y), is linear simple harmonic motion, of amplitude $2 \left(a^2 \cos^2 2\pi \dfrac{x}{\lambda} + \beta^2 \sin^2 2\pi \dfrac{x}{\lambda} \right)^{\frac{1}{2}}$ about this point, of periodic time τ, the line of motion being inclined to the horizontal at an angle ϕ which is given by

$$a \tan \phi = \beta \tan 2\pi \frac{x}{\lambda}.$$

Fig. 31 exhibits this state of affairs schematically, the horizontal line AB having essentially the same specification in this figure as in fig. 30. Furthermore, as fig. 31 already indicates, these linear particle motions are in phase throughout the whole region of the disturbance. Clearly, we have a system of standing waves, as indeed our earlier discussions (see p. 127) would lead us to expect.

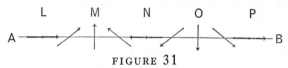

FIGURE 31

Fig. 31 has been drawn to correspond to an interval of x equal to the wavelength λ: $LP = \lambda$. We note that, at intervals of $\dfrac{\lambda}{2}$ along the direction of component wave propagation, the particle motion in the resultant standing wave is entirely vertical (as at M and O in the figure). We might, therefore, imagine a plane vertical boundary, indefinitely thin, placed in the liquid at right angles to the direction of wave propagation at any such point, and we should be forced to conclude that it would be without influence on the overall phenomenon (we are assuming throughout that the liquid is non-viscous). Alternatively, we might consider, not a liquid of 'infinite' (two-dimensional) extent, but a liquid confined in an 'infinitely long' channel between vertical walls at a distance d apart, the liquid being of uniform depth h as before. Standing waves having their crests parallel to the length of the channel would, in such a case, be possible only for wavelengths λ given by

$$2d = n\lambda \qquad (136)$$

n being any positive integer. The particle motion, in these circumstances, in the immediate neighbourhood of the walls, as well as in the immediate neighbourhood of the bottom of the channel, must be parallel to the liquid-solid boundary: equation (136) is the necessary condition (supplementary to the conditions implicit in the results derived or quoted in the last section) for the realisation of this situation. From another point of view we may regard equation (136) as specifying the wavelengths of the normal modes of surface vibration across an infinitely long channel of breadth d containing water of uniform depth. By an obvious extension of phraseology (see p. 21) we may regard these wavelengths (or, more exactly, the 'wave numbers' which are their reciprocals) as constituting a harmonic series. We naturally enquire whether the corresponding frequencies constitute a harmonic series, also. This question is considered in the next section; we shall discover that in general the series of frequencies is not harmonic.

7.4. THE RELATION BETWEEN WAVELENGTH AND FREQUENCY

Let fig. 32 represent a right section of an 'infinitely' long channel, enclosed by vertical walls separated by a distance d and containing water to a uniform depth h. Let RS represent the undisturbed free surface of the water in the channel. Suppose plane waves of wavelength $\lambda = 2d$ to be reflected back and forth across the channel (compare p. 157) so that standing waves are established, constituting surface vibrations in the first normal mode as described above. Let the (small) amplitude of vertical particle motion at R (or S) be B, and the amplitude of horizontal particle motion at N be A (see fig. 31 and equations (135)). Each of these amplitudes is exaggerated in fig. 32—B more so than A. Let MNO, M'NO' represent the extreme profiles of the surface vibrating as here specified. We note that our specification has fixed the wavelength of the disturbance. We wish to calculate its natural frequency.

When the profile of the surface is as represented by MNO (or M'NO') every particle of the liquid is instantaneously at rest (apart from the 'background' thermal motion which does not specifically concern us—compare p. 104). We proceed to calculate the excess potential energy associated with the liquid occupying a length L of the channel in these circumstances. Let us take HJ, HR as rectangular axes, and confine attention to the profile MNO, which we assume to be sinusoidal. Then the y co-ordinate of an arbitrary point on this profile is $h + B \cos 2\pi \dfrac{x}{\lambda}$. We note that there are two contributions to the excess potential energy: a contribution due to gravity and a contribution in terms of interfacial surface energy (see $M\,L\,\&\,T$, § 17.1). Effectively the water normally occupying the volume of which NSON is the right section has been raised to occupy the volume of which NRMN is the right section, and the area of the disturbed surface represented by MNO is greater than that of the undisturbed surface represented by RNS. Let us represent the two contributions by V_g, V_s, respectively.

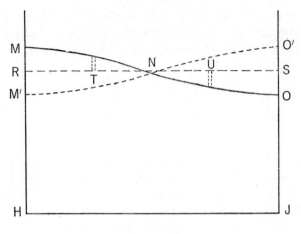

FIGURE 32

In order to calculate V_g, we imagine an elementary volume of liquid centred below U transferred so as to be centred above the corresponding point T (RT = US = x). In this process the mass of liquid involved is $\rho LB \cos 2\pi \dfrac{x}{\lambda} . dx$, if ρ is the measure of the density of the liquid, and the increase of height of the centre of gravity of this mass is $B \cos 2\pi \dfrac{x}{\lambda}$. Integrating over the region RN, we then have

$$
\begin{aligned}
V_g &= g\rho LB^2 \int_0^{\lambda/4} \cos^2 2\pi \frac{x}{\lambda}\, dx \\
&= g\rho LB^2 \frac{\lambda}{8}
\end{aligned}
\tag{137}
$$

where g is the acceleration due to gravity.

Our next step is to calculate the additional area in the disturbed surface. In general, the length of an element of a plane curve is given by $\varDelta s = (\varDelta x^2 + \varDelta y^2)^{\frac{1}{2}}$, so that, when the inclination of the curve to the x-axis is everywhere small,

$$
\varDelta s - \varDelta x = \tfrac{1}{2}\left(\frac{dy}{dx}\right)^2 \varDelta x.
$$

We may use this expression to derive the additional area of water surface in the present case, and multiplying by γ, the measure of the surface tension, we obtain, by suitable integration,

$$
\begin{aligned}
V_s &= \frac{L\gamma}{2}\frac{4\pi^2}{\lambda^2} B^2 \int_0^{\lambda/2} \sin^2 2\pi\frac{x}{\lambda}\, dx \\
&= \frac{\pi^2}{2}\gamma\frac{LB^2}{\lambda}
\end{aligned}
\tag{138}
$$

We have just calculated, in terms of $V_g + V_s$, the excess potential energy associated with the liquid occupying a length L of the channel when the surface profile is as represented by MNO in fig. 32 and the liquid is instantaneously at rest. When, momentarily, the surface of the liquid is horizontal, having the profile represented by RNS in the figure (as it has twice in each complete oscillation), this excess energy has been wholly transformed into kinetic energy of linear simple harmonic motion of the particles of liquid involved in the oscillation. Throughout the oscillation, indeed, the total energy of vibratory motion is constant. In terms of equations (137) and (138) it is given by

$$
E + V = \frac{LB^2}{2}\left(\frac{g\rho\lambda}{4} + \frac{\pi^2\gamma}{\lambda}\right)
\tag{139}
$$

E and V being now the measures of the kinetic and potential energies of all the vibrating particles at an arbitrary instant. For a single particle of mass m executing linear simple harmonic motion of amplitude a and frequency f,

$$
E + V = 2\pi^2 m a^2 f^2
\tag{140}
$$

(M L & T, p. 233). The various particles in the liquid are vibrating with different amplitudes, but with the same frequency. We shall be able to calculate this common frequency, by combining equations (139) and (140), once we have taken full account of the diversity of amplitudes.

In the general case which we have been considering hitherto, h, the depth of liquid in the channel, being entirely arbitrary, the amplitudes of linear particle motion are not strictly the same even for all particles in a given horizontal plane (see pp. 156, 154), and the decrease of amplitude with increasing depth below the surface is different for particles in the neighbourhood of the surface node (at N, fig. 32) from what it is for those in the neighbourhood of the anti-nodes (see p. 154). This is strictly the situation whatever the depth of the liquid, but we have seen that when the depth is greater than a wavelength, or thereabouts, these differences are infinitesimal (compare p. 155), and, this condition being fulfilled, we may regard B of equation (139) as representing the amplitude of linear motion of all the particles in the bounding surface of the liquid, and may further assume that this amplitude decreases exponentially, with increasing distance below the surface, as described in equation (134). This is a situation which is susceptible of simple mathematical treatment: let us first of all, therefore, deal with it—that is with the case of standing waves in a 'deep' channel, when the depth of the liquid in the channel is at least somewhat greater than its breadth. In this case, equation (140) for a single particle, when applied to all the particles of liquid occupying a length L of the channel, leads to the result

$$E+V = 2\pi^2 f^2 L \frac{\lambda}{2}\rho B^2 \int_0^h e^{-4\pi(h-y)/\lambda}dy,$$

or, with negligible error in the case we are considering (in any case our expression for the integrand becomes invalid as $y\to 0$), to the corresponding result

$$E+V = 2\pi^2 f^2 L \frac{\lambda}{2}\rho B^2 \int_0^\infty e^{-4\pi z/\lambda}dz$$

$$= \frac{\pi}{4} f^2 L \lambda^2 \rho B^2 \tag{141}$$

For this calculation it will be remembered that $\dfrac{\lambda}{2}$ is the breadth of the channel—and, as previously, ρ is the measure of the density of the liquid.

We now have two independent expressions for the total energy associated with the system of standing waves of small amplitude occupying a length L of the channel under the conditions that we have postulated $(h > \lambda)$. Equating these expressions, given by equations (139) and (141), respectively, we obtain directly

$$f^2 = \frac{g}{2\pi\lambda} + \frac{2\pi\gamma}{\rho\lambda^3} \tag{142}$$

L

In respect of our chosen conditions, at least, equation (142) provides the relation between wavelength and frequency which, in this section, has been our immediate objective. Of itself, the equation is sufficient to establish the result, which we anticipated at the end of the previous section (p. 158), that, though the wave numbers of the standing waves in a given channel constitute a harmonic series, the corresponding frequencies do not.

7.5. PROGRESSIVE WAVES ON AN INFINITE SURFACE

In an ideal system of plane waves travelling over an infinite surface of liquid, individual particle motion is in ellipses having their major axes in the direction of wave propagation and their minor axes perpendicular to the undisturbed surface of the liquid. The periodic time of such elliptical motion is the same as the periodic time characteristic of the sinusoidal disturbance itself (p. 154). Again, when an infinite surface of liquid is traversed in opposite directions by two sinusoidal wave processes which are identical except for direction of propagation, the resultant disturbance is a system of standing waves in which individual particle motion is rectilinear. The periodic time of this motion is, similarly, the periodic time characteristic of the component systems of plane waves of which the standing waves may be regarded as constituted (p. 157). For the case in which the depth of the liquid is not small ($h > \lambda$), equation (142) relates the frequency of individual particle motion in such a system of standing waves to the wavelength of these waves—and this latter quantity is the same as the wavelength of the component sinusoidal progressive waves into which the standing waves may be resolved. Equation (142), therefore, relates frequency and wavelength for an ideal system of plane progressive waves of small amplitude travelling over the infinite surface of a liquid of constant depth.

Now, in general, the phase velocity of a sinusoidal disturbance of wavelength λ and frequency f is given by the equation $v = f\lambda$. Equation (142) may, therefore, be written

$$v^2 = \frac{g\lambda}{2\pi} + \frac{2\pi\gamma}{\rho\lambda} \qquad (143)$$

—so giving the phase velocity, in the case in question, as a function of the wavelength of the disturbance, and in terms of the acceleration due to gravity and the density and surface tension of the liquid. It will be noted that for very long and for very short waves the phase velocity is large: there is a characteristic wavelength, λ_c, for which this velocity is a minimum. Obviously,

$$\lambda_c = 2\pi\left(\frac{\gamma}{g\rho}\right)^{\frac{1}{2}},$$

and the minimum velocity v_m is given by

$$v_m = \left(\frac{4g\gamma}{\rho}\right)^{\frac{1}{4}}.$$

It has become customary to speak of 'surface waves' when the wavelength of a sinusoidal disturbance is greater than λ_c for the liquid in question, and to say that a disturbance of shorter wavelength is constituted of 'ripples'. For water, at ordinary temperatures, $\lambda_c = 1\cdot72$ cm., $v_m = 23\cdot2$ cm. sec.$^{-1}$.

When the wavelength is very great compared with λ_c, but small compared with the depth of the liquid, equation (143) reduces, approximately, to the expression

$$v^2 = \frac{g\lambda}{2\pi} \tag{144}$$

This expression gives the phase velocity of 'gravity' waves in 'deep' water. Under these conditions the term 'gravity waves' is appropriate, because the phase velocity is independent of the properties of the liquid (provided the viscosity is negligible), being determined, for a given wavelength, by the acceleration due to gravity alone.

Let us consider the corresponding situation in 'shallow' water, that is the case when $\lambda \gg \lambda_c$, also $\lambda \gg h$ (this specification could, of course, refer to waves of extremely great wavelength on the surface of any body of water of constant finite depth). We must attempt, at least under plausible assumptions, to follow through the process of 'working upwards from the region of the bottom' which in § 7.2 (p. 154), for the general case, we declined to follow for reasons of complexity. We reconstruct the argument of § 7.4, and the plausible assumption that we make is that the amplitude of horizontal particle motion is the same, namely A, at all points vertically below N (fig. 32), the position of the node of the standing surface wave.* As before, B is the amplitude of vertical particle motion in the surface at the antinodes (R and S, fig. 32). We shall require to know the relation between B and A. Considering how the standing waves were derived, in § 7.3, from the superposition of oppositely travelling progressive wave trains, we recognise that equations (133) and (128) are relevant to this problem, and that, once the amplitude of horizontal particle motion has been assumed to be independent of depth, these equations lead to the result

$$B = \frac{2\pi A h}{\lambda} \qquad (145)$$

On this assumption, then, $B \ll A$ in the case that we are considering. Moreover, with the horizontal distance, x, measured from HR, as in § 7.4, we conclude that the amplitude of horizontal motion at x is given by $A \sin 2\pi \frac{x}{\lambda}$ (compare equation (135), giving the horizontal displacement, ξ, though from a different origin of x, effectively $\frac{\lambda}{4}$ to the left of HR in fig. 32).

We are now in a position to derive and equate the two expressions for the energy of the standing wave system appropriate to the present case, following the procedure of the previous section. With $\lambda \gg \lambda_c$, of necessity $V_g \gg V_s$, and equation (137), taken by itself, provides one of these expressions. For the other, since $B \ll A$, we compute the total energy of linear particle motion on the assumption that this motion is effectively horizontal throughout the whole body of liquid, the amplitude varying with x (but not with y) in the way that we have mentioned. Then we have (compare equation (141)),

$$E + V = 2\pi^2 f^2 L \rho A^2 \int_0^h dy \int_0^{\lambda/2} \sin^2 2\pi \frac{x}{\lambda} \, dx$$
$$= \frac{\pi^2}{2} f^2 L \lambda h \rho A^2 \qquad (146)$$

---

* The results of the calculation which follows remain essentially unchanged if, instead, we take the maximum amplitude of horizontal motion at height y above the bottom to be $A_0(1+ky)$, with $kh \ll 1$. Then, for example, equation (145) becomes

$$B = \frac{2\pi A_0 h}{\lambda}\left(1+\frac{kh}{2}\right).$$

Equations (146) and (137) now provide the two expressions, which, when equated, yield an equation for f. We have, in fact,

$$f^2 = \frac{1}{4\pi^2}\frac{g}{h}\frac{B^2}{A^2},$$

and, substituting from equation (145), finally,

$$f^2 = \frac{gh}{\lambda^2},$$

or, for the phase velocity of sinusoidal progressive waves, under these conditions,

$$v^2 = gh \tag{147}$$

Let us compare equations (144) and (147): they give the phase velocity of gravity waves in deep and shallow water, respectively. In shallow water ($h \ll \lambda$), obviously, the phase velocity is much smaller, for a disturbance of given wavelength, than the phase velocity of the same disturbance in deep water ($h > \lambda$). Moreover, in shallow water, the phase velocity is independent of wavelength, whereas in deep water it increases, with increase of wavelength, as $\lambda^{\frac{1}{2}}$. In shallow water, the phase velocity decreases as the depth of the water decreases, thus 'long' waves tend to 'break' on a shelving beach. Finally, equation (147) applies, to a good approximation, to very long 'tidal' waves in the open sea; for example the phase velocity of a tidal wave in a region where the depth is 10 fathoms is about 26 knots.

We have now considered various limiting cases; for completeness let us simply quote the general result. When no limitation is placed on the relative magnitudes of λ and h, when it is assumed merely that the amplitude of surface motion is very small compared with the wavelength and that the liquid is ideally mobile, the phase velocity of a sinusoidal plane wave of wavelength λ on an infinite surface of liquid of uniform depth h is given by

$$v^2 = \left(\frac{g\lambda}{2\pi} + \frac{2\pi\gamma}{\rho\lambda}\right)\tanh\frac{2\pi h}{\lambda} \tag{148}$$

Equations (143), (144) and (147) will be recognised as derivable from equation (148) by use of the appropriate approximations.

7.6. THE CONCEPT OF GROUP VELOCITY

For the first time in this book we have encountered, in equation (148)—and in all but one of its simpler versions, an expression indicating that the phase velocity of a wave process is dependent upon the wavelength. In no case which we have previously examined in detail has any such dependence come to light. Fundamentally, our order of treatment has been planned with this aspect of the matter in mind, for there are in fact many natural situations in which wave processes having this particular characteristic are involved. The passage of light through a material medium provides a case in point (see § 8.8). We have intentionally delayed consideration of such processes until now. In general the term 'dispersion' is used to characterise this feature of wave propagation: we say that, in relation to a particular type of disturbance, a medium is 'dispersive' if the phase velocity of the disturbance in the medium varies with the wavelength, however small the amplitude of the disturbance may be. In this section we consider one consequence of dispersion; in so doing we introduce a new concept, that of 'group velocity'. When there is no dispersion, so that a displacement pulse is propagated without change of form (see § 2.7), this concept is of no special significance: in such a case, as we shall see, the group velocity is identical with the unique phase velocity characteristic of the type of disturbance and the medium concerned.

When there is dispersion, the concept of group velocity acquires significance just because, undeniably, there can be no such thing in nature as a strictly sinusoidal disturbance, of whatever type. As we have insisted on a number of occasions (for example, in § 2.5), any such disturbance must be, by definition, truly infinite in both spatial extent and temporal duration. Conversely, any actual disturbance, being finite, cannot behave as a wave process of a single wavelength, although it may be described in terms of a spectral distribution of sinusoidal components (see § 2.12). When there is dispersion, therefore, no actual disturbance can be propagated without some change of form in the process.

Let us, purely for purposes of illustration, consider a 'model' of a finite disturbance in one dimension. Let us assume that the initial displacement, ξ_0, is given, in terms of a one-dimensional co-ordinate, x, by the expression

$$\xi_0 = Ae^{-\mu\left(\frac{x}{\lambda}\right)^2}\cos 2\pi\frac{x}{\lambda} \qquad (149)$$

In this expression, λ appears as the characteristic wavelength of a sinusoidal wave of initial displacement which has been attenuated, symmetrically about the origin, $x=0$, according to the particular 'law' which the exponential factor describes. The parameter μ is a pure number which, for a given λ, is greater the smaller is the range of x over which the initial displacement is significantly different from zero. Equation (149) still implies an infinite (one-dimensional) medium, but it comes much nearer than any simple analytical expression that we have hitherto used has come to a satisfactory formal description of a disturbance which is limited in spatial extent.

If, arbitrarily, we define the space occupied by the initial disturbance as the range of x over which the exponential factor is greater than some given value (small compared with unity), then this range, S, is obviously proportional to $\lambda/\mu^{\frac{1}{2}}$. Let us, therefore, write

$$S = \frac{m}{\sqrt{\mu}}\lambda \qquad (150)$$

where m is a pure number. A little consideration will show that we have not much latitude in our choice of m, in any reasonable definition. The value $m=3$ corresponds to a reduction of the amplitude of the disturbance to about $0\cdot1$ of its central peak at the arbitrary limit $(x=\pm 1\cdot5\lambda/\mu^{\frac{1}{2}})$; $m=5$ corresponds to a reduction to about $0\cdot002$ of the peak amplitude. In what follows we shall be concerned throughout with situations in which $\mu\ll1$. In such situations, clearly, the initial displacement will be significantly different from zero over a range of x many times greater than the fundamental wavelength λ.

Let us now determine the positions of the displacement crests specified in terms of equation (149). These are given by the even-numbered solutions (counting from the solution at the origin) of the equation

$$\frac{d\xi_0}{dx} = 0;$$

the odd-numbered solutions of the same equation give the positions of the troughs of the initial disturbance. We may take the $(2n)$th solution as representative of this whole series. It is implicit in the relation

$$\tan \theta_{2n} = -\frac{\mu}{2\pi^2} \theta_{2n} \qquad (151)$$

where, in general, θ has been written for the phase angle $2\pi x/\lambda$.

Clearly, $(2n-1)\frac{\pi}{2} < \theta_n < n\pi$, thus equation (151) can be re-written, formally, for positive values of n,

$$\tan (2n\pi - \delta_{2n}) = -\frac{\mu}{2\pi^2} (2\pi n - \delta_{2n}),$$

where, generally, $0 < \delta_{2n} < \frac{\pi}{2}$, and $\delta_{2n} > \delta_{2(n-1)}$. When $\mu \ll 1$, even for the smallest values of n, $\delta_{2n} \ll 2\pi n$: we have, therefore, to a good approximation,

$$\tan \delta_{2n} = \frac{n\mu}{\pi},$$

and, in consequence,

$$\tan (\delta_{2n} - \delta_{2(n-1)}) = \frac{\dfrac{\mu}{\pi}}{1 + n(n-1)\dfrac{\mu^2}{\pi^2}}.$$

Similarly, when $\mu \ll 1$, $\delta_{2n} - \delta_{2(n-1)} \ll 1$, for all values of n. Thus, we may simplify further, without significant error, and finally we obtain the result

$$\delta_{2n} - \delta_{2(n-1)} = \frac{\mu}{\pi} \left\{ 1 + n(n-1)\frac{\mu^2}{\pi^2} \right\}^{-1}.$$

Now, let the distance between the $(n-1)$th crest and the nth crest of initial displacement, as enumerated from the central peak, be $\lambda - \epsilon_n$. Then

$$
\begin{aligned}
\epsilon_n &= \frac{\lambda}{2\pi}(\delta_{2n} - \delta_{2(n-1)}) \\
&= \frac{\mu\lambda}{2\pi^2}\left\{1 + n(n-1)\frac{\mu^2}{\pi^2}\right\}^{-1}
\end{aligned}
\tag{152}
$$

Writing $n=1$ in equation (152), we obtain the distance by which the separation of the first crest from the central peak falls short of λ: it is given by

$$
\epsilon_1 = \frac{\mu\lambda}{2\pi^2}
\tag{153}
$$

Again, if N is the value of n at the arbitrary limit of the disturbance as specified by equation (150), then

$$
N = \frac{S}{2\lambda} = \frac{m}{2\sqrt{\mu}}.
$$

We note that, when $\mu \ll 1$, and $3 < m < 5$ (see above), $N > 1$, as indeed we have stated in words already (p. 167). Therefore from equation (152), to sufficient accuracy,

$$
\begin{aligned}
\epsilon_N &= \frac{\mu\lambda}{2\pi^2}\left(1 + \frac{N^2\mu^2}{\pi^2}\right)^{-1} \\
&= \frac{\mu\lambda}{2\pi^2}\left(1 + \frac{m^2\mu}{4\pi^2}\right)^{-1}.
\end{aligned}
$$

Further, under these conditions, $m < 2\pi$ and therefore $m^2\mu \ll 4\pi^2$. In this case, higher order terms in the expansion being neglected, we have

$$
\epsilon_N = \frac{\mu\lambda}{2\pi^2}\left(1 - \frac{m^2\mu}{4\pi^2}\right)
$$

and, therefore,

$$
\frac{\epsilon_1 - \epsilon_N}{\lambda} = \frac{m^2\mu^2}{8\pi^4}
\tag{154}
$$

Let us evaluate the results of our calculation in terms of a numerical example. Let us choose $\mu = 0\cdot01$ and $m=4$. Then $2N=40$, and we are concerned with a symmetrical pattern of initial displacement, as represented by equation (149), which is effectively infinite in extent, but which is concentrated in a central region. Between limits at which the crest amplitude has fallen to 0·02 of its maximum value, this central region of the pattern contains some 40 crests. The distance between successive crests is almost constant over this range (being some 0·05 per cent less than λ, according to equation (153)), but it does, in fact, increase regularly from the centre outwards, the extreme variation being about 2 parts in 10⁶, according to equation (154). (Far beyond the central region, where the crest amplitude is entirely negligible,

the crest-to-crest distance approaches λ: as $n \to \infty$, $\delta_{2n} \to \dfrac{\pi}{2}$.) In

what follows we shall be concerned chiefly with the fact that the crest-to-crest distance varies very slightly—increasing smoothly from the centre outwards—in the arbitrary initial configuration that we are considering.

Hitherto we have spoken only of a pattern of initial displacement. We have fixed our 'model' disturbance in thought, so that we might discuss its geometrical features in detail. Suppose now that equation (149) represents the instantaneous profile of a disturbance, travelling along the positive direction of x, at the instant at which its centre passes through the (arbitrarily chosen) origin. To accept this datum is to make detailed assumptions concerning the velocities as well as the displacements of the particles of our hypothetical (one-dimensional) medium at the instant in question. The situation at any subsequent time t may be broadly described if we can specify the crest-to-crest distance in the neighbourhood of (or 'enclosing') each point of the medium, and the corresponding crest amplitude as a function of time.

If the medium is non-dispersive, the result is simple: the disturbance is propagated indefinitely without change of form. The motion of the particles of the medium is such as to produce this overall result. As the disturbance passes over any particle the amplitude of the particle motion increases, then ultimately decreases again; likewise the effective period of the quasi-periodic motion of the particle varies as the disturbance passes. The acceleration of the particle at any instant is related to the displacement profile in the immediate neighbourhood of the particle, that is to the crest-to-crest distance enclosing the particle at that instant and the corresponding instantaneous displacement amplitude. If the medium is non-dispersive, the effective period of the particle motion is directly proportional to the crest-to-crest distance enclosing the particle at the instant in question. There is no distortion of the disturbance as it is propagated.

If the medium is dispersive, it is still true that the instantaneous particle acceleration is related to the displacement profile in the immediate neighbourhood of the particle, but it is not true that the effective period of the quasi-periodic motion of the particle is instantaneously proportional to the crest-to-crest distance enclosing the particle at that instant. Let us suppose that the phase velocity of a sinusoidal disturbance in the medium increases as the wavelength increases, and let us consider the instantaneous situation, in such a case, in a disturbance of the particular type represented by equation (149). The instantaneous particle accelerations in the centre of the disturbance are such that the effective period of particle motion there is longer, in relation to the period of particle motion in the front or in the rear of the disturbance, than it would be in a non-dispersive medium. Initially the crests of the disturbance move forward more slowly in the centre than elsewhere: as time passes, individual crests move up from the rear, increasing in amplitude and then decreasing again. Always the crests occupying the region of smallest crest-to-crest distance are the most slowly moving of the disturbance; gradually the whole form of the pattern changes. Obviously, if we had started from the assumption that the phase velocity of a sinusoidal disturbance in the medium decreases as the wavelength increases, we should have reached the opposite conclusion: in that case the crests occupying the region of smallest crest-to-crest distance are the most rapidly moving of a disturbance of the particular type that we have been considering.

Our whole discussion has given prominence to the crest-to-crest distance as determinative of the local response of the medium as a disturbance advances. Although it is an unconventional usage of the term, we shall follow Lamb (1904) in designating the crest-to-crest distance 'the local wavelength' of the disturbance. Our discussion in terms of a particular example has been intended as a prior justification of this usage. Adopting it for the general case, we may consider the local wavelength λ (we use the conventional symbol) as a continuous function of x and t, in the one-dimensional propagation problem with which we are concerned.

Now imagine a geometrical point to move along the positive direction of x with velocity $\dfrac{dx}{dt}$. The time variation of the local wavelength in the neighbourhood of this moving point is given by

$$\frac{d\lambda}{dt} = \frac{\partial\lambda}{\partial t} + \frac{\partial\lambda}{\partial x}\frac{dx}{dt} \tag{155}$$

In this expression, the partial derivatives have reference to the instantaneous position of the point. As a special case, let the point move with a crest of the disturbance. The rate of increase of the local wavelength in the neighbourhood of the moving point in this case is the rate at which the crest immediately in front of the reference crest draws away from it. If the instantaneous velocity of the reference crest is v, the instantaneous velocity of the crest next ahead is $v + \lambda\dfrac{\partial v}{\partial x}$, and the rate of increase of the local wavelength around the former crest, at the instant in question, is $\lambda\dfrac{\partial v}{\partial x}$. Particularising equation (155) for this case, we have, therefore, since $\lambda\dfrac{\partial v}{\partial x} \equiv \lambda\dfrac{\partial\lambda}{\partial x}\dfrac{dv}{d\lambda}$,

$$\lambda\frac{dv}{d\lambda}\frac{\partial\lambda}{\partial x} = \frac{\partial\lambda}{\partial t} + v\frac{\partial\lambda}{\partial x} \tag{156}$$

We have used the symbol v for the instantaneous velocity of the reference crest; this usage is consistent with the assumption that we have endeavoured to justify, that instantaneously the forwards velocity of any crest is the phase velocity appropriate to the instantaneous value of the local wavelength in the neighbourhood of the crest.

Let us refer again to the general result represented by equation (155). Instantaneously, at the point x, if a moving reference point has velocity u, given by

$$0 = \frac{\partial\lambda}{\partial t} + u\frac{\partial\lambda}{\partial x} \tag{157}$$

the local wavelength in the immediate neighbourhood of this moving reference point will remain constant. Otherwise stated, the reference point will move with respect to the general pattern of crests in the advancing disturbance so that the crest-to-crest distance in its neighbourhood shows no immediate tendency to change. Suppose, now, that equations (156) and (157) refer to the same x and t, we may then combine these equations, and so obtain the following relation between u and v, namely,

$$u = v - \lambda \frac{dv}{d\lambda} \tag{158}$$

The velocity u, defined in terms of equation (157) and calculable in terms of equation (158), is referred to as the 'group velocity' of a quasi-sinusoidal disturbance ('group'), nearly homogeneous in respect of wavelength λ, travelling in a (dispersive) medium in which a strictly sinusoidal disturbance of that wavelength would be characterised by a phase velocity v.

The concept of group velocity took shape in the writings of Stokes (see p. 256) and Rayleigh (see p. 80) many years before it was formulated by Lamb in the terms that we have here reproduced. Lamb's definition, as we have seen, is based on the constancy of the local wavelength—and so on the constancy of the local phase velocity. If, during a finite interval, a point is moving with uniform velocity in the group and crests pass over the point at a rate which does not vary with time, then that point is moving with the group velocity of the disturbance. In 1877 Osborne Reynolds (see $M\,L\,\&\,T$, p. 251) showed that the group velocity is also the velocity with which, instantaneously, energy is transported by the disturbance. Intuitively, perhaps, the reader will recognise a connection between these two definitions.

In general, when the phase velocity of a sinusoidal disturbance varies with wavelength, the group velocity of a quasi-sinusoidal group will also vary with the dominant wavelength of the group (equation (158)): in a non-dispersive medium, on the other hand, $\left(\frac{dv}{d\lambda}=0\right)$ the group velocity will be identical with the unique phase velocity, whatever the wavelength.

We have been led to a discussion of group velocity through our treatment of surface waves on water. Let us therefore, for sake of specific examples, evaluate the consequences of our general result in relation to the special cases which arise in that connection. For gravity waves in shallow water there is no dispersion (equation (147)), therefore no difference between the group velocity and the unique phase velocity. For gravity waves in deep water, we have (equation (144))

$$v = \left(\frac{g}{2\pi}\right)^{\frac{1}{2}}\lambda^{\frac{1}{2}},$$

thus
$$u = \frac{1}{2}\left(\frac{g}{2\pi}\right)^{\frac{1}{2}}\lambda^{\frac{1}{2}}$$

$$= \frac{1}{2}v.$$

For ripples of very short wavelength, in water which is not too shallow, equation (148) leads to the result

$$v = \left(\frac{2\pi\gamma}{\rho}\right)^{\frac{1}{2}}\lambda^{-\frac{1}{2}}$$

and therefore to
$$u = \frac{3}{2}\left(\frac{2\pi\gamma}{\rho}\right)^{\frac{1}{2}}\lambda^{-\frac{1}{2}}$$

$$= \frac{3}{2}v.$$

As will be observed, these two situations provide specific instances in which the group velocity is, on the one hand, less than, and, on the other, greater than, the phase velocity for all relevant wavelengths.

Finally, there is one purely formal result that should be noted. We have already (p. 157) defined the wave number of a sinusoidal disturbance as the reciprocal of the wavelength—the number of waves per unit length measured in the direction of propagation. This parameter, generally denoted by k, is the space-analogue of the frequency f—the number of vibrations per unit time. Adopting these two parameters, the standard expression for a progressive wave becomes (see equation (11))

$$y = A \sin 2\pi(kx \pm ft),$$

and the expression for the phase velocity is (see equation (12))

$$v = \frac{f}{k}.$$

Then we have
$$\frac{df}{dk} = \frac{d(vk)}{dk}$$

$$= v + k\frac{dv}{d\lambda}\frac{d\lambda}{dk}$$

$$= v - \lambda\frac{dv}{d\lambda}.$$

We therefore obtain, as an alternative expression* for the group velocity u,

$$u = \frac{df}{dk} \qquad (159)$$

* Some writers, also using k for the variable, define 'wave number' as $2\pi/\lambda$. Since the unfortunately named 'angular frequency', ω, is given by $\omega = 2\pi f$, in the notation of these writers, equation (159) becomes

$$u = \frac{d\omega}{dk}.$$

CHAPTER 8

INTERFERENCE AND DIFFRACTION

8.1. GENERAL AND HISTORICAL

The term 'interference' has already been defined, at least paren-
thetically (p. 127). In the context of § 6.1 it was stated quite
generally that when two sinusoidal wave trains, of the same
amplitude and wavelength, are travelling in opposite directions
in an infinite medium, then their 'superposition' results (by
'interference') in a system of 'standing' waves. At the risk of
repetition, it is worth while tracing out once more the steps in the
argument on which this statement is based.

In our original treatment of the problem we were concerned
with the special case of the stretched string (chapter 2). We
showed that, when such a string is vibrating transversely in its
fundamental mode (§ 2.3), or, indeed, in any normal mode
(§ 2.6), individual particle motions are linear and simple harmonic
of the same period, with the phases of these individual motions
the same for all the particles, and the amplitudes varying sinus-
oidally along the length of the string. In § 2.4 we investigated the
consequences of resolving these individual particle motions, in
thought, each into two components, it being postulated that the
two components of each pair should have the same amplitude and
that this common amplitude should be the same in respect of all
the particles in the string. The immediate consequence of this
analysis was the conclusion that, in each pair, one component
must lead and the other follow the actual motion of the particle
by the same phase angle, and that this angle must vary linearly
along the length of the string. Ultimately we recognised that the
leading component motions of all the particles taken together
could be regarded as constituting a progressive wave motion
travelling in one direction along the string, and the following
component motions an exactly similar progressive wave motion
travelling in the other direction. We concluded: 'we may regard
the situation as one in which a single wave process is all the time

travelling back and forth along the string, being reflected without loss at its fixed ends. In this mode of description the actual vibrations may be said to arise from the "interference" of the oppositely travelling waves' (p. 19). Later (p. 30) we showed that 'an infinite string will in fact behave as if it were made up of a linear array of equal finite strings, acting in phase but independently'. In this way the statement made at the beginning of this section, and referring to the interference of similar wave trains in an infinite medium, has its natural origin.

However, it should not be lost sight of that, logically at least, there is a distinction to be drawn between the two statements:

(i) 'standing waves of sinusoidal profile in an infinite medium can for all purposes be regarded as if they were constituted of two exactly similar trains of progressive waves travelling in opposite directions in the medium',

and

(ii) 'if an infinite medium is traversed by two exactly similar trains of sinusoidal progressive waves travelling in opposite directions, the disturbance in the medium will in fact have the character of standing waves of the same wavelength'.

Statement (i) is a purely formal deduction, once the character of the standing wave system is given; statement (ii) masquerades as an independent statement regarding the natural world. The statement made at the beginning of this section has the character of (ii); the argument of § 2.4, here reformulated, justifies (i), not (ii).

If we bear in mind all that we have previously said regarding the unreality of sinusoidal waves in infinite media, we shall admit that we are dangerously near to pure word-spinning here, but we shall also admit that there is a real problem in relation to observable phenomena that is worthy of consideration. Let us pose the problem in ideal form as follows. Let there be two exactly similar sources in an extended medium, separated by a distance very great compared with the effective wavelength common to the two disturbances to which they separately give rise. Let these sources start to emit simultaneously and continue emitting, the intensities (powers) of the two sources being the same. We wish to enquire what is the nature of the disturbance of the medium in the central region, about the line joining the sources.

M

Our present considerations would lead us to suppose that the answer to this question is that in this central region the disturbance will in fact approximate very closely, once a steady state has been reached, to a system of standing waves such as we have discussed. In formulating this answer we have effectively accepted the principle of superposition of two wave processes that 'interfere'. (The verb means, literally, 'to strike one against the other': it was originally used of a horse which strikes the fetlock of one leg with the hoof of another.) By implication, too, we have adopted the point of view that if the question had been extended, and the nature of the disturbance in regions other than the central region had been required, then the same principle of superposition would have proved adequate as basis for an answer.

Here we may recall, in passing, another instance in which we have already adopted the principle of superposition, taking a different example of the resolution of a periodic motion into simple harmonic components as our starting-point. Having defined the meanings of the terms circularly and elliptically polarised wave processes, we wrote (p. 146): 'These are transverse wave processes, and indeed it is equally valid to regard them, not as of a distinct character, but as consisting, in the ideal case, of pairs of plane polarised waves of the same frequency travelling together, the planes of polarisation of the paired (superposed) waves being permanently at right angles. In a similar way we may regard a single plane polarised wave, ideally, as a system of two superposed circularly polarised waves of opposite rotation and the same amplitude.'

In its generality, the principle of superposition, in relation to sinusoidal wave processes, can be attributed without doubt to Thomas Young. In a Bakerian lecture before the Royal Society of London, in 1801, Young enunciated four 'hypotheses' concerning the nature of light and of the luminiferous ether, and nine 'propositions', eight of which had reference to wave motion in general. The eighth proposition stated 'when two undulations, from different origins, coincide either perfectly or very nearly in direction, their joint effect is a combination of the motions belonging to each'.

It is perhaps surprising that this general principle had to wait so long for precise formulation (see p. 7). Newton had indeed relied on it intuitively in suggesting an explanation for a peculiarity in the tides in the gulf of Tongking. He had even foreshadowed a statement of it (*Principia*, book 3, proposition 24), 'It may happen that the tide may be propagated from the ocean through different channels towards the same port, and may pass in less time through some channels than through others, in which case the same generating tide, being thus divided into two or more succeeding one another, may produce by composition new types of tide', but there is no evidence that he found any use for the same principle in relation to the phenomena of sound to which he also gave detailed attention. This is the more surprising, since Newton was the first consistent exponent of the formal procedure of the composition and resolution of vector quantities as an aid to calculation and the understanding of physical phenomena—'so likewise a body moving in the line AD [ABDC being a parallelogram], though by the action of one single force, may be considered as if it had been acted upon by two forces, namely, resolving the single force into two, as AC and AB'—and he was perfectly aware that elliptical motion, in certain circumstances, could be considered as constituted of two linear simple harmonic vibrations. But the composition and resolution of simple harmonic motions in the same straight line was not a problem which exercised him, and it was left to Fresnel, more than a century later, to give the first formal solution of it.

In putting forward the principle of superposition interference Young recognised his role as an innovator; he was entirely convinced of the generality—and originality—of the principle that he was enunciating. He found no evidence of it in the writings of others, he said, 'except some imperfect hints in those inexhaustible but neglected mines of nascent inventions, the works of the great Dr. Robert Hooke, which had never occurred to me at the time that I discovered the law; and except the Newtonian explanation of the combination of tides in the port of Batsha'.

8.2. HUYGENS'S CONSTRUCTION

Young, as we have seen, recognised a vague debt to Hooke, but none to Huygens in relation to the notion of interference. In this he was patently honest, but he was engaged at the time in building up a coherent case for a wave theory of light, and in this broader field of endeavour he was giving new precision to views which had been advocated unsuccessfully by both these men in the seventeenth century. We have already noted (p. 143) that, in the context of the problems of double refraction, Young had found a suggestion of Huygens to be particularly fruitful. That suggestion may be regarded as presaging the extension to crystalline (non-isotropic) media of a general construction which Huygens had already given in relation to pulse propagation in isotropic media. This construction, 'Huygens's construction', is the object of our concern in the present section. Young, and more consciously Fresnel, made much use of it in the treatment of interference effects and of diffraction (see § 8.6). But, before we introduce Huygens's construction, let us give due credit to Hooke—as Young did.

In the scheme of his Bakerian lecture of 1801 (see p. 178), Young stated his first and second hypotheses as follows:

'(i) A luminiferous ether pervades the universe, rare and elastic in a high degree.

(ii) Undulations are excited in this ether whenever a body becomes luminous.'

His first and second propositions were:

'(i) All impulses are propagated in a homogeneous elastic medium with an equable velocity.

(ii) An undulation conceived to originate from the vibration of a single particle must expand through a homogeneous medium in a spherical form, but with different quantities of motion in different parts.'

In 1664 Hooke had written (*Micrographia*, published 1667):

'There is no luminous body but has the parts of it in motion more or less . . . we are to consider . . . the way or manner of the trajection of this motion through the interpos'd pellucid body to the eye . . . it must be a body susceptible and impartible of this motion that will deserve the name of transparent . . . the constitution and motion of the parts must be such that the appulse of the luminous body may be communicated or propagated through it . . . in an homogeneous medium this motion is propagated every way with equal velocity, whence necessarily every pulse or vibration of the luminous body will generate a sphere, which will continually increase, and grow bigger. . . .'

That there is more than a passing resemblance between these statements, separated in time by almost a century and a half, cannot reasonably be questioned.

In Young's third proposition, on the other hand, the borrowing is from Huygens: consideration of it will lead us directly to Huygens's construction. Young wrote:

'(iii) A portion of a spherical undulation, admitted through an aperture into a quiescent medium, will proceed to be further propagated rectilinearly in concentric superfices, terminated laterally by weak and irregular portions of newly diverging undulations.'

The corresponding passage in Huygens's *Traité de la lumière* (see p. 141) may be translated as follows:

'Thus if, for example, an aperture BG were bounded by opaque bodies BH, GI; the wave of light which originates in a point A will always be terminated by the straight lines A[B]C, A[G]E, as has just been shown: those portions of the secondary waves which extend on either side of the space ACE being too feeble to give rise to illumination there.'

This passage was written in 1678. It will readily be admitted that it contains all the elements of Young's statement of 1801. The secondary waves ('ondes particulieres') of the quotation represent Huygens's unique contribution to the wave theories of the later century; they provide the conceptual material for 'Huygens's construction' which we shall now formulate, without further preamble, in modern terms:

'Each element of volume of a medium traversed by a wave process, when the displacement in that volume element is varying, may be considered as the source of a secondary disturbance, propagated throughout the medium as from an isolated source.'

On the basis of the principle here formulated, the progress of a wave front belonging to a disturbance arising in any actual source may be traced out in detail. Thus, if S and S' are geometrical surfaces occupied successively by such a wave front, then S' must everywhere be tangential to a secondary wave assumed to originate in a corresponding element of area of S. Implicit in this statement is the assumption that, at the instant that the wave front passes through S, the primary source may be regarded as extinguished, and as replaced by virtual sources emitting in phase with one another and distributed over the instantaneous wave front in S.

Before we make specific use of this construction, it is worth while commenting on the phrase 'secondary wave' which nowadays is universally adopted, as we have adopted it, in translation of Huygens's 'onde particuliere'. It might appear that the translation does less than justice to the original. Such a charge must indeed be admitted. Huygens's phraseology reflected his belief in an ether of 'very subtle matter' made up of minute particles 'not necessarily all of the same size'. He supposed these particles to be set in motion by the advancing disturbance, and he regarded them as individual sources of the secondary waves. It was natural, therefore, that he should refer to the secondary waves as 'ondes particulieres'. Nowadays this crude mechanical model has been abandoned (see chapter 9), but the construction which Huygens based on his consideration of it is equally valuable in relation to elastic wave propagation in material media and the propagation of electromagnetic waves in 'empty space'.

Let us consider now the very simplest situation. Let a 'point' source Q be situated in an infinite non-dispersive medium. Let S (fig. 33) represent, at time t, the front of a spherical pulse spreading from Q. It is accepted that at time $t + \Delta t$ the front of the pulse will be a sphere S', such that the radial separation of S and S' is $v\Delta t$, if v is the phase velocity of the disturbance in the medium. Obviously, also, S' is tangential to all the spheres of radius $v\Delta t$ which may be drawn about points situated on S. Huygens's construction, as stated earlier in this section (p. 181), is therefore consistent with the accepted facts. Further, if we assume that, at t, the disturbance is confined to a spherical shell of thickness d having S as its outer bounding surface, applying Huygens's construction to every point in this shell we shall conclude that at $t + \Delta t$ the disturbance will be confined to a shell of the same thickness d having S' as its outer surface. Again, use of the construction leads us to a result which is consistent with the facts. However, there is one aspect of the matter which requires further consideration.

As indicated in fig. 33, the complete envelope of the secondary waves originating in S, after a time Δt, is the system of two

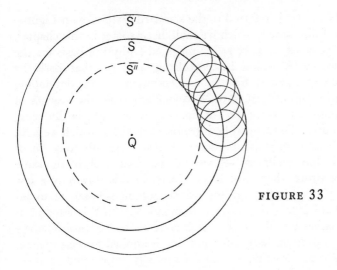

FIGURE 33

concentric spheres, represented by S' and S" in the figure. Only one portion of this envelope—the sphere S'—is relevant to the physical situation that we have postulated: the other portion— the sphere S"—would be relevant to an ideal situation, much more difficult of even approximate realisation than the other, in which a complete spherical pulse was collapsing to a 'focus' at Q. It is because of this aspect of the matter that we were careful to write originally (p. 181), in formulating Huygens's construction, 'then S' must everywhere be tangential to a secondary wave assumed to originate in a corresponding element of area of S'. That is a necessary requirement, but it does not provide a complete specification. Generally, the 'new' wave front is part only of the envelope of the secondary waves originating in the 'old' wave front; only in very special circumstances is it the whole envelope.

If Huygens's construction is regarded merely as an exercise in geometry, there is something strangely arbitrary in the irrelevance of one portion of the envelope for the physical problem. On the other hand, granted this measure of arbitrariness, the geometrical exercise is uniformly successful: in optics it provides the formalism for a satisfactory description not only of reflection and refraction (predicting the correct relation between the phase velocities in the two media in the latter case)—for a systematic account of which the reader is referred to the standard textbooks on Light—but also of diffraction, which we shall discuss later in this chapter. But Huygens, as we have seen, imagined a physical basis for the secondary waves which he postulated, and on that basis he attempted to account for the concentration of the developing disturbance on one part of the envelope only—for the absence of the 'retrogressive wave' (S'' of fig. 33), when light is diverging from a source. To this end he introduced the idea, which we have noted already, that the particles of ether, though they be of 'inconceivable smallness' yet are 'not necessarily all of the same size'. He wrote 'there will be produced in this way only a few secondary waves in the rear, towards the luminous point, a number incapable of giving rise to any illumination'. But this attempt at rationalisation was doomed to lack conviction, for until Young's notion of interference by superposition is applied to the problem, Huygens's construction remains essentially unjustified, a mere recipe for calculation informed only by the brilliant intuition of its author, who in this matter, as in many others, was many generations ahead of his time.

Let us refer back to the 'very simplest situation' which we have already used as illustration: that of the diverging spherical pulse of small thickness, d. Let the region between S_1 and S_2 (fig. 34) represent a small portion of the complete spherical shell occupied by the actual disturbance at time t. Let Q_1Q_2 be a portion of a radius drawn outwards from the point source Q (compare fig. 33) in which the disturbance originated. We accept the principle that the state of the medium within the complete shell of which S_1S_2 is a part is uniquely determined by the state of activity of the source during the short interval of time d/v during which the disturbance arose (and, of necessity, by the properties of the medium, assumed non-dispersive, in which the phase velocity of the disturbance is v). Furthermore, we assume that the state of the medium, everywhere, at any time later than t, is uniquely determined by the state of the medium within the region of the disturbance at t, and by the intrinsic properties of the medium. As before, we are concerned specifically with the state of the medium at time $t + \Delta t$.

Let S_1', S_2' be portions of spheres concentric with S_1, S_2 and of radii greater than the respective radii of these surfaces by $v\Delta t$. Similarly, let S_1'', S_2'' be portions of spheres of radii less than the

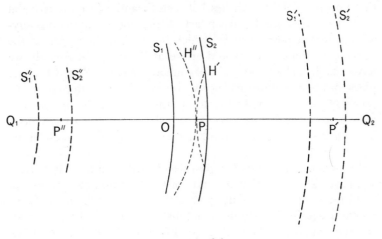

FIGURE 34

FIGURE 34

radii of S_1, S_2, respectively, by the same amount. Our concern is
to understand why, on the basis of the assumptions which we
have just re-stated, we may justifiably conclude that at $t + \Delta t$,
in so far as the field of the diagram is concerned, the disturbance
is confined to the region between S_1' and S_2', being zero elsewhere
—and, in particular, zero within the region between S_1'' and S_2''.
To understand this completely requires an elaboration of analysis
on which we cannot here embark, but some progress may be made
by means of quite simple considerations: sufficient at least to
show that there is a much greater degree of dissymmetry between
the 'direct' and the 'retrogressive' waves than might at first sight
be supposed, if they be imagined merely as developing over the
two sheets of the envelope of the secondary waves of Huygens's
construction.

Let us fix our attention on the state of the medium at P' (in
the region between S_1' and S_2'), at time $t + \Delta t$. Let P, P" be the
corresponding points in the regions between S_1 and S_2, and S_1''
and S_2'', respectively, all three points lying in Q_1Q_2, as shown in
the figure. The term 'corresponding points' here implies that
$P''P = PP' = v\Delta t$. Let H', H" represent in the figure portions of
spherical surfaces, each of radius $v\Delta t$, described about P', P",
respectively. These surfaces touch at P. Then the situation is such
that secondary disturbances originating, at time t, anywhere on

that portion of H' which lies between S_1 and S_2 would arrive at P' at $t + \Delta t$. Similarly, secondary disturbances originating anywhere on that portion of H" which lies within the region of the actual disturbance at t would arrive at P" at $t + \Delta t$. Already we have established an essential dissymmetry between P' and P". The phase of the actual disturbance varies over H', as it does over H"; nowhere over the latter surface is the phase as 'early' as it is anywhere on the former, except at P, where the two surfaces meet. The effects at P' and P" cannot, therefore, be the same at time $t + \Delta t$.

In fact, the dissymmetry goes deeper than we have indicated. We have postulated that the state of the medium, everywhere, at any time later than t, is uniquely determined by the state of the medium within the region of the disturbance at t. In particular, the state of the medium at P' (or P") is so determined over the entire interval from t to $t + \Delta t$. We have considered the situation at $t + \Delta t$ at these two points. This situation, however, is continuous with the successive situations obtaining during the whole interval of length Δt. Indeed, if $OP = x$ (and $v\Delta t > d$), we may regard the history of the state of the medium at P' during the last $(d - x)/v$ units of time of the interval Δt as implicit in the state of the medium between H' and S_2. Similarly, we may regard the state of the medium between H" and S_1 as implying the history of the state of the medium at P" during the last x/v units of time of Δt. Clearly, the sequence of events at P' and P" must be quite different.

As we admitted at the outset, we have not been able to clinch the matter entirely. We have not shown unexceptionably that the assumptions which we have made, in generalising the principle of Huygens, are such as to exclude the retrogressive wave, as we know from experience it must be excluded in any acceptable description of the phenomenon of pulse propagation. We have merely emphasised the dissymmetry of the situation, leaving it to be accepted on trust that this dissymmetry is complete: that the disturbance at P" (fig. 34) is in fact zero throughout, once the pulse has passed, according to our assumptions. The fundamental theory on which this demonstration was later devised, was developed by Poisson (see *M L & T*, p. 256) in 1819. Here we may summarise briefly by saying that for the full justification of Huygens's purely geometrical construction we must consider in some detail the physics of the wave process, we must be satisfied that the nature of the process and the properties of the medium are such that the principle of superposition is valid in their respect, and we must recognise that the conditions in any pulse, the subsequent development of which is in question, are not arbitrary, but the displacements and velocities in its various elements are so related as to express its previous history as a moving entity.

We have attempted to summarise the position, but a little consideration will show that we are still avoiding a major issue. Hitherto, except for passing reference to its many applications, we have discussed Huygens's construction exclusively in relation to a spreading pulse of small thickness. We have formulated the principle of the construction more generally (p. 181), but we have so far restricted detailed consideration of it to this special case. It was indeed in such a context that the construction was first enunciated, and certainly in this context it can be discussed most simply. But we must not lose sight of the fact that the main applications of the construction, since the time of Young, have been in respect of continuous wave trains, rather than pulses. Huygens's notion that light is propagated as a series of unrelated pulses, each of which in imagination could be considered individually, was completely lost in the wave theory of Fresnel, but the construction in terms of secondary waves survived, and increased in usefulness; furthermore, we have claimed its validity in respect of elastic waves in material media, in which connection there is generally no room for differences of opinion in relation to the nature of the disturbance—in many cases we know that we are dealing not with pulses, but with continuous trains of waves nearly harmonic in character. We have not, as yet, justified Huygens's construction in this new context. Essentially, the situation is in many ways different from that that we have discussed hitherto.

Let us refer, once more, to fig. 33, giving new meaning to its various features. Let Q represent a source of constant strength from which a disturbance of well-defined frequency is spreading throughout an 'infinite' isotropic medium in which the phase velocity is v. Except for the continuous outflow of energy from the source, we have, at least in a finite region around Q, a steady-state situation. The amplitude of the disturbance at any point within this region remains constant and there is no sudden change of phase. We note, as another aspect of the process, the steady expansion of each and every wave front: if a particular wave front coincides, at time t, with the sphere of which S is the representation in the figure, the same wave front coincides with S' at $t + \Delta t$, where the radial separation of S and S' is $v\Delta t$. We have only to repeat our previous argument to establish the fact that Huygens's construction is valid, geometrically, as a means of deriving S', the 'new' position of this particular wave front, from S, its 'old' position. But the need for a physical justification remains as before, with the concomitant problem of the absence of the retrogressive wave. It is when we attempt this justification that the differences between the two situations—that of the spreading pulse, on the one hand, and of the radiation from a constant source, on the other —appear most clearly.

The first difference is clear enough. When dealing with the spreading pulse, we were dealing with a situation in which, once the pulse was fully formed, the source remained inactive indefinitely: in our new situation emission from the source continues throughout. Secondly, in respect of the new situation, we are clearly unable to make the simple assumption that previously was valid (see p. 184) 'that the state of the medium, everywhere, at any time later than t, is uniquely determined by the state of the medium within the region of the pulse at t'—for the disturbance effectively fills the whole of space all the time. If we are concerned with the state of the medium at any point at $t + \Delta t$, we have to realise that the points in the medium which are subject to disturbance at t, and are at a distance $v\Delta t$ from our chosen point, lie on the surface of a complete sphere about that point—and that half of them lie farther from the source than does the point itself. It might appear, at first sight, that there could be no simple way of deriving a subsequent from an earlier configuration, in these circumstances. Yet Huygens's geometrical construction succeeds here, as it does in respect of the pulse, and we know, intuitively, that the two situations, different though they may be, must ultimately yield to description in similar terms.

Eventually, justification of the use of Huygens's construction for quasi-sinusoidal diverging waves came through the mathematical investigations of H. L. F. von Helmholtz (see p. 118) and Gustav Robert Kirchhoff (1824-1887), who held professorships of physics, successively, at Breslau, Heidelberg and Berlin—the last, as colleague of Helmholtz, from 1875 until his death. Helmholtz's contribution to this problem was published in 1859, Kirchhoff's in 1882. Almost exactly two centuries after its enunciation, therefore, Huygens's construction was at last thoroughly understood—or very nearly so.

In its original form, as we have repeatedly insisted, Huygens's construction was purely geometrical: it stated nothing concerning amplitudes or intensities. On the other hand it must be clear that the mathematical investigations which justified it in its various contexts, cannot have failed to treat the problem of displacement amplitude in the developing disturbance quantitatively. We have so far omitted to consider this fundamental aspect of the matter in any detail in this section. We shall have to refer to it later in relation to diffraction effects (§ 8.6); here we pass first to a consideration of certain situations of which the main features are commonly classified as characteristic examples of interference. This, though standard terminology, is somewhat misleading: interference by superposition, in Young's sense of the term, is equally involved in most actual situations of which diffraction is traditionally regarded as the distinguishing feature; conversely, many examples of 'interference' involve diffraction, also.

8.3. INTERFERENCE: THE IDEAL CASE

Already, in § 8.1, we have briefly identified the ideal situation in which interference effects should appear uncomplicated by the effects of diffraction. We wrote (p. 177), 'Let us pose the problem in ideal form as follows. Let there be two exactly similar sources in an extended medium, separated by a distance very great compared with the effective wavelength common to the two disturbances to which they separately give rise. . . . We wish to enquire what is the nature of the disturbance of the medium in the central region . . . and . . . in regions other than the central region.' In this section we pursue this enquiry quantitatively. Admittedly dealing with an ideal case, we suppose that the sources are 'point' sources, that they are of equal strength, are characterised by a unique frequency and are emitting in phase with one another. Because we are postulating an ideal situation, we are at liberty to assume that emission from each of these sources is completely unrestricted in time, either past or future—as it must be, if the frequency is single-valued—and that it is isotropic in space. Finally, we impose one further restriction, to safeguard the validity of our subsequent conclusions: that we shall not attempt to specify with any precision the state of the medium in the immediate neighbourhood of either source—that is within a radial distance of a few wavelengths only (see pp. 210, 223).

Suppose, then, that Q_1 and Q_2 (fig. 35) represent the two sources. Let P be any point in the surrounding medium, and let us write $Q_1P = r_1$, $Q_2P = r_2$. If source Q_1 alone were effective, the phase of the disturbance at P, at time t, would be that of Q_1 at some earlier time, say at $t - t_1$. Similarly, if source Q_2 were effective alone, the phase at P at t would be that of Q_2 at $t - t_2$, say. Denoting the phase velocity of the disturbance in the medium by v, we have $t_1 - t_2 = (r_1 - r_2)/v$. Corresponding to this difference in phase transit times, the difference in phase angle is given by $\delta = 2\pi f(r_1 - r_2)/v = 2\pi(r_1 - r_2)/\lambda$, where f denotes the frequency and λ the wavelength of the disturbance.

In the situation that we are considering the two sources are effective together, and, the principle of superposition being accepted, we conclude that the displacement at P, at any time, is the resultant of the individual effects due to the two sources separately. These component effects, as we have seen, are characterised by a constant phase difference δ. However, in order to calculate the resultant displacement explicitly, it is necessary to know the amplitudes of the components as well as their relative phases. Indeed, displacement being a vector quantity, the specification of amplitude involves knowledge of direction as well as of magnitude in each case.

So far as magnitude is concerned, we may assume, in general, that this is inversely proportional to the distance from the source, writing, for our purposes, for two sources of equal strength, $A_1 = A/r_1$, $A_2 = A/r_2$. (This is effectively the inverse-square law of intensity for radiation originating in a source in a non-absorbing medium, energy in simple harmonic motion being proportional to the square of the amplitude.) So far as direction is concerned, our original assumptions, taken strictly, have already limited the possibilities, though they have not obscured the essential problem.

We have assumed that the emission from each source is 'isotropic in space'. Taken strictly, this is in effect an assumption of complete spherical symmetry, which is satisfied only if the dis-

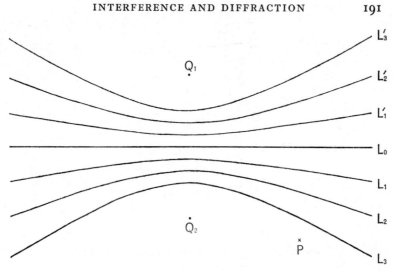

FIGURE 35

turbance is longitudinal—or if it is circularly polarised transverse (see pp. 136, 146). We shall consider these two cases in turn. First, however, we note certain features which are common to them both.

These common features concern the phases of the component displacements, in isolation from the amplitudes. We have seen that, at any point in the medium, the relative phase angle of the component displacements remains constant with time, provided that emission from the sources is continuous. We may enquire, therefore, what are the loci of points characterised by given differences in phase. Obviously, the general equation for such a locus (see above) is $r_1 - r_2 = \delta\lambda/2\pi$. In the plane of fig. 35 this equation, with δ constant, is that of a hyperbola of which Q_1 and Q_2 are the foci. In the limiting case, when $\delta = 0$, the hyperbola becomes the perpendicular bisector of Q_1Q_2. This bisector, L_0, and six representative hyperbolas, L_1, L_2, L_3, L_1', L_2', L_3', are shown in the figure. In the three-dimensional medium of which the figure is the representation, the corresponding loci are hyperboloids of revolution about Q_1Q_2 as axis (L_0 becomes a plane). At distances from the foci very large compared with the interfocal distance, the hyperboloids are hardly distinguishable from conical surfaces having Q_0, the mid-point of Q_1Q_2, as common vertex, to one of which surfaces each hyperboloid approaches asymptotically as the

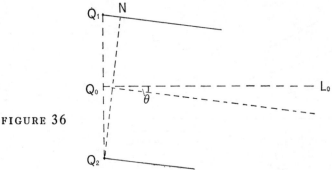

FIGURE 36

distance increases. If $\left(\dfrac{\pi}{2} - \theta\right)$ is the semi-vertical angle of one of these conical surfaces, and if $Q_1Q_2 = d$, brief consideration of fig. 36 will show that the corresponding value of δ is obtained by writing $r_1 - r_2 = Q_1N = d \sin \theta$, Q_2N being perpendicular to Q_1N. In this way δ is given by the equation

$$\delta = \frac{2\pi}{\lambda} d \sin \theta \qquad (160)$$

We return now to a consideration of amplitudes—and, first of all, to the case in which each source emits a longitudinal disturbance. In this case the amplitude of the resultant displacement at any arbitrary point P may be calculated by reference to fig. 37. Here our previous notation is repeated, the angles Q_0PQ_1 and Q_0PQ_2 are denoted by a_1 and a_2, respectively, and $Q_0P = r_0$. We first resolve the component displacement amplitudes, A_1 and A_2, along PQ_0 and at right angles to this direction, and from the geometry of the figure we obtain:

$$\text{along } PQ_0, \; {}_rA_1 = A_1 \cos a_1 = \frac{A}{r_1} \frac{r_1{}^2 + r_0{}^2 - d^2/4}{2r_1r_0}$$

$$(161)$$

$$\phantom{\text{along } PQ_0, \;} {}_rA_2 = A_2 \cos a_2 = \frac{A}{r_2} \frac{r_2{}^2 + r_0{}^2 - d^2/4}{2r_2r_0}$$

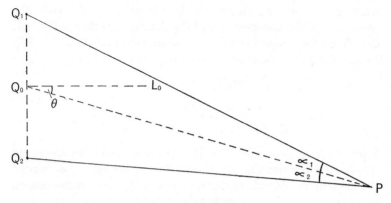

FIGURE 37

perpendicular to PQ_0 (clockwise in the figure),

$$_tA_1 = A_1 \sin \alpha_1 = \frac{A}{r_1} \frac{d}{2r_1} \cos \theta$$

$$-_tA_2 = A_2 \sin \alpha_2 = \frac{A}{r_2} \frac{d}{2r_2} \cos \theta$$

(162)

In the situation that we are considering, $_rA_1$ follows $_rA_2$ in phase by δ, and $_tA_1$ follows $-_tA_2$ by $\pi + \delta$.

Now let us combine $_rA_1$ and $_rA_2$ in order to derive B_r, the amplitude of the 'radial' component of displacement at P. We have (see $M\,L\ \&\ T$, p. 91)

$$B_r^2 = {}_rA_1{}^2 + {}_rA_2{}^2 + 2{}_rA_1\,{}_rA_2 \cos \delta$$

(163)

Similarly, for the amplitude of the 'transverse' component of displacement at P, we have

$$B_t^2 = {}_tA_1{}^2 + {}_tA_2{}^2 + 2{}_tA_1\,{}_tA_2 \cos \delta$$

(164)

We note that, in general, the radial and transverse components of displacement at P are not in phase with one another, since the ratios $_rA_1/_rA_2$ and $-_tA_1/_tA_2$ are not the same. As a consequence, the 'particle motion' at P is not rectilinear, but the total energy of such motion is proportional to $B_r^2 + B_t^2$, in spite of this difference in phase. Let us denote by U the total energy per unit volume of the medium at P: we may then write

$$U = c(B_r^2 + B_t^2),$$

N

where c is a constant. In a particular situation, c will involve the frequency of the disturbance and the density, or other parameter, describing the properties of the medium (see $M L \, \& \, T$, p. 233). Substituting from equations (161)-(164), we now have

$$U = c\{A_1{}^2 + A_2{}^2 + 2A_1A_2 \cos{(\alpha_1 + \alpha_2)} \cos{\delta}\}$$
$$= cA^2 \left\{ \frac{1}{r_1{}^2} + \frac{1}{r_2{}^2} + \frac{2}{r_1r_2} \cos{\frac{2\pi}{\lambda}} (r_1 - r_2) \cos{(\alpha_1 + \alpha_2)} \right\} \qquad (165)$$

Equation (165) is interesting in showing that, under the combined influence of the two sources of disturbance, the energy density of the medium is everywhere finite, except at Q_0. Only at this central point is the medium permanently undisturbed. Any other conclusion—for example the conclusion that over any finite surface U could be equal to zero—would be difficult to reconcile with our intuitive belief, not too precariously based on common experience, that, in spite of interference, the medium of our problem must be the vehicle of energy passing out radially from the two sources which we have placed at Q_1 and Q_2. We assume that there cannot be any absolute barrier to this flow of energy through any finite region of space, in the ideal case which we are considering. We may express the implications of equation (165), from another point of view, as follows. Those hyperboloids of fig. 35 for which $\cos \delta = -1$ (*i.e.* those for which $r_1 - r_2 = (2n+1)\lambda/2$, n being any integer) are not loci of points of zero disturbance in the medium; they are merely loci of points at which the component disturbances from the sources are 180° out of phase with one another. At large distances (i.e. when $r_0 \gg d$) these loci approximate very closely to loci of minimum disturbance.

Having treated the case of longitudinal disturbances in some detail, we may deal more briefly with the other case—that in which the sources are supposed to emit transverse disturbances which are circularly polarised. Let us refer back to fig. 37 in respect of this situation. In this new situation the first step is to resolve each circularly polarised disturbance at P into plane polarised components in directions at right angles, of equal amplitude and of phase difference $\pi/2$ (see p. 146). For each disturbance we may choose the direction at right angles to the plane Q_1Q_2P as the vibration direction of one of these components. Then the other component lies in that plane. The components in the plane

Q_1Q_2P have in general different amplitudes and different directions (at right angles, respectively, to Q_1P and Q_2P) and are characterised by the phase difference δ. We must deal with them as we dealt with the individual disturbances A_1 and A_2 of the previous case, resolving them along and at right angles to PQ_0, combining them in pairs, and again combining the resultants so obtained. The components at right angles to the plane Q_1Q_2P, we combine directly. They have the same direction, though in general different amplitudes, and their phase difference also is δ. Finally, the resultant of these components has to be combined with that of the others. In this way an expression for the energy density equivalent to equation (165) is eventually obtained. It may be written, adapting our previous notation to the new situation,

$$U = cA^2 \left\{ \frac{1}{r_1^2} + \frac{1}{r_2^2} + \frac{1}{r_1 r_2} \left(1 + \cos\left(a_1 + a_2\right)\right) \cos \frac{2\pi}{\lambda} \left(r_1 - r_2\right) \right\} \quad (166)$$

Hitherto our discussion has been entirely unspecific: we have taken P as an arbitrary point, and have imposed no further condition on its location except that it be not within a distance of a few wavelengths of either source. There are, however, two special conditions which we might impose which are of particular relevance to various experimental arrangements by means of which interference effects are commonly demonstrated. According to the first of these conditions, P is restricted to lie within a small distance of Q_0L_0 (fig. 37), a perpendicular bisector of Q_1Q_2, and to be at a relatively great distance from $Q_0(r_0 \gg d)$; according to the second special condition, P must lie within a small distance of the line on which the sources themselves lie, and in this case it need not be at a great distance from the sources. Let us consider these two configurations in turn. In each case we shall fix attention on the state of disturbance of the medium at points lying in a geometrical plane, this plane, in the first case, being at right angles to Q_0L_0, and, in the second case, at right angles to Q_1Q_2. In the second case we shall consider separately the two possible situations—first, that in which the plane lies in the region between the sources, then the situation in which it lies outside this region.

Qualitatively, it is easy to determine the pattern of disturbance over the small area of plane at right angles to Q_0L_0 with which we are concerned in the first case. The hyperboloids of fig. 35

intersect this plane in a series of lines which, to a first approximation, are straight and parallel. Across the centre of the pattern, the common direction of these lines is at right angles to Q_1Q_2. We fix attention on the lines corresponding to the various values of δ given by $r_1-r_2=n\lambda$ (i.e. by $\delta=2\pi n$), where n is any integer. When r_0/d is large enough, these lines are the loci of maximum disturbance in the plane (see equation (165)). Quantitatively, we wish to determine the spacing of these lines.

For this purpose, let x_n be the distance of the nth line from the central line $(n=0)$, and let the value of r_0 for the central line be written as l (l is then the perpendicular distance of either source from the plane). If the distance x_n is measured across the centre of the pattern, we may write, without any approximation,

$$\left\{l^2+\left(x_n+\frac{d}{2}\right)^2\right\}^{\frac{1}{2}}-\left\{l^2+\left(x_n-\frac{d}{2}\right)^2\right\}^{\frac{1}{2}}=n\lambda.$$

We have already imposed the condition $l\gg d$; if, also, $l\gg x_n$, we obtain, to second-order accuracy,

$$\left(x_n+\frac{d}{2}\right)^2-\left(x_n-\frac{d}{2}\right)^2=2n\lambda l,$$

or
$$x_n=\frac{n\lambda l}{d} \tag{167}$$

On the basis of equation (167), x_n is directly proportional to n; we conclude, therefore, that the loci of maximum disturbance are equally spaced. We see, moreover, that the condition $l\gg x_n$, requisite for the validity of equation (167), implies the prior condition $d\gg n\lambda$. This, then, is the condition that over a plane of 'small' linear dimensions at a 'large' distance from two point sources, in the disposition that we are considering, there shall be at least n lines of maximum disturbance on each side of the central disturbance maximum. There is one further point of interest in our analysis: it is that the approximation which validates equation (167) is equivalent to replacing the hyperboloids of fig. 35 by the conical surfaces to which at large distances they approach asymptotically. If we write $\delta=2\pi n$ in equation (160), and $x_n/l=\tan\theta$ in equation (167), these equations are seen to be identical when θ is very small ($l\gg x_n$).

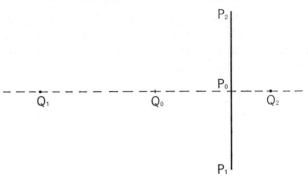

FIGURE 38

When $\delta = (2n+1)\pi$, in the case that we are considering, the loci are those of minimum disturbance. It is easy to see that, over the small plane area at distance l, these disturbance minima lie midway between the maxima whose positions are specified by equation (167). If we are dealing with longitudinal disturbances, we can calculate the ratio of the intensities of maximum and minimum disturbance, using equation (165). Employing an obvious notation, writing $r_1 = r_2 = l$, $\cos(a_1 + a_2) = 1 - \dfrac{d^2}{2l^2}$ (all to second-order accuracy), we have, after further simplification,

$$\frac{I_{\max}}{I_{\min}} = \frac{U_{\max}}{U_{\min}} = \frac{4l^2}{d^2}.$$

This ratio is always very large when $l \gg d$; for d constant, it becomes larger as l increases. In the other case, that of circularly polarised transverse disturbances, when equation (166) applies, we have, similarly,

$$\frac{I_{\max}}{I_{\min}} = \frac{8l^2}{d^2}.$$

We turn now to the second special configuration mentioned on p. 195, that of points in a plane of small area at right angles to the line containing the sources. Fig. 38 represents the situation when this plane (of which P_1P_2 is the trace in the figure) lies in the region between the sources. We retain our previous notation, except that now we write $Q_0P_0 = l$. Very clearly, in this case, the loci of points of constant phase difference δ are circles having

P_0 as centre. Writing δ_0 for the phase difference at P_0, we have $\delta_0 = 4\pi l/\lambda$. Then, if x_n is the radius of the circular locus corresponding to phase difference $\delta_0 - 2\pi n$ (δ decreases outwards from P_0 in the plane, in this case),

$$\left\{ \left(\frac{d}{2}+l\right)^2 + x_n{}^2 \right\}^{\frac{1}{2}} - \left\{ \left(\frac{d}{2}-l\right)^2 + x_n{}^2 \right\}^{\frac{1}{2}} = 2l - n\lambda,$$

or, also to second-order accuracy,

$$x_n{}^2 \left\{ \frac{1}{\dfrac{d}{2}-l} - \frac{1}{\dfrac{d}{2}+l} \right\} = 2n\lambda,$$

or

$$x_n{}^2 = \frac{n\lambda}{l} \left(\frac{d^2}{4} - l^2 \right) \qquad (168)$$

When the plane $P_1 P_2$ lies outside the region $Q_1 Q_2$, if we again denote the distance $Q_0 P_0$ by l, we have, similarly, $\delta_0 = 2\pi d/\lambda$, and, to the same order of accuracy as before,

$$x_n{}^2 = \frac{2n\lambda}{d} \left(l^2 - \frac{d^2}{4} \right) \qquad (169)$$

Evaluating the results that we have obtained, we see that, when the plane lies between the sources, the phase difference at the centre of the pattern varies continuously as the plane is moved. In this way the disturbance at the centre passes through a succession of maxima and minima of intensity. Also, the scale of the pattern changes. The circular loci of maximum disturbance are more widely spaced, the nearer the plane is to the mid-point Q_0. Finally, when the plane passes through Q_0 the phase difference is zero over its whole area, and the variation of intensity over its surface is not very marked. When the plane lies outside the region of the sources, on the other hand, the phase difference at the centre of the pattern is seen to be independent of the precise position of the plane. The intensity at the centre, therefore, decreases monotonically as the plane is moved away from the nearer source. Again, however, the scale of the pattern changes as the plane is moved. The circular loci of maximum disturbance expand continuously as l increases. It is interesting to compare the scale of the circular pattern characteristic of this case, when l becomes very great ($l \gg d$), with that of the approximately linear pattern described by equation (167) and characteristic of the disturbance over the central region of a plane having its mid-point on a perpendicular bisector of Q_1Q_2 and at a great distance from the sources. When we speak generally of the pattern characteristic of the disturbance in either plane, we are thinking particularly— as throughout this discussion—of the pattern of loci of points of constant phase difference, the loci constituting the pattern being such that the defining phase difference changes by 2π as between one such locus and the next.

For the linear pattern of the 'broadside' position, we may slightly refine our previous notation (p. 196) and in equation (167) write $x_n/l = \tan \theta_{nb}$. Similarly, in equation (169), relative to the 'end-on' position, we may write $x_n/l = \tan \theta_{ne}$. Then, when $l \gg d$ in each case, we have

$$\tan \theta_{nb} = \frac{n\lambda}{d}, \quad \tan^2 \theta_{ne} = \frac{2n\lambda}{d},$$

or
$$\tan^2 \theta_{ne} = 2 \tan \theta_{nb}.$$

In each configuration we are concerned exclusively with small angles ($\theta_{ne}, \theta_{nb} \ll 1$); we conclude, therefore, that the angular radius of the nth circular locus in the plane in the end-on position is considerably greater than the angular separation of the nth linear locus from the central locus in the plane in the broadside position, or, expressing the same result in symbols, that $\theta_{ne} \gg \theta_{nb}$. It should be understood, of course, that all the angles involved in this statement are angles subtended at Q_0, the mid-point of the sources.

8.4. INTERFERENCE: SOME PRACTICAL CONSIDERATIONS

In the last section we considered in some detail the phenomenon of the interference, by superposition, of two wave processes in the simplest of ideal cases—and we gave separate attention to two special situations 'of particular relevance to various experimental arrangements by means of which interference effects are commonly demonstrated' (p. 195). It will be our object, in the next section, to refer briefly to some of those arrangements. First, however, we indicate, in general terms, how far from the ideal of our earlier considerations most of these arrangements must actually be.

In the ideal case we postulated two point sources in an infinite medium, 'empty' except for the sources. The reader may have noticed that we were careful not to introduce any observer, or instrument of detection, into our hypothetical situation. We discussed, rather, the state of disturbance over the surface of a geometrical plane variously located in the medium. It need hardly be remarked that point sources are not physical realities, nor is any actual medium infinite in extent. But it is verging on pedantry to insist on these fine distinctions: a medium sufficiently extensive for all practical purposes is generally available, and provided that the outgoing wave from a source of small dimensions is spherically symmetrical the fact that the source is of finite size is of little consequence. A more serious complication is that in most actual arrangements the medium is far from 'empty' except for the sources. There must be, for purposes of quantitative observation, some instrument of detection—at the very least a photographic plate, or screen, rather than an immaterial geometrical plane. And, more often than not, the free development of the spherical disturbances is restricted and modified by apertures, or lenses, or other devices. Whenever a wave front is so restricted, diffraction occurs, and our previous analysis is no longer applicable in detail.

The most serious complication of all, however, arises with the sources themselves. In the ideal case we postulated that the disturbances originating in the two sources should be 'completely unrestricted in time, either past or future', that they should be of equal and unvarying intensity, of precisely the same frequency for each source, and, at any instant, in phase at their respective origins. If the other conditions were fulfilled, the last would indeed be trivial: our analysis would remain essentially unchanged if the emitting sources were characterised by a constant phase difference Δ, rather than zero, as we have supposed. Even the condition of equal frequencies is not absolutely essential, if the prior conditions are satisfied. If the two frequencies were very nearly the same, the interference patterns, over planes of small area such as we have discussed, would not be obliterated: they would merely be modified, exhibiting periodic variations in time. The 'beating' of musical notes of very nearly equal pitch (see $M L \mathrel{\&} T$, p. 91) is an example of this effect—though its spatial aspects are rarely appreciated. Finally, the condition that the intensities of the two sources should be the same, when taken alone, is far from determinative. Our analysis could well deal with the situation of unequal sources; again, interference effects would result—if the other conditions were fulfilled—but the disturbance minima would be everywhere less marked. The patterns themselves would remain basically the same.

No, the essence of the complication, in relation to the sources, lies in the first condition: we have postulated that the disturbances shall be of unvarying intensity, completely unrestricted in time. In one respect this condition is exactly comparable with the condition that the medium shall be of infinite extent, and, in this respect, being realists, we may easily relax it, so far as the former condition was relaxed. Thus, it will be sufficient if, throughout the duration of any experiment, we require that the sources remain of constant strength, and emit continuously, without abrupt changes of phase at the origin. With this relaxation, it might be thought that the complication is reduced to negligible proportions—but to accept this conclusion is to admit a hidden assumption, which in some cases may not be justified.

Fundamentally, the issue depends on whether or not we understand and can specify fully the physical process by which the source emits energy. If the source is a macroscopic mechanical system maintained in a simple mode of vibration, we can probably satisfy ourselves that such vibration can be maintained continuously over a long period of time. In that event it is not impracticable to build two 'exactly similar' sources and obtain interference effects under conditions approximating fairly closely to the ideal that we have described. We have, in fact, already admitted the phenomenon of beats in music as belonging to the class of interference phenomena—even though, in such a case, the two 'macroscopic mechanical systems', the vibrating strings or air columns, are not exactly similar, but only nearly so. Again, in recent times, the technique of the electromagnetic generation of 'microwaves' (see p. 224) has been developed far beyond the limits of earlier anticipation. We can now construct sources of such radiation, tuned to the same frequency within very narrow limits, which will emit steadily over long periods of time. Near-ideal interference experiments with two such sources are obviously possible.

With certain sources of sound, then, and with microwaves of

electromagnetic origin, the conditions that we have laid down for an ideal experiment can be approximately satisfied. But it remains a fact of history that, throughout the nineteenth century and the first half of the twentieth, the phenomena of interference have been studied most systematically with visible light. Here the situation is entirely different. No one has succeeded in observing simple interference effects, of the character that we have described in the last section, using two independent sources of light. This statement remains true of 'exactly similar' sources which the spectroscope shows to emit light of one spectral line only. Already, in 1807, Young was as clear as he could be on this point. He wrote: 'In order that the effects of two portions of light may be thus combined, it is necessary that they be derived from the same origin, and that they arrive at the same point by different paths, in directions not much deviating from each other.' And he added (though this aspect of the matter is not our immediate concern): 'This deviation may be produced in one or both of the portions by diffraction, by reflection, by refraction, or by any of these effects combined.' Young's main contention is reminiscent of Newton's remark concerning the tides of Batsha (see p. 179): 'It may happen that the tide may be propagated from the ocean through different channels towards the same port . . . in which case the same generating tide, being thus divided . . . may produce by composition new types of tide.' We are left wondering whether the similarity of formulation is fortuitous, or whether Young imagined that the state of affairs in an ordinary source of light might be as generally chaotic as that on the surface of the ocean which, in spite of its apparent waywardness, yet rises and falls with a regular rhythm.

We are not called upon to romanticise the situation, however, but rather to seek an answer to our problem from experience—in the first place from our accumulated knowledge of light sources generally, and, in the second, from precise experiment designed to elucidate the situation. In the first place, then, let us recall that a common source of light in these days is a volume of gas, at low pressure, through which an electric discharge is passing. Obviously, in this case, the molecules of gas are, on the average, so far apart that they must be regarded as acting independently (even if they were put into states of emission in acts of collision they would be acting independently during the emission process).

Admittedly this is an extreme case, but even the luminosity of a candle flame is in the main that of small particles of soot raised to incandescence by the combustion. The conclusion is generally inescapable: 'artificial' light sources in common use are not simple vibrating systems—any one of them is constituted of a large number of independent elements, and we have no reason to expect that the contributions of these various elements to the total emission from any source shall, at any instant, be in phase with one another. We shall return to this aspect of the matter later (see p. 206), meanwhile let us refer to the second component of our experience, that derived 'from precise experiment'.

Armand Hippolyte Louis Fizeau (1819-1896), a Frenchman of independent means, was the first to examine systematically the way in which the distinctness of the circular 'fringes' in an interference pattern observed with quasi-homogeneous light varies with the difference in optical path of the interfering beams. Using light from a sodium flame he found (1862) that the contrast or 'visibility' of the fringes gradually decreased, as the path difference in the centre of the pattern was increased from a small number of wavelengths to about 500 wavelengths, then increased again to a maximum when the path difference was about 1000 wavelengths, and so on, periodically. He followed this process through 52 cycles, until the total path difference was some 50,000 wavelengths, or about 3 cm. Fizeau gave the correct explanation of what he had observed: as may be verified by use of a prism spectrometer of moderate resolving power, the quasi-homogeneous yellow light of the sodium flame has two components of which the effective wavelengths differ by about 1 part in 10^3. With this composite light, the pattern observed is the sum (by intensities) of two patterns of insensibly different colour; these are sometimes in step (over a not too large region), sometimes out of step with one another, depending upon the mean path difference involved. When the two patterns are in step the contrast characteristic of either is exhibited in their combined effect; when they are out of step their combination results in a field of almost uniform illumination. There is no steady interference between light of the one wavelength (colour) and the other, but for each component some effect of interference persists even though the path difference is increased to 50,000 wavelengths. We write 'even though', here, in anticipation of later results, but it should be pointed out that if the light from the source were strictly monochromatic the visibility of the fringes would remain constant (at least in the case of plane waves) however great the path difference became.

The work of Fizeau was taken up, nearly thirty years later, by Albert Abraham Michelson (1852-1931), a Pole, who emigrated to America as a boy, and held professorships of physics, successively, at the Case school, Cleveland, Clark university and the university of Chicago. Having developed apparatus of much greater flexibility, Michelson examined many sources of quasi-homogeneous light by the fringe-visibility method, establishing in that way the nature of the 'fine structure' of several spectrum lines. As a result of this work he recognised that some of these lines are essentially single—that is that they consist of one distinct component only. He found that in such cases the fringe visibility decreases with increasing path difference in a characteristic manner: it does not remain constant. We may conclude that, even in such cases, the single component, although we may be correct in regarding it as a 'unique' radiation from the point of view of atomic physics, is not strictly monochromatic: it is characterised by an individual frequency (or wavelength) spectrum which is continuous over a very narrow range of the parameter in question —the spectrum line has a 'natural width'. Alternatively, we may say, and this is a more direct statement for our present purposes, that the radiation from the source is emitted in wave trains of finite length. That these are broadly equivalent statements may easily be accepted in view of the discussions of an earlier section (see p. 42). In the case of a particular 'singlet' red line in the spectrum of cadmium vapour (wavelength 6.438×10^{-5} cm.), for example, Michelson found that the fringes lost contrast steadily, to become almost invisible when the path difference was some 30 cm. In this case, and within our present scheme of interpretation, this distance may be taken as a fair estimate of the effective length of the separate wave trains emitted by the source. When, by different optical paths, two portions of such a train arrive at the point of observation, displaced one with respect to the other by more than the train-length, interference is impossible. When, alternatively, two such portions arrive at a given point, with relative displacement considerably less than the train-length, interference occurs—but only over the very short interval of time (about 10^{-9} sec. in the case of the cadmium red light) required for the interfering portions of the trains to pass the point in question. When there is a persistent pattern of fringes on a screen we can only conclude that the optical system is such that between every point effective in the source and any arbitrarily chosen point on the screen the path difference for the two interfering portions of the beam is essentially the same. Only in that way would the phase relations of successive pairs of interfering wave trains necessarily be identical. This, then, is the primary condition for the achievement of persistent interference patterns with visible light—and the various experimental arrangements to be described briefly in the next section were originally designed, consciously or intuitively, to ensure its fulfilment.

In the foregoing discussion we have attempted to account for the detailed appearance of an interference pattern observed with quasi-homogeneous light—that is, for the scale of the pattern and the distribution of intensity in it (particularly for the contrast between the regions of maximum and minimum illumination)— in terms of the assumption that emission from the source is in the form of wave trains of a definite train-length, and of a dominant wavelength characteristic of an atomic, or, at least, a very small-scale, process occurring in the very large number of luminous elements which go to make up the macroscopic source. This point of view gives to the interference pattern a rapidly fluctuating structure in time (we have mentioned that the arrival time of a single wave train may be of the order of 10^{-9} sec.), but a stable structure in space. There is nothing intrinsically implausible in this analysis: the fluctuations in time which it involves are likely to be much too rapid to be detected visually—or by photographic means. But we have given no indication of the amount of energy which we regard as carried by a single wave train—and in the last paragraph we used a form of words which at least implied that we were supposing that the two interfering portions of any wave train would have passed over the point of observation before the corresponding portions of the next wave train arrived. We wrote in that place of 'successive pairs of interfering wave trains'. These two aspects of the matter—the energy in a single train and the possible overlapping—are not unrelated, as a simple calculation will show.

Let us take the case of the cadmium vapour source previously mentioned, for which the train-length is of the order of 30 cm.

Unless the effective portion of such a source emits (at random in time) considerably fewer than 10^9 wave trains per second, there must occur, at the source, a relatively large amount of overlapping of successive trains. If the luminous power of the source is 0·1 watt, there will be considerable overlapping, then, unless the energy in each train is large compared with 10^{-10} joule, or 10^{-3} erg. In macroscopic terms this is a small quantity of energy, but in respect of atomic systems it is a very large amount—and in such a source we must almost certainly consider the single atom as the independent emitter. According to Einstein's relation (see *M L & T*, p. 276 and p. 134), if an atom of cadmium were to emit 10^{-3} erg of energy its mass would decrease by roughly 0·7 units on the atomic scale (say from 112 to 111·3 atomic mass units, or by about 10^{-24} g.). It would be contrary to all our ideas of the permanence of atoms to admit such a possibility: we must rather conclude that in the field of a 0·1 watt source any small region is at any instant transmitting very many independent wave trains simultaneously: indeed, if we make the argument fully realistic, we must in these circumstances interpret 'very many' as of the order of a hundred million.

We must not shirk the issue, therefore, within the framework of our scheme of interpretation, of the overlapping of wave trains in the two portions of the beam which are brought to a common point in the plane of observation, when quasi-homogeneous light is used in an interference experiment. Granted that we can explain the various features of the interference pattern in terms of the history of a single characteristic wave train, as it is divided in its passage through the apparatus and brought together again in the observer's field of view, we have still to convince ourselves that our scheme of interpretation is a tenable one, once it is recognised that, in almost every such experiment, each point in the field is at every instant receiving a multitude of such pairs of interfering portions of wave trains randomly related to one another in relative phase. We accept that, in respect of a given point in the plane of observation, the optical system imposes the same difference of phase on the two portions into which each incident wave train is divided, but we must necessarily assume that the overlapping incident trains (and therefore the overlapping resultants to which they give rise in the region of the plane of observation) are entirely independent, that is that their phase angles (at any instant) are randomly distributed between the limits 0 and 2π.

We do not propose to treat this problem in its generality, but a simpler problem the solution of which should be sufficiently definite to assure us that in the more complicated case the result would be similar. If that be the upshot, our general scheme of interpretation of interference effects with quasi-homogeneous light will be justified as self-consistent. Our real problem, let us repeat, is to determine the resultant intensity due to a very large flux of overlapping wave trains of finite length. These wave trains may be regarded as of constant form (determined by the precise path difference characteristic of the point of observation), but their individual arrival times are randomly distributed. The average number of such trains in passage at any instant is N (itself a large number) and their phases are entirely independent. The simpler problem that we shall set ourselves here is to determine the intensity due to superposed wave motions, each strictly sinusoidal and of the same amplitude, having randomly distributed phases. This problem was first considered by Rayleigh in 1880, more than ten years before the experiments of Michelson gave ground for the more refined notion of finite wave trains which we have been discussing. In 1880 Rayleigh had regarded his investigation as of direct relevance to the physical situation in an actual light source made up of innumerable centres of disturbance, and he spoke of it colloquially as the problem of the two candles. When he had solved the problem he wrote, 'In this way . . . we may properly say that two candles are twice as bright as one.'

Here, indeed, we shall not even treat Rayleigh's original problem rigorously, but a special case of it which he later gave (1910) as embodying all its essential features. Instead of assuming that the phases of the N component wave motions at any instant are randomly distributed between 0 and 2π, we shall suppose that only two values of the phase angle are possible, namely δ and $\delta + \pi$, and that for any component it is equally as likely that the phase angle has the one value as that it has the other. On this basis, if the displacement amplitude at any point, due to one component wave motion acting alone, is represented by A, the resultant amplitude, when the N components are acting together, may be any one of the integral multiples of A given by the series

$$NA, (N-2)A, (N-4)A, \ldots (N-2N)A.$$

We may suppose that the first of these possible values corresponds to the (very unlikely) event that the phase of every component is δ; then the last possible value in the series $(-NA)$ will correspond to the (equally unlikely) event that the phase of every component wave motion is $\delta + \pi$. The essence of our problem now is to obtain a general expression for the probability that the resultant amplitude is in fact $(N - 2n)A$—or, what is the same thing, that the resultant intensity is proportional to $(N - 2n)^2 A^2$—and from this to evaluate the 'expectation value' of the intensity, namely the value which would be deduced as an average from a large number of independent 'trials', if that number could be increased indefinitely. And, let it be remarked in parenthesis, our 'real' problem, involving the finite wave trains, has this aspect of multiple trials built into its structure: our treatment of Rayleigh's simplified problem, therefore, does full justice at least to this aspect of the real situation.

The probability that the resultant amplitude is $(N - 2n)A$, in Rayleigh's problem, is the probability that, of the N components, precisely $N - n$ have phase angle δ, and n phase angle $\delta + \pi$ (on the basis of our previous identification). Now, any arbitrary assignment of phase to the N components has intrinsic probability $1/2^N$, when only two (equally likely) possibilities are available at each step. On the other hand, the number of ways of choosing n (and rejecting $N - n$) out of N components is $N!/n!(N-n)!$. Thus the probability that the resultant amplitude is $(N - 2n)A$ is given by

$$P(n) = \frac{1}{2^N} \frac{N!}{n! \, (N-n)!},$$

and the corresponding contribution to I, the expectation value of the intensity is given by

$$I(n) = c \cdot \frac{1}{2^N} \frac{N!}{n! \, (N-n)!} (N - 2n)^2 A^2,$$

where cA^2 is written for the intensity which would be observed if one component were acting alone. In this connection we note that our probabilities are correctly 'normalised', since

$$\sum_0^N P(n) = \frac{1}{2^N} (1 + 1)^N = 1.$$

Our immediate problem is to evaluate the sum given by

$$I = \sum_{0}^{N} I(n),$$

or by

$$I = \frac{cA^2}{2^N} \sum_{0}^{N} \frac{N!}{n! \, (N-n)!} \, (N-2n)^2.$$

We note that

$$(e^x + e^{-x})^N = e^{Nx} + Ne^{(N-2)x} + \frac{N(N-1)}{1.2} e^{(N-4)x} + \ldots + e^{-Nx},$$

so that

$$\tfrac{1}{2} \sum_{0}^{N} \frac{N!}{n! \, (N-n)!} \, (N-2n)^2$$

may be identified as the coefficient of x^2 in this expression. Alternatively, we have

$$e^x + e^{-x} = 2 \left(1 + \frac{x^2}{2!} + \frac{x^4}{4!} + \ldots \right),$$

thus the coefficient of x^2 in the expansion of $(e^x + e^{-x})^N$ is clearly $2^N \, (N/2!)$. Obviously, therefore,

$$\sum_{0}^{N} \frac{N!}{n! \, (N-n)!} \, (N-2n)^2 = 2^N N,$$

and

$$I = cNA^2 \tag{170}$$

We conclude that the expectation value of the intensity in this case is exactly the same as would be calculated on the assumption that each component wave train transports its own portion of energy, apparently uninfluenced by the other trains which are in course of propagation at the same time. We note, moreover, that this final result does not depend on the assumption that N is a very large number; properly interpreted, equation (170) is valid for any value of N. This is as far as we can take the justification of our scheme of interpretation of interference effects with quasi-homogeneous light, but it will probably be agreed that we have gone a long way towards rendering that scheme a reasonably acceptable one. That was our modest aim.

At this point there is only one further comment that should properly be made. In 1909, G. I. Taylor (b. 1886), who had taken his degree at Cambridge in the previous year, carried out an

o

experiment in which he examined photographically the interference effects in a diffraction pattern as they depended on the
intensity of the light source employed. With his weakest source,
an exposure of some three months was required. Taylor found no
difference at all in the sharpness of the fringes, whatever the
strength of the source and the consequent time of exposure. This
result is precisely what we should expect according to our scheme
of interpretation. We have already suggested (p. 206) that an
appropriate value for the energy associated with a single wave
train, according to that scheme, might well be of the order of
10^{-11} erg. In Taylor's experiment, with his weakest source, the
mean energy density of radiation within his apparatus was not
much more than 10^{-16} erg cm.$^{-3}$. In such circumstances, almost
certainly, we should conclude that overlapping of successive wave
trains was of negligible account. In more recent years, other
experimenters, adopting more conventional arrangements for the
realisation of optical interference, have verified and extended
Taylor's observations. There can be no doubting the general
result.

8.5. INTERFERENCE: SOME EXPERIMENTAL ARRANGEMENTS

It is not our intention in this section to give a systematic account
of the various experimental arrangements—or even of the various
classes of experimental arrangement—by which interference
effects have been demonstrated and studied, but rather to give a
brief description of some arrangements which have been of
importance historically. We shall also give a more detailed discussion of one series of experiments which brings to our attention
an aspect of a situation which we have hitherto ignored, namely
the state of affairs in an ideal spherical wave in the neighbourhood
of the origin. It will be recalled that in § 8.3 we specifically excluded
consideration of that region of the field (p. 190). Under these two
heads we shall confine attention to experiments in optics.

We have seen that the notion of interference by superposition
of sinusoidal wave processes originated with Thomas Young
(p. 178). In the field of optics Young began by recognising that
certain phenomena, already very fully described by Newton, could
be explained on this basis more convincingly than on the basis of
the corpuscular theory of the Newtonians. Young himself wrote
(1807) of 'a very extensive class of phenomena . . . none of which

have been explained on the supposition of emanation, in a manner sufficiently minute or comprehensive to satisfy the most candid even of the advocates for the projectile system; while on the other hand all of them may be at once understood, from the effect of the interference of double lights. . . '. Phenomena of the class in question had first been noticed by Robert Boyle (see *M L & T*, p. 278). Then, a year or two later, Robert Hooke gave a description of some of them in *Micrographia* (see p. 180); finally, in 1675, some ten years later again, Newton communicated to the Royal Society a full account of them. When his *Opticks* came to be published in 1704, book 2 of that treatise was devoted to their consideration. We generally refer to these effects as the 'colours of thin plates'; 'Newton's rings', as they are commonly called, provide their best-known manifestation.

Essentially, in all these cases, we have light incident on a thin film, for example a soap film or a film of air enclosed between plates of glass, and partially reflected (and partially transmitted) at each surface of separation. In particular, if we view the film along the direction of the incident light, we may expect to observe interference effects arising from the superposition of the reflected beams—the beam reflected from the first and that reflected from the second bounding surface of the film. It is clear that these two interfering beams have been produced from a single beam incident on the film, so fulfilling Young's primary condition (p. 202). We commonly say that they have been produced by the method of 'division of amplitude'—in that part of the light is reflected and part transmitted at each surface, as we have indicated already.

It will be remembered that Young classified the methods by which the divided portions of a beam of light might be brought to interference as 'deviation . . . in one or both of the portions by diffraction, by reflection, by refraction, or by any of these effects combined'. In respect of Newton's rings, and the colours of thin plates, it is obviously a case of reflection of both portions; and, because the development of the wave front of the incident light is not essentially restricted in this arrangement, diffraction plays no important part.

When Young had satisfied himself that the observations of Newton and Hooke and Boyle could be explained in terms of the new notion of interference, he demonstrated the effect himself in another context, making use of diffraction to bring the inter-

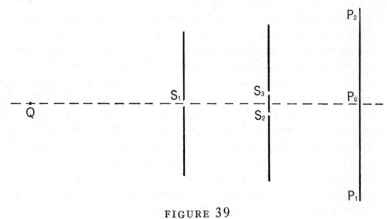

FIGURE 39

fering portions of the divided beam together. 'The simplest case appears to be', he wrote, 'when a beam of homogeneous light falls on a screen in which there are two very small holes or slits, which may be considered as centres of divergence, from whence the light is diffracted in every direction. In this case, when the two newly formed beams are received on a surface placed so as to intercept them, their light is divided by dark stripes into portions nearly equal, but becoming wider as the surface is more remote from the apertures . . . and wider also in the same proportion as the apertures are closer to each other.' Fig. 39 illustrates the arrangement schematically. Q represents the source of light (Young used the sun for this purpose) and P_1P_2 the screen on which the interference pattern is observed. S_1 is a slit (or pinhole) severely restricting the incident light and so illuminating the exactly similar parallel slits (or pinholes) S_2 and S_3 by diffraction. P_0 is the central point of the fringe system. Light reaches the region of the screen around P_0 solely by reason of the further diffraction of the already diffracted light as it passes through S_2, S_3. Ideally, the conditions for interference may be perfectly realised in Young's arrangement, but in practice the distribution of intensity on the screen is likely to be largely influenced by the pattern of diffraction characteristic of the individual slits S_2, S_3 (see p. 227). In order to avoid this effect it would be necessary to make the slits so narrow that it would be difficult to obtain an interference pattern of sufficient intensity for easy observation.

The disadvantages of Young's arrangement, from the point of

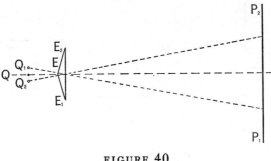

view of intensity, if a pure interference pattern is required, were overcome by Fresnel some ten years later. Fresnel employed two arrangements, the one utilising refraction, and the other reflection, to bring the two portions of a divided beam to interference. Fresnel's bi-prism arrangement is illustrated schematically in fig. 40. A line source Q is placed parallel to and equidistant from the two refracting edges, E_1, E_2, of a prism of large angle (the angle about E, the other edge of the prism being very little less than 180°). The screen P_1P_2 is perpendicular to the plane of symmetry of the system as shown. If the equal small refracting angles are of magnitude a, the deviation of light passing through either half of the prism in a principal plane is very closely $(\mu-1)a$, where μ is the refractive index of the glass of the prism. To fair approximation, therefore, over the region on the far side of the prism, the source simulates two parallel sources Q_1 and Q_2, in a plane through Q parallel to the screen, and so disposed that $\angle Q_1EQ_2 = 2(\mu-1)a$. Light from these two virtual sources overlaps, on the far side of the prism in the region indicated by the dotted lines on the figure. The angular width of this region, as seen from E, is also $2(\mu-1)a$.

Fig. 41 illustrates the other arrangement used by Fresnel. Two plane mirrors, M_1M, M_2M, inclined to one another at a small angle a, are so arranged that their reflecting surfaces intersect in a line through M. Parallel to this line of intersection is a line source Q. Q_1 and Q_2 represent the virtual images of Q formed in the mirrors. Obviously, Q, Q_1 and Q_2 are equidistant from M, and $\angle Q_1MQ_2 = 2a$. In the region P_1MP_2 in the figure, the two beams of light appearing to originate in Q_1 and Q_2, respectively,

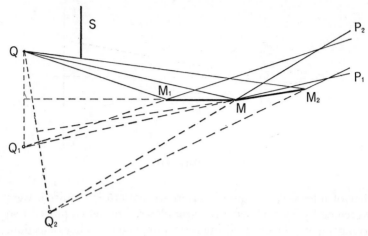

FIGURE 41

overlap, and the usual two-source interference pattern may be observed. In the central portion of this pattern, more completely than in the central portion of the pattern obtained with the bi-prism, the disturbing effects of diffraction are of negligible importance. In fig. 41, S represents an opaque screen shielding the region of observation from the direct light from the source. Earlier we referred to Newton's arrangement for observing interference effects with thin films as employing the method of division of amplitude. In the same context we may refer to Fresnel's arrangements, of the bi-prism and the mirrors, as using the method of division of the wave front.

An interesting variant of Fresnel's arrangement of mirrors was devised by Humphrey Lloyd (1800-1881), professor of physics, and colleague and collaborator of Hamilton in Dublin (see *M L & T*, p. 77). Lloyd made use of only one single (unsilvered) mirror, in a manner illustrated in fig. 42. As before, Q represents a line source of light parallel to the reflecting surface M_1M_2. Q_1 is the virtual image of Q, and interference effects are observed on a screen S, placed parallel to the plane containing Q and Q_1. Clearly, these effects are confined to the region of which $P_1M_2M_1P_2$ is the boundary in the figure.

It might be thought that the arrangement illustrated in fig. 42 is at a disadvantage in comparison with the two arrangements du

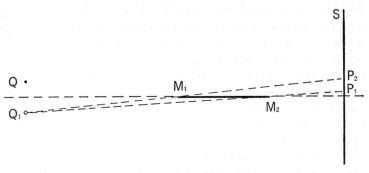

FIGURE 42

to Fresnel, in that not more than one-half of the interference pattern may be observed (and that only when the screen abuts on the mirror at M_2), but it has a compensating advantage to which reference will now be made. This advantage arises from an aspect of symmetry which Lloyd's arrangement possesses and which the others do not. It is axiomatic that the experimenter will normally be concerned to obtain the maximum possible intensity in the interference pattern that he is studying. To do this he will use a source slit (Q in figs. 40-42) which is as wide as is consistent with good definition of the fringes. Now we have seen that each element of the source slit must be regarded as an independent centre of disturbance, and the observed interference pattern as exhibiting the sum (by intensities) of the elementary patterns due to these independent disturbances. When the width of the source slit is finite, therefore, in either of Fresnel's arrangements, a little consideration of figs. 40 and 41 will show that the centres of the elementary patterns will be distributed on the screen over a rectangular area of the precise dimensions of the source slit itself. The resultant pattern, therefore, will be 'blurred', overall, in a direction at right angles to the fringes, through a broadening of every feature of the ideal pattern by an amount equal to the width of the slit. Unless the slit is considerably narrower than the separation of successive fringes, the definition of the resultant pattern will thus be greatly reduced. In Lloyd's arrangement no similar overall blurring occurs.

Considering fig. 42 in relation to a source slit of finite width, we see that the geometrical centres of all the elementary patterns lie in the same straight line—the line in which the plane of the reflecting surface M_1M_2 intersects the screen S. At the centre of the pattern, therefore, there is no blurring. In this case, however, the effective separation of the elementary sources (the quantity d of equation (167)) varies, and in consequence the spacing of the fringes varies from one elementary pattern to another. If $d/2$ is the perpendicular distance of the mid-point of the source slit from the plane M_1M_2, and w is the width of the slit, it is easy to show, in terms of equation (167), that blurring to the extent of one fringe width does not occur until the nth fringe from the centre is reached, where $n = d/2w$. A pattern, well-developed in the central region, can thus be obtained with a source slit of width equal to one-tenth of its distance from the plane of the mirror. In either of Fresnel's arrangements, with a source slit of similar width ($w = d/20$) it would be necessary for the screen to be at a distance considerably greater than $d^2/20\lambda$ for fringes of moderate definition to be obtained over any portion of the screen. For light of wavelength 5×10^{-5} cm., for example, and an effective source separation of 2 mm., the distance of the screen for satisfactory observation of the fringes must be considerably in excess of 40 cm. Such a requirement is inimical to the primary necessity, at least in respect of simple demonstrations, to achieve the greatest possible intensity of light in the fringe system to be studied.

There is another aspect of Lloyd's arrangement, also related to its symmetry characteristics, which, though not a matter of practical convenience, leads to an experimental observation which is of considerable importance for theory. In this aspect Lloyd's arrangement is asymmetrical, whereas Fresnel's are symmetrical arrangements. In Fresnel's arrangements the two portions of the incident beam which are brought to interference in each case have had the same history: with the bi-prism each portion has suffered refraction, with the mirror each portion has suffered reflection. In Lloyd's arrangement one portion of the light arrives at the screen directly from the source, only the other portion has been reflected from the upper plane surface of the glass. Lloyd found, in his case, with the screen abutting on the far end of the mirror, that the fringe bordering the surface of the mirror was a dark fringe, whatever light was used. Normally, we expect the central fringe in a two-source interference pattern in the broadside position (see p. 195) to be a bright fringe, for all wavelengths. In order to explain Lloyd's observation it is necessary to assume that there is an abrupt change of phase angle, of magnitude π, when light of any wavelength, is reflected, in air, from a glass plate. We cannot here enter into the considerations which exhibit this result as the natural consequence of basic theoretical assumptions, we merely state that the result is a general one, valid in all circumstances in which light, travelling in a medium in which the phase velocity is v, is reflected at the bounding surface of a second medium in which the phase velocity (for the same frequency) is less than v. The situation is analogous to many others discussed earlier in this book; the simplest analogue is that of the sinusoidal wave reflected at the fixed end of a stretched string (compare p. 30).

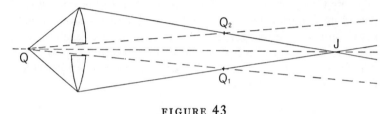

FIGURE 43

Fresnel's bi-prism arrangement suffers from another disadvantage beyond that already mentioned. A prism of small angle does not form a true (virtual) image of a line object, to the extent that a lens does: light from such an object traversing the prism at an angle with the diffracting edge very different from 90° does not appear to diverge from a well-defined image. From the point of view of the interference experiment there is a loss of intensity in the pattern and a background of diffuse illumination on the screen. This particular disadvantage can be largely overcome by using a split lens instead of the bi-prism. The first arrangement of this kind, due to Billet, is illustrated in fig. 43. A double convex lens is cut in two along a plane through the axis, and the two halves are then separated symmetrically by a small distance in a direction at right angles to the plane of section. A pin-hole source Q (or a short line source parallel to the plane of section) is centred on the original axis of the undivided lens. Real images of the source are formed at Q_1Q_2, and the normal broadside-position two-source interference pattern may be observed on a screen placed at right angles to the axis some distance beyond J, the point of intersection of the extreme rays in the plane of the figure.

The second possibility with the split lens is to separate the two halves in a direction parallel to the axis. This arrangement was described by G. Meslin in 1893. We shall discuss it in some detail: it is the arrangement by which the peculiar properties of a spherical wave in the neighbourhood of the origin, to which reference was made at the beginning of this section (p. 210), may be demonstrated most simply. Meslin's split-lens arrangement is illustrated in fig. 44. We use the same notation as previously, and we recognise, first of all, that interference effects are possible only in the relatively restricted region lying between Q_1 and Q_2, the real images of the source, and represented by Q_1Q_2J in the figure. We note that even in this region only one-half of the symmetrical pattern of fringes is to be expected (as in Lloyd's mirror arrangement), and we see that for the first time we have an example of a two-source system effective in the end-on position (see p. 197). The fringes, therefore, are circular (or, to be precise, semicircular) fringes, centred on the axis.

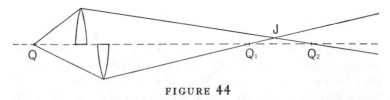

FIGURE 44

In § 8.3 we discussed the ideal case corresponding to this situation with the aid of fig. 38, which we repeat here for sake of convenience. Essentially, fig. 38 shows an enlargement of the region Q_1Q_2J of fig. 44, with a screen P_1P_2 inserted for observation of the fringes. For our previous calculation Q_1 and Q_2 represented separate sources from which interfering beams were incident on P_1P_2 from opposite directions. Consequently the state of interference at P_0, the centre of the pattern, varied with the position of the 'screen'. Now Q_1 represents a real, and Q_2 a virtual, source; light is incident on the screen from the side of Q_1 only, one portion diverging from Q_1 and the other converging towards Q_2. The axial ray is common to the two beams, and the path difference at P_0 is zero for all positions of the screen. If x_n, as before, is the radius of the (now semicircular) fringe for all points on which the equivalent

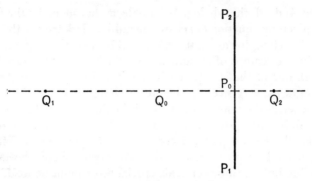

FIGURE 38 (REPEAT)

path difference is $n\lambda$, and if other symbols have their previous meanings, we have, in the new situation,

$$\left\{\left(\frac{d}{2}+l\right)^2+x_n{}^2\right\}^{\frac{1}{2}}-\left(\frac{d}{2}+l\right)+\left\{\left(\frac{d}{2}-l\right)^2+x_n{}^2\right\}^{\frac{1}{2}}-\left(\frac{d}{2}-l\right)=n\lambda.$$

To second-order accuracy, therefore,

$$x_n{}^2\left\{\frac{1}{\frac{d}{2}+l}+\frac{1}{\frac{d}{2}-l}\right\}=2n\lambda,$$

or
$$x_n{}^2=\frac{2n\lambda}{d}\left(\frac{d^2}{4}-l^2\right) \tag{171}$$

According to equation (171), the scale of the fringe system is greatest when the screen is situated midway between Q_1 and Q_2 $(l=0)$, and, when it is in that position, the radius of the first fringe counting from the centre is given by $x_1{}^2=\lambda d/2$. If, for example, Q_1 and Q_2 are separated by 4 cm., with light of wavelength 5×10^{-5} cm., the radius of the first fringe is 0·1 mm. It is obvious that in such a case a low-powered microscope, rather than a viewing screen, is necessary for the observation of the fringes.

When the fringes in Meslin's arrangement are viewed in the manner just described it is found that the central spot is dark. From simple considerations we should expect a bright spot, since, as we have seen, the corresponding geometrical path difference is zero. Indeed, the whole pattern reflects this anomaly: the fringe radii given by equation (171) are the radii of dark fringes throughout. In seeking for an explanation of this anomalous effect, there is only one feature of asymmetry to which it may reasonably be related: one of the interfering beams has already passed through a point of convergence (Q_1) before reaching the plane of observation, whereas the other has not. If this be the essence of the matter, then, if it were possible to examine the fringes in the region beyond the second point of convergence (beyond Q_2 in fig. 44), there should be no anomaly—the centre spot should be bright. With Meslin's arrangement this crucial test cannot be made.

The anomaly of the dark centre, which we have just described as exhibited in Meslin's experiment, had, in fact, first been observed in 1890 by L. G. Gouy. Gouy gave the explanation that we have hinted at, but as he, too, was unable to observe the fringes on both sides of the point of convergence he cannot be said to have clinched the matter experimentally. Gouy employed a white-light source, and a system of two mirrors as illustrated in fig. 45. MN is the common normal, at M, to a plane mirror M_1M and a concave mirror M_2M, which abut over a finite distance including this point. The source is placed at Q, on the axis of the mirror M_2M, farther from the mirror than the centre of curvature. Q_1 is the virtual image of Q formed by M_1M, and Q_2 the real image formed by M_2M. Interference takes place within the region represented by $P_1Q_2P_2$ in the figure, and is best observed in the neighbourhood of Q_2P_1 (on which line the centre of the half-pattern is located) and at a fairly considerable distance from Q_2 (in order that the intensities of interfering beams shall not be too different). In this region Gouy observed, using white light, a system of coloured fringes with a black central spot. Obviously, there was no possibility of his observing fringes in the region of MQ_2. Had he been able to do so, believing the anomaly to depend on an effect taking place about the point of convergence (Q_2, in this case), he would have expected to find the normal pattern with a white centre between that point and the mirror.

Since 1893 many experimenters have examined the problem which Gouy's observations originally posed, and have confirmed his predictions. In the field of optics complete success was first attained using polarised light in an ingenious arrangement which made it possible to obtain two images, such as Q_1 and Q_2 of

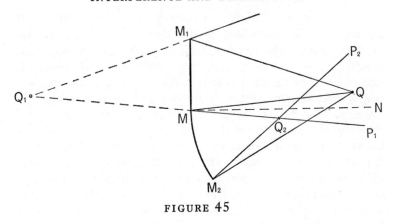

FIGURE 45

fig. 44, using for each the full aperture of a compound lens of doubly-refracting material. The method was employed first of all by Pieter Zeeman (1865-1943). We cannot digress in this place to describe Zeeman's experiment, or later versions of it by which his results were refined and extended; suffice to say, taking fig. 44 again to refer to the new situation, that to the left of Q_1, or to the right of Q_2 in the figure, normal interference patterns with bright centres are in fact observed, whereas between Q_1 and Q_2, as we have already seen, anomalous patterns with dark centres are obtained. We conclude that when a luminous disturbance (and it is indeed true of any wave process) passes through a point of convergence the net result is an 'anomalous' change of phase angle, along any path through the point, of magnitude π.

In evaluating this result, we may compare it, if only for interest —for there is no fundamental similarity in the two effects—with that which we deduced from the half-pattern with a dark centre obtained in Lloyd's mirror arrangement (p. 216). In that case we spoke of 'an abrupt change of phase angle', when light travelling in an optically less dense medium is reflected at the bounding surface of a more-dense medium. We may justify this form of words, practically at least, by pointing out that the wavelength of visible light is roughly a thousand times greater than the thickness of the layer (or the order of an atomic diameter in depth) over which the properties of the media on the two sides of their geometrical surface of separation may be expected to vary. In relation to the phase change through a point of convergence, however, the situation is different. No discontinuity of material is involved, and we are virtually compelled to the view, on perfectly general grounds, that the phase change must be gradual. If we accept this conclusion, we shall find it almost impossible to reject the corollary, that one-half of the total change occurs as the disturbance converges towards the centre, the other half as it subsequently diverges. Our basic assumption is that the effect is a general necessity of geometry, not the result of particular circumstances involving the physical character of the radiation or of the medium.

Exploring the view that we have just expressed, let us consider the ideal case of a spherical wave of unique frequency diverging from a point source—or its converse, that of a similar wave converging to a point 'sink' in an infinite non-absorbing medium. Our first requirement is an expression corresponding to that of equation (114), which we deduced for plane waves under similarly ideal conditions. The full solution for spherical waves of sound was given by Rayleigh in 1878. We may write it, for a diverging wave, without particular reference to any specified type of wave process, as follows:

$$\xi = \frac{A}{r} \left\{ \sin 2\pi \left(\frac{r}{\lambda} - \frac{t}{\tau} \right) + \frac{\lambda}{2\pi r} \cos 2\pi \left(\frac{r}{\lambda} - \frac{t}{\tau} \right) \right\} \qquad (172)$$

Here A is a constant, r is the radial distance from the centre of the wave, ξ is the 'displacement' appropriate to the case in question, and λ and τ have their usual significance. Equation (172) may be written

$$\xi = \frac{A'}{r} \sin \left\{ 2\pi \left(\frac{r}{\lambda} - \frac{t}{\tau} \right) + \delta \right\} \qquad (173)$$

where $$A' = A \left(1 + \frac{\lambda^2}{4\pi^2 r^2} \right)^{\frac{1}{2}}, \quad \tan \delta = \frac{\lambda}{2\pi r}.$$

We see that the angle δ decreases from $\frac{\pi}{2}$ to zero, as r increases, and indeed may be taken as zero when r is greater than a very few wavelengths ($\delta = \frac{\pi}{4}$ when $r = 0.159\lambda$, $\delta = 0.158$ radians when $r = \lambda$). Again $A' > A$ throughout, but only when $r < \lambda$ is the relative difference $(A' - A)/A$ significantly greater than 1 per cent.

(Hereby our previous assumption (p. 190), that the displacement amplitude in a spherical wave varies inversely as the radius, is justified—for we were not then concerned with 'the state of the medium . . . within a radial distance of a few wavelengths' from the source.)

Regarding the variation of δ, with which we are mainly concerned in this discussion, we note first of all that, in the case of a converging wave, equation (173) becomes

$$\xi = \frac{A'}{r} \sin \left\{ 2\pi \left(\frac{r}{\lambda} + \frac{t}{\tau} \right) + \delta \right\} \qquad (174)$$

With this equation, and equation (173), we are able to follow the progress of a spherical wave as it converges to a centre and then diverges again. In the process of convergence, as r decreases, δ increases from 0 to $\frac{\pi}{2}$: it is as if the distance covered had been, judged by the condition in a plane wave of the same type and frequency, less than the actual distance by one-quarter of a wavelength. As the wave diverges again, r increases and δ decreases from $\frac{\pi}{2}$ to 0. Again, in comparison with a plane wave, it is as if the spherical wave had covered a distance less by $\frac{\lambda}{4}$ than the actual distance. To provide another point of view, let us calculate the phase velocity—the value of $\frac{\partial r}{\partial t}$ for which the phase angle remains constant. We find, on the basis either of equation (173) or of equation (174), that the phase velocity at a distance r from the centre is given by

$$v' = v \left(1 + \frac{\lambda^2}{4\pi^2 r^2} \right) \qquad (175)$$

where $v \; (= \lambda/\tau)$ is the phase velocity in a plane wave of the same frequency. Equation (175) shows that the phase velocity increases, in a converging wave, to become instantaneously infinite at the centre; then it decreases again as the wave diverges. Only within a region of about three wavelengths diameter around the centre is v' more than 1 per cent different from v, but, as the wave collapses into and expands out of that region, the acceleration of phase is sufficient for an overall gain of 93 per cent of the full gain of π radians which characterises the complete process of convergence 'from infinity' and divergence 'to infinity' again.

Summarising our discussion of Gouy's experiment and its phenomenological explanation, we may say that appeal to the theory of the ideal case of spherical wave propagation in an infinite medium has provided a formal description which appears to fit the facts in every particular. This is a highly satisfactory result, but we should be careful not to interpret it too literally. We must not forget that neither in Gouy's arrangement, nor in any of the more sophisticated versions which later experimenters have used, is a complete spherical wave employed. In every case the wave front is restricted by apertures, of lenses or mirrors, and a full description of the observations necessarily involves aspects of diffraction which must modify the outcome in detail. Indeed, in recent years, when the availability of microwave sources has made possible the study of the phenomenon on a larger scale, these modifications have been the subject of systematic investigation. For our purposes, however, we may reasonably conclude that the anomaly of the dark centre in Gouy's experiment has finally been resolved. That the effect should occur was implicit in Rayleigh's solution of the equation for spherical waves in 1878, but he did not predict its occurrence, and it was left to Gouy to discover it twelve years later by direct experiment.

8.6. DIFFRACTION

It was Robert Hooke's misfortune to have been anticipated, by a few years, in the discovery of both interference and diffraction effects with visible light—though, almost certainly, he was an independent discoverer in each case. We have referred (p. 211) to his anticipation by Boyle in respect of the colours of thin plates (interference). In respect of diffraction, Francesco Maria Grimaldi (1618-1663) must be accorded priority. In a work entitled (in short) *Physico-Mathesis de Lumine* and published two years after his death, an account is given of observations which Grimaldi made on the shadows cast by objects, of various shapes, which he placed in the narrow beam of sunlight admitted through a small aperture into a darkened room. Hooke made many similar observations in 1672, but they, too, remained unpublished throughout the lifetime of their author: an account of them appeared in 1705, two years after Hooke's death, in his *Posthumous Works*. Newton's *Opticks* had been published in the previous year: there systematic observations on the shadows cast in monochromatic light were described carefully for the first time. Qualitatively, the combined results of these three observers—Grimaldi, Hooke and Newton—may be summarised in the statement that, when the source of light is of very small dimensions, the edges of shadows of opaque objects are not sharp, but are bordered, inside and outside the geometrical shadow-edge, by dark and bright fringes. The linear scale of these effects, other factors being the same, is smaller for blue light than for red. Newton gave the name 'inflexion' to this phenomenon, which he attempted—not very convincingly—to account for on the corpuscular hypothesis. The term 'diffraction', now in universal use, is Grimaldi's.

In an earlier section we defined diffraction in the positive assertion (p. 200), 'Whenever a wave front is restricted by apertures, or lenses, or other devices, diffraction occurs.' This is essentially Fresnel's dictum, first clearly formulated in 1818. We shall discuss his elaboration of it presently: meanwhile it is appropriate to review very briefly the period of a little more than a century which passed between the publication of the *Opticks* and the submission of Fresnel's memoir on 'Diffraction' to the Académie des Sciences on 29 July 1818. During this period, very roughly the eighteenth century of the present era, no one (before Young) effectively disputed Newton's view that light is essentially corpuscular in nature—nor did anyone advance this view, by predicting, on the basis of it, any effect which was later confirmed by experiment. In a period when there is no unifying theory challenging the experimenter, diverse observations are apt to have little impact on men of science. This was certainly the case in optics in the century which we are now considering. There were new observations in plenty, many of them made by professional astronomers, but they were not incorporated into a general body of theoretical knowledge, and the descriptions of them in the literature were soon forgotten. Thus, in 1723, Maraldi published in Paris an account of observations of the shadows cast by small spheres of different sizes. He reported having observed a central bright spot at whatever axial distance within the conical shadow he placed his screen. David Rittenhouse (1732-1796), while treasurer of Pennsylvania, made a diffraction grating and de-

P

scribed its properties in 1786. Each of these publications was potentially of great significance, but by the turn of the century both were forgotten. Young, reviewing the history of the subject in 1807, made no mention of either of them. In 1787, at Padua, Comparetti described many new observations of his own, in a book, *De Luce Inflexa et Coloribus*. Young wrote: 'Comparetti's experiments on inflexion have every appearance of accuracy, but they are much too intricate to be compared with each other, or with those of former observers.' Some ten years after these words were written, the whole subject had been revolutionised by the work of Fresnel.

We have referred to Fresnel many times already, and first (p. 144) for his collaboration with Arago, and through Arago with Young, in relation to the phenomena of polarised light. That was only one of Fresnel's several contributions to optics made within a period of twelve years, for that was the full span of his life as a scientist. All these contributions were made outside his normal professional activities, for he was a civil engineer by training, employed by the French government, and they were made in spite of poor health. Indeed, they were all but abandoned, two years before his death, as his strength failed him. As Malus had done, and, at thirty-nine, only two years older than he had been, Fresnel died from tuberculosis on 14 July 1827.

From the experimental side, Fresnel's contribution to the study of diffraction is important chiefly for his disproof of the then currently held view that reflection of light at the edges of an obstacle plays an essential part in the formation of the fringes which are observed outside the limits of the geometrical shadow. He not only established by accurate measurement that the positions of the fringes are not such as to admit of this explanation, but he carried out a series of careful experiments which showed that any influence of the material of the obstacle, or of the nature of the edges by which the beam is limited, is, at most, very small indeed. The conclusion appeared to him to be inescapable: the entire phenomenon must be explicable in terms of the restriction of the wave front, simply, the physical means by which that restriction is brought about being of no consequence.

Having thus seized on the essence of the matter, in its phenomenological aspect, Fresnel proceeded to develop a quantitative theory. For the first time Huygens's construction became more than an exercise in three-dimensional geometry (see p. 189)—for it was on the basis of that construction, and Young's principle of superposition, that Fresnel developed his theory. In his prize memoir, Fresnel treated three cases in detail: the case of the opaque screen bounded by a straight edge, the case of the parallel-sided slit, and that of the parallel-sided opaque strip (the exact complement of the slit). The basic problem was to determine, for each point in the plane of observation, the effect arising from the secondary sources in that portion of the complete wave front which, in relation to the point in question, was not obscured by the obstacle. For this purpose Fresnel devised a method of dividing the wave front into elementary zones, the effects of which could be summed without much difficulty—and because the examples which he treated originally were all such that the effective boundaries were rectilinear, so the elementary zones were, in these applications, elongated. Fresnel called these zones 'spindles': in current terminology they are sometimes referred to as 'lunes'. Another, and for certain purposes a simpler, method is to divide the wave front into annular zones. We shall discuss the problem of the circular obstacle on the basis of that method—and we shall not, in fact, discuss any other specific problem in detail. Our purposes, in this section, are strictly limited, and the case of the circular obstacle will serve as well as any towards their realisation.

In point of history, the question of diffraction by a circular obstacle provided the test case for Fresnel's theory. As we have stated, it was not treated in the memoir which was submitted to the Académie des Sciences in July 1818. But Poisson, one of the committee of award, as a check on the argument which Fresnel had applied to the parallel-sided strip, applied the same argument to the opaque circle (or sphere). He was led to the wholly unexpected conclusion that, with a point source on the axis, the intensity on the axis, and within the shadow, should, at least at large distances, everywhere be the same as if the obstacle were not there. He was so convinced, so it is said, that this conclusion must be contrary to experience, that he requested Arago, who was also a member of the committee, to test the matter by experiment. Arago (repeating, in effect, the long-forgotten experiment of Maraldi, see p. 225) found in favour of Fresnel. Thereafter, Poisson—and his brother doubters, Laplace and Biot—capitulated, and the announcement of the award of the prize to Fresnel was made in March 1819. Seven years later the prize-winning memoir was published in full: by that time the triumph of the wave theory of light was well-nigh complete.

Before we introduce the circular obstacle into our discussion directly, let us consider certain aspects of the geometry of an uninterrupted wave front diverging from a point source, of well-defined frequency and constant strength, situated in an infinite and uniform medium. Let Q (fig. 46) represent the source, and S a portion of the spherical wave front under consideration, at time t. Let P be the point of observation, for the purposes of our discussion. The plane of the diagram is any plane containing Q and P. At the instant in question let ρ be the radius of the wave front, and let QP intersect the wave front in O. We may refer to O as the pole of S in respect of P. Let $OP = \sigma$. Let M be an arbitrary point on the wave front, and let $MP = r$, $\angle PQM = \theta$. Then, if the figure be rotated about QP, the locus of M is a small circle on the sphere of the wave front, and the radius of this small circle is $\rho \sin \theta$. Consider now the annular zone lying between this small circle and the corresponding small circle through M′, a point very close to M. If $\angle MQM' = \varDelta\theta$, the area of the zone is given, to the first order in $\varDelta\theta$, by

$$\varDelta S = 2\pi\rho \sin \theta \,.\, \rho\varDelta\theta.$$

But, in respect of $\triangle$ PQM,

$$r^2 = \rho^2 + (\rho + \sigma)^2 - 2\rho(\rho + \sigma) \cos \theta.$$

Thus, if M′P $= r + \varDelta r$, to the same approximation as before,

$$r\varDelta r = \rho(\rho + \sigma) \sin \theta\varDelta\theta,$$

and we obtain, by substitution,

$$\varDelta S = \frac{2\pi\rho r}{\rho + \sigma} \varDelta r \qquad (176)$$

In the limit, equation (176) implies an interesting result which we shall now derive. If MM′ is a sufficiently small distance— small, say, with respect to λ, the wavelength of the radiation— then each point in the elementary annular zone bears the same relation to P: regarded as a secondary source, in relation to P, any small element of this zone may therefore be considered as exactly equivalent to any other small element of the same area. This being

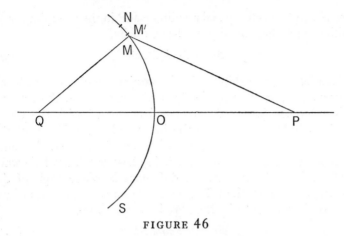

FIGURE 46

the case, if the elementary zone were effective in isolation, the disturbance at P would have amplitude directly proportional to the area of the zone, and inversely proportional to r, the distance of P from each point in the zone (p. 190). The only other variable factor which might intervene (we are leaving out of account any possible complication arising from polarisation effects) is an 'obliquity factor' depending upon the angle between QM, the direction of the actual flow of energy from the source, and MP, the direction of hypothetical flow from the fictitious secondary source at M. Let us denote the angle between these two directions by ϕ; then we may write, for the amplitude of the disturbance at P if the elementary zone were effective alone,

$$\Delta a = \frac{cAk(\phi)}{r}\Delta S \qquad (177)$$

Here A is the actual displacement amplitude over the wave front S, $k(\phi)$ is the obliquity factor that we have introduced (we naturally take $k(0)=1$), and c is a constant so far as our particular problem is involved. We note, in passing, that Δa and A being of the same dimensions, the factor k being non-dimensional, and ΔS representing an area, c must be of the dimension L^{-1}. We shall return to this point later (see p. 235). Meanwhile, we substitute from equation (176) for $\Delta S/r$ and obtain

$$\Delta a = 2\pi cAk(\phi)\frac{\rho}{\rho+\sigma}\Delta r.$$

Now $A\rho/(\rho+\sigma)$ is the actual amplitude at P in the diverging wave. Writing a for this quantity, we have, finally,

$$\Delta a = 2\pi c k(\phi) a \Delta r \qquad (178)$$

Equation (178) exhibits the interesting result to which we referred. It appears most clearly if we translate Δr, the extreme path difference (assumed very small compared with the wavelength λ) between points on the inner and outer fringes of the elementary zone and P, the point of observation, into a difference in phase. The actual disturbance is in phase over the whole wave front S, thus $\Delta\delta$, the extreme difference in phase angle of the secondary waves reaching P from points on the two edges of the zone, is given by $\Delta\delta = 2\pi\Delta r/\lambda$. We have, therefore,

$$\Delta a = c k(\phi) \lambda a \Delta \delta \qquad (179)$$

Equation (179) shows that if, beyond the small circle through an arbitrary point M on the wave front S, we construct a series of contiguous elementary annular zones of such radii that the amplitudes of their effects at P are the same for all, then, provided that only a small range of ϕ is involved (so that $k(\phi)$ may be taken as constant throughout), the range of phase angle at P corresponding to each such zone is also the same. Indeed, for elementary zones so constructed, we may say that their individual effects at P are equal in amplitude and uniformly spaced in phase.

Let us now construct, with the small circle through M as its inner boundary, a 'half-period' zone of which the outer boundary is the small circle through N (fig. 46). A half-period zone, commonly referred to as a Fresnel zone, is defined as one for which the extreme path difference to the point of observation is one-half wavelength; in the present case we have, therefore, $NP - MP = \lambda/2$. The range of ϕ over this half-period zone will be small if QP is very large compared with λ, and if the wave front at the instant in question is neither very close to Q, nor very close to P. We shall assume that these conditions are in fact fulfilled, and we shall proceed to apply the result embodied in equation (179) to deduce the effect at P of the half-period zone, considered in isolation from the rest of the wave front. The range of phase angle, at P, of the secondary disturbances arising in the various elements of the half-period zone is, by definition, π. According to equation (179), therefore, if we choose these elements suitably, we obtain,

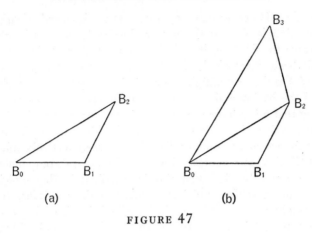

B_3

B_2

B_2

B_0 B_1

B_0 B_1

(a)   (b)

FIGURE 47

at P, n (a large number) of simple harmonic displacement components, each of amplitude $ck(\phi)\lambda a\pi/n$, and each different in phase from the next by π/n radians. In this approximation to the actual situation, the number n can be as large as we choose—and, the larger n is, the more exact is the approximation.

We have already, in this chapter (p. 193), used the parallelogram law in order to obtain the resultant of two simple harmonic displacement components which are collinear. The extension of this vectorial method of calculation to deal with a large number of such components is perfectly straightforward. Fig. 47 (a), for example, is the vector diagram exhibiting the parallelogram law in relation to the composition of two collinear simple harmonic motions of which the amplitudes and relative phases are represented by the vectors B_0B_1, B_1B_2 respectively. We have accepted the conclusion (see $M\,L\,\&\,T$, p. 90 for proof) that the vector B_0B_2 represents the resultant simple harmonic motion in both amplitude and phase. Suppose that a third component simple harmonic motion is involved, and let its amplitude and relative phase be represented by B_2B_3 (fig. 47 (b)). Then the resultant of all three simple harmonic motions may obviously be obtained by combining this component with the resultant of the first two— and $\triangle B_0B_2B_3$ exhibits this composition, by the parallelogram law, precisely as $\triangle B_0B_1B_2$ exhibits the previous composition of the other components. The vector B_0B_3 therefore represents in full the resultant of the three component simple harmonic motions in question. However many components are involved, clearly the construction is similar: the vector closing the vectorial polygon represents the final resultant in both amplitude and phase.

This basic principle having been established, we may accept fig. 48 (a) as the vectorial diagram relative to our present problem, that of the half-period zone, drawn with $n = 6$. (We are not pretending that 6 is a large number—only the diagram is simpler for a smaller value of n—but we are assuming that the displacements due to the various secondary disturbances are effectively collinear at P.) The vectors representing the elementary components in the figure are the six equal chords inscribed in the semicircle. The diameter of the semicircle represents the resultant. In the limit, as n becomes very large, the inscribed chords of the vectorial diagram merge into the arc of the semicircle, and ultimately fig. 48 (b) provides the relevant representation. In this diagram the length of the semicircular arc represents the amplitude which would have resulted at P if the secondary disturbances from the elements of the half-period zone had all been in phase there; the length of the diameter represents the resultant amplitude at P actually determined by the differences of phase. On the basis of the result previously obtained (p. 230), then, the length of the semicircular arc in the diagram is a measure of the quantity $ck(\phi)\lambda a\pi$, and we conclude that m, the amplitude at P due to the half-period zone MN considered in isolation, is given by

$$m = 2ck(\phi)\lambda a \qquad (180)$$

—for the ratio of the lengths of diameter and arc is $2/\pi$. Furthermore, we conclude that the phase of this resultant disturbance is midway between the extreme phases of the elementary secondary disturbances originating in the half-period zone, for the diameter of the semicircle of fig. 48 (b) is parallel to the tangent at its mid-point.

Hitherto we have considered only a single Fresnel zone, having its inner boundary determined by the point of observation and by an arbitrarily chosen point on the wave front. Let us now divide the whole wave front into Fresnel zones centred on the pole O (fig. 46), and let m_1, m_2, ... be the amplitudes, at P, of the secondary disturbances due to these zones taken individually. We number the zones outwards from the pole. Now it is the essence of Fresnel's theory, that the effect at P, when the wave front has

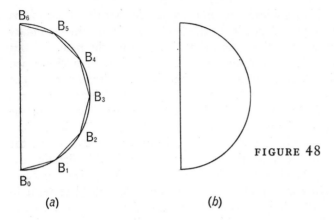

FIGURE 48

(a)   (b)

expanded to include that point, is given by combining these secondary disturbances with due regard to phase. But the phase of each secondary disturbance, as we have just seen, is characteristic of the elementary disturbance arising from the mid-element of the Fresnel zone to which it is ascribed. Moreover, the zones being half-period zones, these mid-elements are successively more and more distant from P by a constant interval of $\lambda/2$. The phases of the secondary disturbances from succeeding zones, therefore, form a regular series, with constant angular difference π: in relation to the secondary disturbance from the central zone, the others lag in phase by π, 2π, . . . radians, respectively. With this result established, the composition of the secondary disturbances is a simple matter. We are, in fact, able to write

$$a = m_1 - m_2 + m_3 - \ldots - (-1)^t m_t \qquad (181)$$

(it will be recalled that we have already (p. 230) identified a as 'the actual amplitude at P in the diverging wave').

In equation (181), m_t is obviously intended to represent the amplitude of the secondary disturbance due to the 'last' Fresnel zone on the wave front, in relation to P. Something must be said in this connection, for there is an element of indefiniteness in it. Clearly, the last zone will not in general be a full half-period zone, nor will the effective phase lag of the secondary disturbance due to it be an integral multiple of π. Strictly, therefore, the last term in equation (181), as it stands, is incorrectly formulated: this is a conclusion which we cannot logically refute. Supposing that the term itself is significant, we must conclude that the phase of the disturbance at P depends, in the final analysis, on the secondary disturbance from the zone most distant from the pole. All our intuitive notions tell against such a conclusion. Fresnel escaped from this dilemma by assuming that the obliquity factor, $k(\phi)$ of equations (177) to (180), decreases to zero as ϕ increases to $\pi/2$ (and remains zero for $\pi/2 < \phi < \pi$). Hence our notation m_l: the 'last' zone on the wave front, according to Fresnel's assumption, is that from which the secondary disturbance travelling in the direction of P is tangential to the wave front. In this direction the intensity of the disturbance is effectively zero. There is no problem involved in the failure correctly to formulate the last term in equation (181) if its magnitude is altogether negligible. In any case, we have not to consider secondary disturbances reaching P from the 'inside' of the expanding wave front S, only those originating over that portion of the wave front 'visible' from P at the instant in question. We shall accept Fresnel's 'solution' here, merely remarking that as a self-justified treatment of the problem it did not escape criticism from later theorists. It must indeed be regarded as having been superseded—though not seriously discredited—in the work of Helmholtz and Kirchhoff (see p. 188)— and in more recent work.

We note, then, that the terms in equation (181) are finite in number, and we accept Fresnel's (admittedly too bold) assumption that the last terms become vanishingly small. On this basis we may re-write the equation in either of the two forms

$$a = \frac{m_1}{2} + \left(\frac{m_1 + m_3}{2} - m_2\right) + \left(\frac{m_3 + m_5}{2} - m_4\right) + \dots \quad (182)$$

and

$$a = \left(m_1 - \frac{m_2}{2}\right) - \left(\frac{m_2 + m_4}{2} - m_3\right) - \left(\frac{m_4 + m_6}{2} - m_5\right) - \dots \quad (183)$$

without paying particular attention to the end term of the series in either case. Recognising that the only variable factor in the amplitudes m_1, m_2, ... is the obliquity factor $k(\phi)$ (see equation (180)), and that this factor varies very slowly from one zone to the next, we conclude that all quantities of the form $\left(\frac{m_l + m_{l+2}}{2} - m_{l+1}\right)$ in equations (182) and (183) are very small indeed. Moreover, these quantities must in general be smaller the greater is l. If these small quantities are all of the same sign, then the conclusion from the two equations is simple: the magnitude of a must be intermediate between $m_1/2$ and $m_1 - m_2/2$. This conclusion is not essentially modified if the sign of the small quantities changes once or twice in the series (it would be difficult to justify many alternations in sign on physical grounds, in any actual case). We write therefore

$$\frac{m_1}{2} < a < m_1 - \frac{m_2}{2} \quad \text{or} \quad \frac{m_1}{2} > a > m_1 - \frac{m_2}{2},$$

depending upon whether $m_1 > m_2$ or $m_1 < m_2$. In either event, since m_1 and m_2 can differ only in the second order, we may write, at least to first-order accuracy,

$$a = \frac{m_1}{2} \tag{184}$$

We conclude, in words, that the amplitude, at any point of observation in the field of a point source, in the absence of any restriction on the expanding waves, is one-half of that which would result if, between the source and the point of observation, and perpendicular to the line joining them, an 'infinite' screen were interposed pierced only by a circular aperture, centred about the pole of the wave front at the screen, and of diameter equal to that of the first Fresnel zone. The treatment that we have given, leading through equations (182) and (183) to this result, was given first by Arthur Schuster (1851-1934), professor of physics at Manchester, in 1891.

Let us digress, at this point, and combine equations (180) and (184). Using an obvious notation, we have

$$m_1 = 2a = 2ck(\phi_1)\lambda a.$$

Now ϕ_1 differs insignificantly from zero, and, by definition (p. 229), $k(0) = 1$. Thus

$$c\lambda = 1 \tag{185}$$

We have already concluded that the dimensions of the constant c of equation (177) are L^{-1} (p. 229); equation (185) shows that c is precisely the wave number of the homogeneous radiation with which we are concerned. It would, indeed, have been difficult to have suggested any other quantity of dimensions L^{-1} which could possibly have been involved in the physical problem to which equation (177) refers, but why the wave number should be involved at all is not necessarily obvious when the matter is first considered. In any case, our detailed analysis has now shown that it is the wave number, simply, and not some multiple of it, which enters into the expression (as we have formulated it) for the amplitude, at some distant point, of the secondary disturbance arising in an elementary area of primary wave front as in Fresnel's theory.

We have now considered the question of the amplitude at an arbitrary point of observation in the unrestricted field of a point source, and in this connection have obtained a consistent description of the expanding wave in terms of Fresnel's theory. But our description is not complete until the question of phase is satisfactorily disposed of also. We therefore revert to this matter here. We note, first of all, that it is implicit in the form of equation (181) that the resultant disturbance at the point of observation has the same phase as the secondary disturbance due to the central half-period zone. But the latter, as we have shown, is the phase 'characteristic of the elementary disturbance arising from the mid-element of the zone' (p. 233). Thus, the phase of the resultant disturbance at P (the point of observation) is that of an elementary secondary disturbance diverging from a point on the wave front distant $OP + \dfrac{\lambda}{4}$ from P, where O is the pole of the wave front in respect of P, as in our previous discussion (see fig. 46). The question at issue is whether there is any contradiction between this statement, which derives directly from Fresnel's theory, and the statement to which there can certainly be no exception, for it poses the problem which Fresnel's theory is designed to treat, that the phase of the resultant disturbance at P is that of the primary wave which diverged from Q and passed through O at the instant at which the elementary secondary disturbance of the previous statement is supposed to have originated. For some seventy years it was suspected that there was, in fact, a contradiction between these two statements, since the distance which the primary wave has to traverse from O to P is less by $\dfrac{\lambda}{4}$

than the distance which the elementary secondary wave originating in the mid-element of the first Fresnel zone has to traverse in the same time, if the two statements are to be concordant. But the theoretical investigations of Rayleigh, and the experiments of Gouy and others, which we described in the last section (pp. 220-224) eventually dispelled this suspicion: we now realise that the phase velocity of a diverging wave is 'abnormally' great near the origin, and that we should be inconsistent in our application of Fresnel's ideas if we did not take this fact into account in relation to the secondary disturbances which, following Huygens, he assumed to diverge from points on the primary wave front. From O to P (fig. 46) the phase velocity of the primary disturbance is essentially that of an ideal plane wave; the elementary secondary disturbance, with which the primary wave is being compared, gains in phase as it diverges, so that within a few wavelengths the additional geometrical path length of $\dfrac{\lambda}{4}$ is exactly compensated.

There is thus no contradiction between the two statements that we formulated, and we may regard the question of phase in Fresnel's theory as satisfactorily disposed of.

We are at last in a position to return to the case of the circular obstacle, to which we addressed ourselves at the outset (p. 227). Let the small circle through the arbitrary point M on the wave front S (fig. 46) be the boundary of such an obstacle. By confining attention to the effect at P, we are considering only the situation on the axis, and within the geometrical shadow. This is Poisson's problem of 1818. We have, in fact, already carried through all the analysis necessary for its solution. In outline, the procedure is as follows. Starting from the boundary of the obstacle, we divide the wave front S into Fresnel zones. We apply Schuster's method of summation. Just as before, we conclude that the amplitude of the resultant disturbance at P is one-half of the amplitude which would result if the first zone effective (the zone MN of fig. 46) were effective alone. Using an obvious notation, combining equations (180), (184) and (185), we may write

$$a_{\mathrm{P}} = k(\phi_\sigma)a \qquad (186)$$

σ being the distance of P from the obstacle (or the pole O), as before. This is the result which Arago verified by experiment. Apart from the slow variation due to the obliquity factor $k(\phi_\sigma)$, the amplitude of the disturbance on the axis is independent of the size of the obstacle—and exactly the same as it would be if the obstacle were removed.

We have been dealing hitherto with diffraction phenomena in the field of a point source—with effects modifying the precisely sharp boundaries which would characterise the shadows of 'obstacles' placed in such a field, if radiation from the source were indeed propagated 'in straight lines' in all circumstances. In optics, shadow patterns are generally of much less concern to the experimenter than are focused images—and in a great proportion of optical instruments restriction of wave fronts occurs under approximately plane-wave conditions. It needs no principle which we have not already formulated to treat the problems arising in this connection—Fresnel's basic theoretical ideas are as relevant here as they were in relation to 'shadow' diffraction—but the convention has grown up, and taken root, to distinguish the one type of situation from the other. We speak of diffraction effects in shadows as Fresnel diffraction phenomena, and of similar effects in the focal plane of an optical instrument as Fraunhofer diffraction phenomena. In the former case the diffracting obstacles and apertures are generally situated in a region where the wave fronts have significant curvature; in the latter generally where the wave fronts are effectively plane. The distinction, let it be repeated, is a matter of practice, of the application of theory, not of the theory itself. If it is a question of the formal development of the theory to suit the individual problem, it is usually the case that the mathematics is simpler for phenomena of the Fraunhofer class than for those of the other. From the restricted, but technically very cogent, point of view of the designer of optical instruments, it is natural to conclude, with Rayleigh, that Fraunhofer diffraction phenomena are the 'more important': that is not our conclusion, for the purposes of this book. The basic theoretical ideas arise most generally in a discussion of phenomena of the Fresnel class: that is how we have introduced them here.

Joseph von Fraunhofer (1787-1826) was an almost exact contemporary of Fresnel. Born a year earlier than the Frenchman, like him, Fraunhofer contracted tuberculosis and died at the same early age. He was the eleventh child of a Bavarian glazier, left an orphan at the age of eleven. Apprenticed to a master glass-cutter in Munich after the death of his parents, he survived the collapse of the house in which he lived with his employer, and the lean years which followed, to attract the interest of a partner in a newly established firm of mechanical and optical instrument makers. He accepted employment as optician in his patron's firm in 1806, was made a partner in 1814 and became sole manager in 1818. Fraunhofer's experimental work on diffraction was carried out mainly between 1817 and 1823: it was directed almost entirely towards increasing his understanding of the optical properties of the instruments which he was called upon to design. During this period, almost by accident, he re-discovered (see p. 225) the dispersive action of the optical (diffraction) grating—and he followed up his discovery with great experimental skill and physical insight. Earlier (1814-1817) his main contributions had been in the field of spectroscopy (as this field would now be named). Wollaston (see p. 142) had observed and recorded the presence of seven dark lines in the spectrum of sunlight in 1802; Fraunhofer re-discovered the lines and extended and systematised knowledge of them, and of similar features in the spectra of moonlight and of the light of the brighter stars, with rare success. His determinations of wavelength were not bettered in accuracy for fifty years.

The optical instrument industry of S.E. Germany, in the nineteenth century, threw up two men who contributed greatly to the fundamentals of their subject—and thereby to the pre-eminence, in succession, of the firms by which they were employed, and which they eventually managed. Joseph von Fraunhofer was the first of these: the second was Ernst Abbe (1840-1905), the son of a poor labourer. It would be difficult to judge one of them greater than the other in native genius. In this chapter, however, we shall not be concerned with Abbe's contributions; though some of them increased our understanding of the importance of diffraction effects, they are more appropriately discussed in a textbook on optics than here.

8.7. BABINET'S PRINCIPLE

In the last section (p. 226) we accepted Fresnel's experimental result 'that any influence of the material of the obstacle, or of the nature of the edges by which the beam is limited, is, at most very small indeed'. This result related specifically to diffraction effects observed with visible light, but, by implication we accepted it as basis for the treatment of diffraction effects generally, assuming 'that the entire phenomenon must be explicable in terms of the restriction of the wave front, simply, the physical means by which that restriction is brought about being of no consequence'.

If we take this assumption at its face value, and examine it critically, we shall see that it implies a state of affairs that we cannot altogether believe in. In most cases, and evidently so in the situations in optics which Fresnel investigated, it must represent a very close approximation to the truth, but it cannot be a rigorously valid assumption in any case. For consider a point source in an infinite medium. Our assumption commits us to the view that if an ideally thin disk-shaped obstacle were so placed in the medium that the source lay on the axis of the disk, then the vibratory condition of the medium over the whole of the un-obscured portion of the sphere, containing the circumference of the disk in its surface and having the source as its centre, would be precisely the same as if the disk were not there. We are committed to the view that, whether the surface of the obstacle facing the source reflects or absorbs the radiation which reaches it, the same statement is admissible: right up to the edge of the obstacle, the amplitude of the disturbance in the medium (over the sphere in question) is the same as it would be if no obstacle were there. The more sophisticated theories of optical diffraction of the later nineteenth century (see pp. 188, 234) were in some measure directed towards removing this formal blemish in the theory of Fresnel: in great measure they were successful in that respect— and in justifying the simpler theory pragmatically, so that it can now be used with some confidence, as we have indeed used it, as a basis of calculation in regard to actual phenomena. Here we carry its application one stage farther, deriving a result which is a generalisation of a principle first enunciated by Jacques Babinet (1794-1872) in 1837.

Babinet's principle has to do, strictly, with diffraction effects of the Fraunhofer type. It is concerned with effects observed in the focal plane of an optical instrument when obstacles are placed within the aperture which admits light to the instrument. In respect of this aperture it defines 'complementary screens' as two 'screens' covering the aperture in such a way that the clear portions of the one screen correspond exactly with the opaque portions of the other screen, and *vice versa*. Thus, for example, a screen pierced by a single hole, and an obstacle of precisely the same dimensions as the hole in the screen and similarly placed in the aperture admitting light to the instrument, are 'complementary screens' in Babinet's sense. The principle in question states that, for any point in the focal plane where the illumination is zero when light enters the instrument through the unrestricted aperture, the intensities of illumination are the same when first one and then the other of a pair of complementary screens is used to restrict the aperture. This result follows directly from the basic assumptions of Fresnel which we have just been discussing. For the effect, at any point in the focal plane, due to light entering through the unrestricted aperture, can obviously be resolved into the component effects due to those portions of the incident light which traverse two portions of the aperture which are complementary in the sense that the two portions together make up the whole aperture. Now, if Fresnel's assumptions are valid, these component effects are the same as would be observed with complementary screens limiting the aperture in the appropriate manner. If, with the unrestricted aperture, the resultant effect is zero at the point in question, clearly the amplitudes of the component vibrations must be equal and their phases opposite. Intensities being determined by the squares of the amplitudes (without reference to phase), the intensities observed in the corresponding experiment with the two complementary screens must evidently be the same.

In the above, we have deduced Babinet's principle from Fresnel's assumption; now we proceed to its generalisation as originally intended. In this process we take account of phase specifically; thereby the principle becomes enlarged in scope. So enlarged, it applies equally to cases of Fresnel diffraction and Fraunhofer diffraction—always granted the effective validity of Fresnel's basic assumption which provides its ultimate justification. In the process of generalisation the definition of complementary screens is not changed in essence; we merely note that in the wider context the definition is not dependent on the notion of the aperture of an optical instrument which has a well-defined 'entrance-pupil' for incident light. When it is not so dependent, pairs of screens which by definition are complementary will generally appear as 'infinite' screens.

In the wider context, then, we first state the truism that, if the effect, at any time, at any point in the field of radiation of a point

Q

source situated in an otherwise empty and infinite medium, may be deduced (as we have indicated on pp. 182-189) from a knowledge of the state of the medium at some previous time over a suitably chosen wave front, then that effect may be regarded as the resultant of the effects contributed by any two portions of the wave front which together make up the whole. We next take in the Fresnel assumption, then the truism takes the form of a general statement that at any point in such a field of radiation, when two complementary screens are employed in succession, the actual vibrations are such that if they were to be compounded (with due regard to relative phase) the resultant would be precisely the vibration which would be effective, at the point in question, if neither screen were interposed. This general statement is an expression of Babinet's principle in its extended form.

As an example of a situation to which the generalised principle applies, let us take as our pair of complementary 'screens' a circular obstacle and a 'real' screen with a circular hole in it. The radius of the hole is the same as that of the obstacle, and we confine attention to the 'illumination' along the axis of the system when the point source is also on the axis (on the other side of the 'screen', in each arrangement, and at a specified distance from it). We have already in effect considered the distribution of amplitude and intensity along the axis of a circular obstacle under these conditions (p. 237), and our earlier discussion (pp. 228-237) enables us to evaluate the corresponding distribution for the circular hole by a simple extension of the argument. The only change of emphasis that is necessary is that whereas previously we were discussing the effect at a single (arbitrary) axial point, assuming the size of the obstacle to vary, now we are thinking in terms of a given obstacle (or the complementary hole) and an axial point the position of which is itself subject to variation.

Previously, we decided that, apart from the effect of the obliquity factor, the amplitude of the disturbance at an arbitrary point on the axis of a circular obstacle is 'precisely the same as it would be if the obstacle were removed'. In the case of the circular hole, on the other hand (if the hole is not too large—see below), if we imagine the axial point brought up from infinity, then at a distance σ_1, say, the wave front as limited by the hole will constitute just a single Fresnel zone in respect of the point. At a closer distance σ_2, the 'visible' wave front will constitute just two Fresnel zones, and so on. On this basis we conclude (compare equations (181)-(184)), that at the points distant σ_2, σ_4, . . . the amplitude of the axial disturbance is very small indeed, whereas at the points distant σ_1, σ_3, σ_5, . . . it is very closely twice that which would be effective if the screen were removed. At these axial points, when the wave front is limited by a circular hole in a screen, the intensity of the axial disturbance is very closely four times as great as it would be if there were no screen interposed. To summarise, then, for the two complementary screens in this arrangement: along the axis of one (the obstacle) the intensity decreases monotonically with increasing distance from the screen, being everywhere, except at small distances, indistinguishable from the intensity in the absence of the screen; along the axis of the other (the hole) the intensity, whilst following a similar general trend, oscillates regularly between a value which is effectively zero (at certain distances) and a value (at intermediate distances) which is closely four times the normal intensity in the absence of the screen. This summarising statement, however, is incomplete, because it deals only with intensities; since it says nothing about phase, the generalised Babinet principle is not immediately relevant to it. Obviously, we must continue the matter farther in order to elicit that relevance. We do this by use of the vectorial diagram.

In fig. 48 (*b*) we gave the vectorial diagram for a single Fresnel zone, neglecting the variation of the obliquity factor over the width of the zone. Thereafter, we calculated the effect of an unrestricted wave front at an external point by summing algebraically the individual contributions of the very many Fresnel zones of which (with respect to that point) it was regarded as constituted. To provide the more detailed treatment which we now require, we construct the vectorial diagram for the whole wave front. Fig. 49 exhibits this diagram—admittedly severely distorted in that the total number of zones indicated in the figure is considerably smaller than the number that we have tacitly assumed in the algebraic treatment to which we have referred. But the essential features of the diagram are not lost in this distortion. Again, the diagram has obviously been drawn, for simplicity, on the assumption that the obliquity factor, $k(\phi)$ of the algebraic treatment, decreases monotonically as the obliquity, ϕ, increases. This is not a serious distortion, either.

It does not require any long explanation of fig. 49 to establish

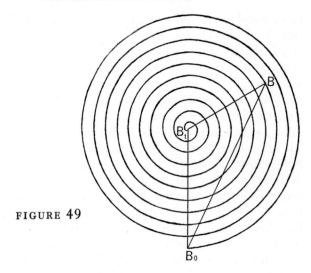

FIGURE 49

the fact that B_0B_t is the vector representing in amplitude and phase the disturbance, at the point of observation when the whole wave front is unrestricted. The length of this vector is $m_1/2$, in terms of equation (184). Similarly BB_t is the vector representing, at the point in question, the disturbance when a circular obstacle obscures a central portion of the wave front (some $4\frac{2}{3}$ Fresnel zones, as the figure has been drawn). Finally, B_0B is the vector representing the disturbance at the point when the central region previously obscured is alone effective. The vectorial triangle B_0BB_t then exemplifies the generalised Babinet principle for the case we are considering.

Obviously, fig. 49 (correctly drawn) refers specifically to a single axial point of observation—and a single value of the axial distance from source to screen. If the latter distance is kept constant, and the distance of the point of observation is gradually reduced from infinity, the figure changes progressively—without, of course, changing its essential character. In the first place, the whole scale of the figure expands, for the amplitude, in the absence of any screen, is inversely proportional to the distance from the point of observation to the source—the distance $(\rho + \sigma)$ of our previous notation (see p. 228). In the second place, the number of complete coils in the spiral of the figure decreases. This is a trivial effect at first; indeed the number of spirals is not halved until the point of observation approaches fairly close to the screen. (These last statements are based on the Fresnel assumption that the 'last' zone is that from which the secondary wave reaches the point of observation in a direction tangential to the wave front—see p. 234. Then the number of zones is proportional to the extreme path difference $\sigma\{(1+2\rho/\sigma)^{\frac{1}{2}}-1\}$, and this quantity changes by less than 5 per cent whilst σ decreases from infinity to 10ρ. It is not halved until σ has decreased to $0\cdot25\rho$.) Finally, the position of the point B in the diagram changes progressively. When the point of observation is at infinity, the representative point B lies within the outermost half coil of the spiral provided $d<2(\lambda\rho)^{\frac{1}{2}}$. Here d is the diameter of the hole (or obstacle) and λ is the wavelength of the radiation concerned. Whatever the actual position of B corresponding to the point at infinity, however, as σ decreases B traverses the spiral inwards towards its centre. Again using our previous notation, when $r=\rho$, B is still only twice as far from B_0, in angular measure around the spiral, as it was when r and σ were infinite. Thereafter, the motion of B becomes more rapid. When r (or σ)$=0\cdot25\rho$, B is roughly five times its original angular distance from B_0. (The angular distance of B from B_0 is given by $2(\rho+\sigma)\epsilon/(r+\sigma)$, where ϵ is the value of this quantity when $r\to\sigma\to\infty$.) When the point of observation is at any of the distances σ_1, σ_3, σ_5, . . . specified in our preliminary discussion (p. 242), obviously B is diametrically opposite to B_0: when σ is any of σ_2, σ_4, . . . B is near to B_0, in the radius drawn to that point from the centre of the spiral. Evidently, throughout all these changes, as we have demonstrated for the arbitrary case, the generalised Babinet principle applies.

8.8. FROM DOPPLER'S PRINCIPLE TO THE ČERENKOV EFFECT

The result which generally goes by the name of Doppler's principle was in fact enunciated independently by three scientists in about as many years. However, present usage is not, therefore, necessarily unjust: it almost certainly assigns priority correctly. The other two originators were Babinet, whose contributions in another context we discussed in the last section, and a Scottish engineer, John Scott Russell (1808-1882). Scott Russell was a man of many activities—he was, for example, one of the joint secretaries of the Great Exhibition of 1851. His early life had set the pattern of variety: he had attended classes at the universities of St. Andrews, Edinburgh and Glasgow, before graduating from the last-named at the age of sixteen. As a professional physicist, however, his experience was limited to one year only. When he was twenty-four 'he was engaged to give the natural philosophy course at the university of Edinburgh, the chair having become vacant by the death of Sir John Leslie'. During that year, another twenty-four-year-old, James David Forbes (1809-1868), was elected to the vacant professorship, and thereafter Scott Russell was able to devote his full attention to his personal researches. These took the form of large-scale experiments on waves on water. It was somewhat later (1844), during this phase of his career, that he drew attention to a peculiar feature of wave propagation in such circumstances, and so provided what is probably the first accurate description of a phenomenon which we have considered already, in an earlier section (§ 7.6), under the heading 'The concept of group velocity'.

Christian Doppler (1803-1853) eventually became professor of physics at Vienna. He put forward the principle that we are now to discuss in 1842. The fact that the implications of the principle for observational astronomy were clarified by Fizeau some six years later has led certain writers to adopt the double designation, the Doppler-Fizeau principle. From what we have already said, if there is to be a bracketing of names, this is not the most appropriate one.

Qualitatively, Doppler's principle states that changes in the relative motion of a source of quasi-homogeneous radiation and an observer involve changes in the frequency of the radiation as observed. This statement does not appear to indicate a topic which has a natural place in a chapter dealing with interference and diffraction. Such justification as there is for its inclusion here comes from the fact that it may be discussed—as the other topics to be considered in this section may also be discussed—very profitably by use of Huygens's construction.

We shall consider first the case in which the source is moving, with uniform rectilinear velocity v_s through a medium in which the disturbance is propagated with velocity v, and the observer is at rest. In fig. 50, X'X represents the line of motion of the source, and Q_0, Q_1, Q_2, . . . its positions at a series of equally spaced instants t, $t + \tau$, $t + 2\tau$, . . ., τ being the characteristic period

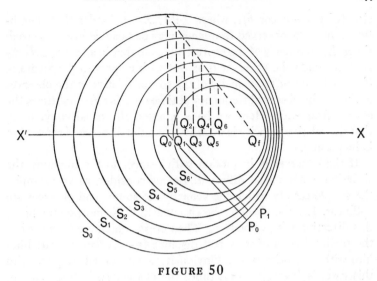

FIGURE 50

of the radiation which it emits. S_0, S_1, S_2 . . . are the traces in the plane of the figure of spheres centred at Q_0, Q_1, Q_2, . . ., respectively, and of radii vT, $v(T-\tau)$, $v(T-2\tau)$. . . . Obviously, S_0, S_1, S_2 . . . represent, at time $t+T$ (when the source is at Q_f), the positions of 'corresponding' wave fronts in process of diverging from the moving centre. In particular, if S_0 is the locus of a wave crest, then S_1, S_2 . . . are the loci of succeeding crests in the general disturbance. For an observer at rest at a point in the line Q_0X, crests which are separated in the medium by an inter-crest distance $(v-v_s)\tau$ are approaching with velocity v: for such an observer, then, the frequency of the incident radiation is $v/(v-v_s)\tau$ or $v/(v-v_s)$ times the characteristic frequency of the source. Similarly, for a stationary observer in Q_0X', the effective wavelength of the incident radiation is $(v+v_s)\tau$ and the effective frequency is less than that of the source in the ratio $v:v+v_s$.

Consider now an observer situated at P_0 on S_0. At time $t+T$, when the source is at Q_f, the direction of incidence of the radiation reaching him is along Q_0P_0. If $T\gg\tau$—that is, if the distance of the observer is in general very many wavelengths from the line of motion of the source—the instantaneous value of the effective wavelength of this incident radiation is the projection of P_1P_0 on Q_0P_0 (Q_1P_1 having been drawn parallel to Q_0P_0), that is very closely by $(v - v_s \cos \theta)\tau$, where $\angle P_0 Q_0 X = \theta$. Under these conditions, then, the observed frequency may be taken as $v/(v - v_s \cos \theta)$ times the frequency of the source. We note that in all these circumstances, when the observer is at rest with respect to the medium, if we write v_r for the velocity of the source relative to the observer at time t, the observed frequency at time $t + T$ is $v/(v + v_r)$ times the source frequency. Here we have adopted the usual convention, that the relative velocity is positive when the distance of separation is increasing.

If the observer is in motion with respect to the medium, the situation is somewhat different. Let us consider, as an example, the simple case in which the velocities of source and observer are collinear. Let the observer be situated in $Q_0 X$ and be moving in this direction with velocity v_0. Then crests which are separated in the medium by an inter-crest distance $(v - v_s)\tau$ are approaching him with a velocity $v - v_0$. Obviously, the observed frequency, in this case, is $(v - v_0)/(v - v_s)$ times the characteristic frequency of the source. The relative velocity of source and observer is now $v_0 - v_s$, and the result valid in the previous case, that the observed frequency is less than the emitted frequency in the ratio $v : v + v_r$, in this more general case is valid only in the limit when $v_0 \ll v$, $v_s \ll v$.

As we have already implied, Doppler was originally concerned with the relevance of his newly enunciated principle in the field of observational astronomy (in particular, in relation to the spectra of double stars—pairs of stars which revolve in orbits around their centre of mass—see $M L$ & T, p. 214): in that field we have to do almost exclusively with velocities of source and observer which are very small compared with the velocity of light. Then, certainly, the relative velocity only is in question—if we can accept our analysis as giving a satisfactory account of the physical phenomenon itself. Empirically, there is a wealth of evidence in support of this naïve view: line-of-sight velocities deduced on the basis of the optical Doppler effect make good sense in our general picture of the heavens—in respect of the rotation of the planets, the motions of double stars, star 'streaming', and other effects more subtle than these. But we should not overlook a philosophical difficulty. Our analysis is built on the concept of the propagating medium. In relation to elastic waves this is a real physical system; in relation to light—so far as the astronomical problem is concerned—it is empty space. The notion that velocities can be specified uniquely with respect to empty space seems to imply the underlying notion of absolute rest which the modern physicist has come to repudiate (see $M\,L\,\&\,T$, p. 132). It is one of the successes of Einstein's theory of relativity, which we cannot enter into here, that, whilst denying validity to the concept of absolute rest, it so reformulates the problem that the undeniable facts of observation are accounted for, and Doppler's result for the change of frequency due to relative motion of source and observer is reinstated in the domain of optical phenomena as formally correct—at least to the first order in the usually very small quantity v_r/v.

In the domain of elastic waves the limitation $v_r \ll v$ is not a naturally imposed limitation: nowadays even large bodies travelling through the atmosphere at speeds greater than the speed of sound in air are not uncommon. Moreover, in the domain of surface waves we recall the fact (see p. 163) that on the surface of water at ordinary temperatures waves may be propagated with a velocity as small as some 15 yards per minute. That is much less than a normal walking-pace. If the observer is moving with a velocity greater than the velocity of propagation of the disturbance in the medium, whilst the velocity of the source is less than this characteristic value, provided that he starts in a region where the medium is initially undisturbed the observer will obviously remain permanently out of range of the disturbance, as long as his velocity is suitably directed. But this is clearly a trivial result: a much more interesting situation arises when the velocity of the source is greater than the characteristic velocity of wave propagation. We proceed, therefore, to consider this situation in some detail.

In fig. 50 we used Huygens's construction for an analysis of the case in which $v_s < v$. Fig. 51 has been similarly constructed for $v_s > v$, using the same notation as before. In this case, as the figure indicates, there is a conical surface, having its apex at Q_f, the instantaneous position of the source, and semi-vertical angle ϕ

given by $\phi = \sin^{-1}\left(\dfrac{v}{v_s}\right)$, which separates an undisturbed region of

the medium from the disturbed region. This surface is represented in the figure by its trace, AQ_fA'. The surface is not a true wave front in that it is not a locus of constant phase, but it is a real surface of discontinuity. At any point which lies instantaneously on this surface (which moves bodily with the source) the local

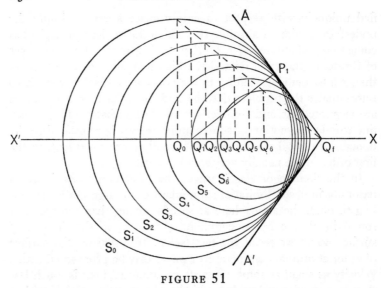

FIGURE 51

disturbance advances in a direction at right angles to the surface. This description of the situation is a perfectly general one: even in the ideal case, in which a source had been in motion in an infinite medium for an infinitely long past time, there would still, at any instant, be an infinite region of the medium, ahead of the source and around it, as yet free from disturbance.

Here we leave the Doppler effect, and proceed to consider a closely related phenomenon. Hitherto, we have consistently idealised the situation, at least in one respect. We have assumed a point source of quasi-homogeneous radiation moving with uniform rectilinear velocity. Strictly, there is no such natural object as a point source of radiation. Let us now proceed to the other extreme, and use fig. 51 for the discussion of a physical situation which is more realistic. Let us regard $X'X$ as the line of motion of the centre of mass of a real body (say, a rifle bullet) which has an axis of symmetry which all the time lies in $X'X$ as the body moves. In order to make fig. 51 fully applicable, let us assume that our moving body in fact has a sharp 'nose' of not too large apical angle. Let us also assume that the medium is non-dispersive. The moving body is no 'source of radiation', in our previous sense—that is, it contains no vibrating system of any kind—but, moving through the real medium, it causes a local compression in the immediate region of the nose. When the motion of the body is steady, the state of strain of the medium in the region of the nose is constant. A state of strain in the medium cannot, however, remain localised: it will be dissipated as a spreading pulse. When the body is in motion with a velocity greater than the velocity of pulse propagation in the medium, fig. 51 shows that the elementary pulses of strain, propagated from successive elements of path of the body, will coalesce and form a conical pulse-sheet of small thickness. AQ_fA' is the trace of this sheet in the figure, and, as before, this feature moves as if attached to the point of origin of the disturbance, namely the nose of the moving body in the case that we are considering. Outside this sheet the medium is strictly undisturbed, and inside it, also, it is generally quiescent. In so far as we can employ the notion of phase, when a pulse is in question, we may say that the boundary of the spreading pulse-sheet is a locus of constant phase. It is therefore more correct to regard this bounding surface as a true wave front than so to regard the corresponding boundary in the previous case of the radiating source for which fig. 51 was originally drawn.

Referring back to fig. 50, now, and re-interpreting it for our present purposes, we see at once that, when the velocity of the real body is less than the velocity of pulse propagation in the medium, there is no surface over which the elementary pulses coalesce into a continuous pulse-sheet; that is, there is no 'bow-wave', no outgoing disturbance of finite amplitude regularly propagated with the velocity characteristic of the medium in question.

Let us look at the phenomenon of the bow-wave from the point of view of a stationary observer. Let Q_1P_1 (fig. 51) be normal to AQ_f, part of the trace of the wave at the instant for which the figure is drawn. An observer situated at P_1 receives the wave at that instant, and the disturbance which he registers obviously originated when the nose of the moving body was passing through Q_1, some time previously. At that previous instant, the relative velocity of the body and the observer was $-v_s \sin \phi$, where ϕ is the semi-vertical angle of the cone of the wave. Now, as we have already concluded, $\sin \phi = v/v_s$, thus at that previous instant the relative velocity in question was $-v$. This is a general result: a stationary observer receives, from a body in uniform motion, that part of the bow-wave which originated when his distance from the moving body was decreasing at a rate equal to the velocity of propagation of the disturbance in the medium. A little reflection will show that this result is an almost self-evident deduction from Huygens's principle, applied directly to the particular question at issue.

In the case of a body in uniform rectilinear motion the condition $v_r = -v$ cannot be satisfied more than once in respect of any particular observer at rest in the medium. If, however, the motion of the body is rectilinear and accelerated, and if, initially, $v_s < v$, this condition may be satisfied twice. On each occasion a disturbance will arise which has considerable amplitude at the observer, as the result of the superposition of the elementary pulses derived from a finite length of path of the body. These considerations have been advanced in explanation of the 'supersonic bangs' which are sometimes heard on the ground when an aircraft in the vicinity exceeds the speed of sound. In such a case, when changes of direction of the aircraft, as well as changes of air-speed, are likely, it is entirely possible for a stationary observer to hear more than two 'bangs' whilst the aircraft is in his neighbourhood.

The Čerenkov effect, the last of the miscellaneous effects to be considered in this section, is the analogue, in optics, of the phenomenon of the bow-wave generated by macroscopic bodies in sufficiently rapid motion in material media. In the Čerenkov effect the moving body is an electron, or other elementary charged particle, which is traversing a transparent material medium with a velocity greater than the phase velocity of visible light in the medium. If n is the refractive index of the medium for light of wavelength λ (measured in empty space), it is a consequence of the wave theory of Young, later verified by Fizeau (see p. 183), that the phase velocity of the light in the medium is c/n, c being the unique value of the phase velocity in empty space. In a practical case $n > 1$—and the transparent medium is dispersive, so that n varies with λ. It is possible, therefore, for the charged particle to be moving through the medium with a velocity greater than c/n, and, if our description of the effect is the correct one, when this condition is satisfied for any wavelength, for light of that wavelength to be involved in the Čerenkov effect.

When an elementary charged particle moves through a material medium the only type of strain which it is capable of setting up in the medium is electrical in nature: if, then, the generation of light is attributed to the process of dissipation of this strain, we are already committed to a view of the nature of light waves which regards them as in essence an electrical phenomenon. To pursue this matter here would be to anticipate the discussion of the next chapter; suffice to say that the Čerenkov effect requires an electromagnetic theory of light for its satisfactory interpretation.

Accepting the statement that the effect that we are discussing is the analogue of the phenomenon of the bow-wave in purely mechanical systems, and overlooking the details of the physical process of light generation, we should expect to find the following result. For a charged particle traversing a transparent material medium with velocity v, there should originate in the medium in the immediate neighbourhood of the path of the particle, and be propagated exclusively in a direction $\cos^{-1}(c/nv)$ to its direction of motion (the only direction in which the elementary disturbances reinforce one another), light of wavelength λ for which the refractive index of the medium is n. This is essentially the result which was established experimentally by Čerenkov in the years 1934-1937, and which has been abundantly verified by the many investigators who have followed him.

The Čerenkov effect remained undiscovered for so long because, in relation to the other phenomena which result from the passage of charged particles through matter, it is a phenomenon of very small intensity. The early workers in radioactivity had noticed the light emitted from very active preparations of radium salts contained in glass vessels. The first demonstration that visible light having a continuous spectrum of wavelength is emitted from pure water when radioactive radiations pass through the water was made by L. Mallet, who published a series of papers on the subject during the period 1926-1929. This work was largely forgotten until it had been effectively repeated and extended by Čerenkov some eight years later, and until, in particular, an acceptable theory of the effect had been elaborated. This was achieved by I. M. Frank and I. E. Tamm in 1937.

Pavel Alekseyevich Čerenkov (b. 1904) carried out the definitive investigation that we have been describing whilst still a postgraduate student working under the direction of S. I. Vavilov in Moscow. He had taught in a secondary school from 1928 to 1930, before embarking on his studies for a higher degree. Jointly with Frank and Tamm, he was awarded the Nobel prize for physics in 1958.

CHAPTER 9

THE WAVE-PARTICLE DUALITY

9.1. LIGHT AS AN ELECTROMAGNETIC WAVE PROCESS

Not systematically, but at some length, in earlier sections of this book, we have discussed various aspects of the debate between those who followed Newton and regarded a beam of light as essentially a stream of discrete particles and those who accepted Young's development of the rudimentary ideas of Hooke and Huygens and conceived of it as a process propagated in a medium without transport of matter. We have considered in turn the phenomena of polarisation (§ 6.5) and diffraction (§ 8.6) and have concluded (p. 144) that 'for all practical purposes, the debate . . . was settled' by Fresnel's memoir on 'Diffraction' in 1818. But we added, in parenthesis, 'at least for eighty years!'—that was to foreshadow the experimental discoveries that we shall be considering in a later section (p. 276)—and we were careful to qualify our statement by the opening phrase 'for all practical purposes'. For all practical purposes the debate was settled in favour of the views of Young and Fresnel, but (see p. 145) the development of an acceptable physical theory of the wave process 'had to await the genius of Maxwell'.

James Clerk Maxwell (1831-1879) began to consider the problem in 1855, at the age of twenty-four, shortly after he had obtained his degree at Cambridge. Ten years later his monumental paper 'A Dynamical Theory of the Electromagnetic Field' was published by the Royal Society. Of that paper E. T. Whittaker has written (1951), 'in it the architecture of his system was displayed, stripped of all the scaffolding by aid of which it had been first erected'. In retrospect, it may be regarded as marking the first enunciation of an electromagnetic theory of light as a coherent unity. Maxwell was to amplify the theory later, particularly in a paper published in 1868, and in the second volume of his *Treatise on Electricity and Magnetism* (1873), but the physical ideas upon which the theory was founded are already present in the paper of

1865. The essential distinction between a corpuscular theory of radiation and a wave theory, classically estimated, is, as we have stated, that, according to the former, matter is transported, according to the latter, energy. The essential novelty in Maxwell's wave theory of light consisted in this, that he postulated that the transport was of electromagnetic strain energy through the medium, not of mechanical energy, under the traditional categories of the potential and kinetic energies of the ultimate parts of the medium.

We should endeavour to understand some of the difficulties which faced those who attempted to provide a physical basis for a wave theory of light before Maxwell. They were confronted with the inescapable facts that light is propagated through 'empty' space with a unique velocity, and that, being susceptible of complete polarisation, it has the character of a wave motion in which the 'displacement' is a purely transverse displacement. Moreover, the velocity of propagation is immensely greater than that of any other wave process—or, at least, that was the situation as it appeared to those who considered the problem during the period of roughly forty years which passed between the death of Fresnel and the publication of Maxwell's paper.

The fact of wave propagation through 'empty' space was taken to imply that space is not truly empty, but is filled with an all-pervading medium possessing well-defined physical properties. This was no new idea: the notion of such an 'ether' goes back at least as far as Descartes (1596-1650), we have noted Huygens's use of it (p. 182), and it was tentatively employed by Newton—even to add refinement to his corpuscular theory of light. It had persisted throughout the eighteenth century, when 'aethers were invented . . . to constitute electric atmospheres and magnetic effluvia . . . till all space had been filled three or four times over with aethers' (Maxwell). Joseph Priestley (see *M L & T*, p. 277) had protested against this multiplicity of invention in 1767, asking pertinently 'Is there any electric fluid *sui generis* at all, distinct from the luminiferous aether?', but it was not until the time of Fresnel that the facts were available by which further speculation could be checked. Then it appeared that the properties of the luminiferous ether had to be such that, whereas it was incapable of transmitting a longitudinal disturbance, it could sustain and transmit a transverse disturbance with the enormously great velocity with which light was known to be propagated. These are stringent requirements: if we are thinking in terms of elastic vibrations, gross matter does not exhibit the requisite combination of properties in any one of its three states, solid, liquid or gas —and, in any case, the absolute magnitude of the velocity provides clear indication that argument by analogy must be hazardous, so great is the range of extrapolation involved. In spite of these considerations, the ablest mathematical physicists of the first half of the nineteenth century wrestled with the problem with great singleness of purpose—though without convincing success—and for many years after the publication of Maxwell's theory the fascination of the subject scarcely declined. Active concern with a mechanical model of the ether did not take on the character of an ineffectual idiosyncrasy until the century had closed. It would take us too far outside our subject, however, to discuss here any of this work—that of A. L. Cauchy (1789-1857), F. E. Neumann (1798-1895) or G. G. Stokes (1819-1903), for example, which is characteristic of the first period, before Maxwell's theory was formulated, or that of Kelvin (1824-1907) which belongs to both periods. We turn, rather, to a consideration of the basic ideas of the electromagnetic theory itself.

Initially, the two subjects, electricity and magnetism, were studied independently one of the other. More than a century before any comparable account of electrical phenomena had been written, William Gilbert (1544-1603) had placed the fundamental facts of magnetism on record in a systematic order, yet the discovery of quantitative 'laws', in each subject, had to await the same development—certain improvements in experimental technique which did not mature until the close of the eighteenth century. It is true that in 1750 John Michell (1724-1793), recently having taken his degree at Cambridge, published an analysis of the observations made by others on the forces between magnets, from the time of Newton until his own day, and satisfied himself that in that case, as with Newtonian gravitation, 'each pole attracts or repels exactly equally, at equal distances, in every direction . . . the attraction and repulsion of magnets decreases, as the squares of the distances from the respective poles increase'. It is true, also, that Priestley, with brilliant intuition, drew the correct conclusion (1767) 'that the attraction of electricity is subject to the same laws with that of gravitation, and is therefore according to the [inverse] square of the distances'—and this on the basis of what was little more than a qualitative experiment, in which no forces were measured. (Henry Cavendish (1731-1810) carried out a similar experiment a few years later, and drew from it the same conclusion, but he did not publish any account of his work.) However, in each case, in respect of magnetic poles and electric charges, a direct quantitative demonstration of the validity of the inverse-square law was not forthcoming until C. A. Coulomb (1736-1806) used the torsion balance for this purpose in 1785. Coulomb had re-discovered the principle of this instrument, which was first developed by Michell some years previously. (In 1798 it was used by Cavendish for the determination of the gravitational constant—see *M L & T*, § 10.5.) We may summarise the situation by saying that by the beginning of the nineteenth century, though the really definitive experimental verifications were to come later, the basic laws of force were accepted as established—that is, the laws of electrostatic and magnetostatic attraction and repulsion between charges. Regarding the nature of the elementary charge (or pole), electric or magnetic, however, it can only be insisted that each was, equally with the other, still a question of free speculation and debate.

The basic laws of force having been accepted, the way was open for the definition of units of measurement of charge and pole. We imagine, therefore, ideal situations in which disembodied charges (or poles) are situated in vacuum, and unit charge (or pole) is conventionally defined as that which, at unit distance, repels an exactly similar entity with unit force. On these two definitions, respectively, the separate systems of measurement appropriate to phenomena in electrostatics and magnetostatics were built up in the early years of the nineteenth century.

During the same period two experimental discoveries greatly enlarged the field of our enquiry. In 1800 Alessandro Volta (1745-1827), professor of natural philosophy at Pavia, devised for the first time a method of obtaining a 'steady' current of electricity in a metallic conductor. For more than fifty years physicists and others had investigated the effects of discharging batteries of Leyden jars through wires, through liquid conductors, and even through their friends, but little quantitative order had appeared in the phenomena which they had observed. With the introduction of the voltaic pile an entirely new approach became possible. The

R

second experimental discovery to which we have alluded was among those thus made possible by the first: in 1820, after an unsuccessful attempt to observe the effect during a lecture in Copenhagen, Hans Christian Oersted (1777-1851) discovered the deflection of a compass needle due to the action of a steady current flowing in a neighbouring wire. A connection between magnetic and electrical phenomena had long been suspected: here was the first clear instance of such an effect. Here also was a phenomenon which could be made the basis of a method of current measurement, once its 'laws' were understood. This understanding was not long delayed. Within a matter of two months the fundamental facts had been elicited through the experiments of Jean Baptiste Biot (1774-1862) and Félix Savart (1791-1841), and in less than five years André Marie Ampère (1775-1836) had raised, on these experiments and others of his own, a coherent structure of co-ordinating theory. Briefly—though incompletely—stated, the crucial experimental fact is that the force on a magnetic pole due to a steady 'linear' current is the resultant of the elementary forces due to the current as it passes through each short element of the wire which carries it, the force ascribed to any such element being directly proportional to the length of the element and inversely proportional to the square of the distance of the element from the pole. It is a matter of conventional definition (of current strength) to add that the magnitude of the resultant force is directly proportional to that of the current in such a case.

The incompleteness of this statement (of the Biot-Savart law) relates to our omission to specify the direction of the force. Yet, if the incomplete statement is valid as far as it goes, and if the force on a pole placed at the centre of a circular current-carrying coil is not identically zero, then that force must be at right angles to the plane of the coil. This in fact is the case. Conventionally, then, unit current, in the 'electromagnetic' system of units, is defined as that current which, flowing in unit length of arc of a circular coil of unit radius, exerts unit force on unit pole placed in vacuum at the centre of the coil.

By using modern terms in this account of century-and-a-half-old controversies, we have obscured one important point—indeed, the point on which our future argument hangs. We have implicitly assumed that the 'steady' effects, observed in the neighbourhood of wires joining the plates of a voltaic pile externally, are due to the continuous transfer of electricity from one plate to the other—just as (by definition) the transient effects in the neighbourhood of wires joining the plates of initially charged Leyden jars are to be ascribed to such transfer. We have assumed (to express the matter less directly in terms of experiment) that static electricity and current electricity are essentially the same. Very properly, physicists of the early nineteenth century were much concerned with this problem. Over the years from 1801 to 1833, from the limited investigations of W. H. Wollaston (see p. 142) to the very thorough investigations of Michael Faraday (1791-1867), evidence accumulated for the correctness of this point of view. From the last-mentioned date (1833), its correctness was no longer held in question by any scientist of repute.

This, then, is the position that we have finally reached. Electric charge may be measured, in the electrostatic system of units, in terms of the empirical law

$$F = \frac{q_1 q_2}{r^2} \tag{187}$$

Here the symbols have their traditional meanings. Electric current may be measured, in the electromagnetic system of units, in the arrangement of the circular coil, in terms of the law

$$F = \frac{2\pi i m}{r} \tag{188}$$

where, again, the symbols are the traditional symbols. The quantity m, the magnetic pole strength, may be measured, in the same units, in terms of the law of Michell and Gauss,

$$F = \frac{m_1 m_2}{r^2} \tag{189}$$

A current i flowing for a time t transports an electric charge q given by

$$q = it \tag{190}$$

This equation is valid for either system of measurement.

Suppose, now, that the magnitudes of the fundamental units of length and time are changed. We wish to investigate the effects of these changes on the magnitudes of the derived units in terms of which electric charge is measured in the two systems. We can have no reason to expect *a priori* that the two units, defined on the basis of entirely different physical procedures, would be of the same magnitude, but we should expect, intuitively, that the ratio of their magnitudes would be independent of any change in the magnitudes of the fundamental units of length and time. This intuitive expectation is based on the conviction that electricity is one and the same, whether its effects belong to the traditional domain of electrostatics or to that of electromagnetics—and it is obviously conditional on the assumption that in equations (187)-(190) all the various factors entering into the physical phenomenon are explicitly expressed. We need not evaluate in detail the dimensions of the two units of charge to discover that our expectation proves false in the upshot. On the basis of equation (187), we have directly, for the electrostatic unit,

$$[q_e] = L^1[F^{\frac{1}{2}}] \tag{191}$$

and, for the electromagnetic unit, from equations (188)-(190) we obtain

$$[q_m] = T^1[F^{\frac{1}{2}}] \tag{192}$$

It is clear from equations (191) and (192) that the ratio of the magnitudes of the two units of charge of the traditional systems is not independent of changes in the magnitudes of the fundamental units of length and time. There is one exception to this statement: in the special case in which these changes are themselves in the same ratio, so that the magnitude of the unit of velocity remains constant, the ratio of the magnitudes of the units of charge is likewise constant.

The year 1833, the year of Faraday's virtual proof of the identity of static and current electricity, may be regarded as marking the end of a period. The comments of our last paragraph are such as a discerning critic (possibly with a twentieth-century cast of mind!) might have made at that time. Had he been commenting on the situation again twenty years later he would have brought new knowledge to his task. He would have realised that the assumption that equations (187)-(190) contain all the factors involved in the physical situations which they purport to describe is untenable, and he would not, therefore, have been surprised at the apparent paradox involved in the dimensional equations deduced from them. In 1837 Faraday had himself re-discovered a result which had remained for sixty years recorded but un-published in the papers of Henry Cavendish (see also p. 257): the mechanical force between electric charges situated in an insulating medium depends upon the medium. The force is in general less in a material medium than in vacuum, the separation of the charges being the same. If the factor of diminution is $1/\epsilon$ ($\epsilon > 1$), the quantity ϵ is the 'specific inductive capacity' of the medium, according to Faraday. Nowadays we use the term 'dielectric constant' or 'permittivity' for this quantity. In any case, equation (187) assumes the modified form

$$F = \frac{q_1 q_2}{\epsilon r^2} \qquad (193)$$

A similar modification of equation (189) was introduced by Kelvin in 1851. In the magnetic case the result is more difficult to argue from experiment, since isolated magnetic poles have no physical reality. But Kelvin's arguments were convincing: a factor μ, representing a property of the medium, must be inserted in the equation for the force, giving it the form

$$F = \frac{m_1 m_2}{\mu r^2} \qquad (194)$$

The physical quantity of which μ is the measure still retains the name which Kelvin assigned to it: it is the 'magnetic permeability' of the medium in which the poles are situated.

Taking equations (193), (188), (194) and (190) as basis, and repeating our previous dimensional analysis, we now have

$$[q_e] = L^1 [\epsilon^{\frac{1}{2}}][F^{\frac{1}{2}}]$$
$$[q_m] = T^1 [\mu^{-\frac{1}{2}}][F^{\frac{1}{2}}]$$

and, if the dimensions of the two units are the same—which was our original expectation—

$$\left[\left(\frac{1}{\mu\epsilon}\right)^{\frac{1}{2}}\right] = L^1 T^{-1} \qquad (195)$$

We do not know what dimensions to assign to the units of measure-ment of dielectric constant (permittivity) and magnetic permea-bility—indeed it is reasonable to assume that they involve some other fundamental unit than those of mass, length and time—but we conclude that these quantities are of such a nature that their measures may properly appear in a physically significant equation of the form

$$\left(\frac{1}{\mu\epsilon}\right)^{\frac{1}{2}} = kv \tag{196}$$

where v is a velocity characteristic of the medium to which they refer, and k is a pure number. Here one point should be noted very precisely; in equation (196) the numerical quantities μ and ϵ are the measures of the permeability and permittivity of the medium in some at present unspecified, single, self-consistent, system of units which is applicable throughout the entire range of the unified subject electricity-and-magnetism. In respect of equations (193) and (194), re-defining the units on which the electrostatic and electromagnetic systems of measurement are based, we continued to assume, quite arbitrarily, that for empty space $\epsilon = 1$, $\mu = 1$. We cannot begin to discuss the significance of equation (196) unless we abandon that two-fold assumption—unless, that is, we distinguish between the 'relative' permittivity and 'relative' permeability, the measures of which are involved in the earlier equations, and the corresponding 'absolute' quantities which are represented in equation (196).

There are obviously many different ways of assimilating the two historical systems of measurement. Let us assimilate them by transforming all measures made in the electrostatic system into the measures appropriate to the electromagnetic system of measurement. Then in this unified system the measure of the absolute permeability of empty space is still unity. On the other hand, if the magnitude of the electromagnetic unit of charge is R times greater than that of the electrostatic unit, the measure of a given charge in electromagnetic units is smaller in the ratio $1:R$ than its measure in electrostatic units, and in this case the measure of an absolute permittivity (in electromagnetic units) is also smaller than the corresponding relative permittivity, but in the ratio $1:R^2$ (see equation (193)). In the unified system, therefore, the measure of the absolute permittivity of empty space is $1/R^2$. Inserting values in equation (196), as we are now in a position to do, we obtain, for empty space,

$$kv = R \tag{197}$$

The implication of equation (197) is just this, that the number R, the ratio of the two units of electric charge, arbitrarily defined from what appeared in the early days of the subject to be wholly independent observations, is a definite multiple k of the measure, in the appropriate units of length and time, of a unique velocity characteristic of a physical property of empty space. If we do not reject this implication out of hand as untenable, we cannot avoid the conclusion that the characteristic velocity in question has reference to an electromagnetic property of empty space (or of a hypothetical ether, if we adopt the idiom of the last century). Writing in 1910, Joseph Larmor (1857-1942) expressed the matter forcibly as follows. 'The emergence of a definite absolute velocity such as this, out of a comparison of two different ways of approaching the same quantity, entitles us to assert that the two ways can be consolidated into a single dynamical theory only by some development in which this velocity comes to play an actual part. Thus the hypothesis of the mere existence of some complete dynamical theory was enough to show, in the stage which electrical science had reached under Gauss and Weber, that there is a definite physical velocity involved in and underlying electrical phenomena, which it would have been hardly possible to imagine as other than a velocity of propagation of electrical effects of some kind. The time was thus ripe for the reconstruction of electric theory by Faraday and Maxwell.'

If we seek to date the time to which Larmor refers at the end of this quotation, then the years 1851 to 1855 provide the natural interim period. As we have seen, in 1851 Kelvin introduced the concept magnetic permeability and in 1855, or thereabouts, Maxwell began to build on the work of Faraday the 'single dynamical theory' which was necessary for the process of consolidation. Larmor refers earlier to Gauss and Weber.

Karl Friedrich Gauss (1777-1855), was professor of mathematics and astronomy at Göttingen from 1807 until his death. Wilhelm Eduard Weber (1804-1891) became his colleague on appointment as professor of physics at the same university in 1831. Weber also held office until he died, but with an intermission during the years 1837 to 1849 when he was deprived of his post for political reasons. During part of this time (1843-1849) he was professor at the university of Leipzig. In 1845 Gauss wrote to him there, that he had long been considering an extension of electrical theory which would involve the assumption of modes of interaction of electrical charges other than those already known from direct experiment and would lead to the (then equally hypothetical) conclusion that electric actions are propagated through space with a finite velocity. Ten years later, at the time of his death, Gauss had not succeeded in this object which he had had in mind for so long.

In the following year Weber, in collaboration with Rudolph Kohlrausch (1809-1858), made the first experimental determination of the ratio of the two units of charge. They obtained the result $R = 3\cdot107 \times 10^{10}$. In the next year again (1857) Kirchhoff (see p. 188) developed a theory on the basis of which it appeared that a signal in a long telegraph wire of circular cross-section and infinite conductivity would be propagated with a velocity of which the measure would be R, and he drew attention to the fact that according to the experiment of Weber and Kohlrausch it seemed likely that this velocity would be identical with the velocity of light in empty space. But Kirchhoff's theoretical interest was confined to the wire: he did not discuss his result in its bearing on the properties of the space in which the wire was situated. That view of the matter arose with Maxwell.

Maxwell's decisive contribution was that he argued his way to an acceptable form for the additional mode of interaction for which Gauss had been searching. His work was not derivative from Gauss's, rather was it built on Faraday's, as we have already stated, and on Kelvin's. We may approach Maxwell's basic assumption by considering first a wholly ideal (unrealisable) situation in which an infinite homogeneous conducting medium is traversed by a current of which the direction of flow is everywhere the same (say, parallel to a particular line X'X) and of which the density is constant (that is, the current per unit area perpendicular to X'X is the same at every point). This situation is unrealisable, if for no other reason, because there is no return flow of current. Then since, due to a linear current element, there is no component of magnetic field parallel to the current direction, we must conclude, from considerations of symmetry, that the magnetic field intensity is everywhere zero in these entirely hypothetical circumstances. This result, which is obvious on the basis of perfectly general arguments, would have been obtained explicitly if we had written down, in terms of the Biot-Savart law, an expression for the field at an arbitrary point, due to an arbitrarily chosen current filament, and had proceeded to a suitable (vectorial) summation over the whole medium. In such a calculation the basic quantity determining the magnitude of the contribution due to each current filament would be the current density in the medium, the measure of which we denote by j. The dimensions of the unit of current density are obviously given by

$$[j] = [q]L^{-2}T^{-1},$$

where, as previously, q denotes the measure of a charge.

Let us now consider the equally unrealisable case of an infinite homogeneous non-conducting medium in which the electric field intensity is, at any instant, everywhere of the same magnitude, E, and the same direction. In this case there can be no current involving the transport of charge, but we can construct a physical quantity, having reference to the electrical state of the medium, the derived unit of which quantity has the dimensions $[q]L^{-2}$, so that the rate of change of this quantity (we are assuming that E may vary with time) is measured in a unit which has the same dimensions as the unit of current density. The quantity in question was named the 'electric displacement' in the medium by Maxwell. We denote its measure by D, and adopt Maxwell's definition

$$D = \frac{\epsilon E}{4\pi}.$$

We confirm our statement about the dimensions of the unit of electric displacement, by deriving those of electric intensity (mechanical force per unit charge) first, using equation (193). We have

$$[E] = [q]L^{-2}[\epsilon^{-1}],$$

thus the statement $\quad [D] = [q]L^{-2}$

follows immediately, and

$$\left[\frac{dD}{dt}\right] = [q]L^{-2}T^{-1} = [j],$$

as we averred. It was Maxwell's decisive contribution to the theory of the electromagnetic field to assert that the quantity $\frac{dD}{dt}$, which he called the displacement current, is indeed a vector quantity with which a magnetic field is associated in the same way as it is associated with a current density in a continuous medium. There was at that time no direct experimental result which necessitated this conclusion, but, without some such addition to the theoretical basis of the subject, there remained, in the background it is true, the implicit presupposition that the propagation of electric and magnetic effects is instantaneous. To Maxwell—as to Gauss before him—this presupposition was anathema.

When Maxwell developed the implications of the extended theory which he had proposed, the result emerged that the velocity of propagation of electromagnetic effects in a non-conducting medium is given precisely by the simple formula

$$v = \left(\frac{1}{\mu\epsilon}\right)^{\frac{1}{2}}.$$

Maxwell pointed out that it was permissible to conclude that Weber and Kohlrausch had already, in effect, determined this velocity experimentally as $3\cdot1 \times 10^{10}$ cm. sec.$^{-1}$ (see p. 264), and because of the remarkable coincidence in numerical values, he continued (1862), 'We can scarcely avoid the inference that light consists in the transverse undulations of the same medium which is the cause of electric and magnetic phenomena.' There were other grounds for this inference besides the mere numerical coincidence, as we shall presently indicate; meanwhile it is useful to examine further the new concepts of displacement and displacement current, the inclusion of which in the theory led to the result which made the inference possible.

To a naïve twentieth-century experimental physicist the notion of electrical displacement in a non-conducting material medium is a natural notion, once his views on the atomic constitution of matter and the electrical structure of atoms are granted. An applied electric field can be expected to produce a 'polarisation' of atoms and molecules—an effective separation of the centres of the positive and negative charges in the atom or molecule along the direction of the field. But Maxwell, despite the evidence of Faraday's work on electrolysis (1834), did not seriously entertain such views: 'The electrification of a molecule', he wrote (1873), 'though easily spoken of is not so easily conceived.' Moreover, for purposes of his theory, he had assumed his media to be continuous and homogeneous, that is he had disregarded their atomicity altogether. By such restrictions the theory had been rendered in some measure artificial (in its original form, for example, it was unable to provide a satisfactory account of dispersion), but Maxwell was thereby relieved from undue anxiety regarding the physical significance attaching to the electric displacement in empty space. The twentieth-century physicist, however, finds no atoms or molecules in empty space to be polarised by the applied field. Maxwell was assailed by no such difficulty: for him the all-pervading ether had the requisite property; the presence of 'embedded' matter merely modified the effect.

Very soon after Maxwell died, the experiments of Michelson (see p. 204) and E. W. Morley (1838-1923) raised the first doubts in the minds of many concerning the plausibility of the idea of such an all-pervading physical medium. These experiments were carried out in 1881 and 1887, and others followed to reinforce the doubts which had been raised. Gradually, the notion of a physical ether lost its usefulness. Larmor, possibly the last of the great 'classical' physicists to survey the problem, wrote, somewhat obscurely, it must be admitted, 'The ether may even be considered to be a dynamical specification of space itself.' That was in 1910. Five years previously, Albert Einstein (1879-1955) had formulated a non-classical theory—the theory of special relativity—which 'explained' the experimental results of Michelson and the others, in the sense of bringing the various observed effects together within a self-consistent mathematical system. In Einstein's theory not only was the idea of a physical ether abandoned altogether, but to some extent the notion of three-dimensional space itself (as a continuum entirely distinct from the one-dimensional continuum time) was abandoned also. In 1910 Larmor had not assimilated these novel ideas, but in the years that followed, as more and more experimental facts were seen to be consonant with them, they came to be accepted as essential to our understanding of the world. In particular, the basic assumption (loosely expressed) that two observers in uniform relative motion, one with respect to the other, must necessarily deduce the same physical laws from similar sets of observations made on the same physical phenomena, has assumed the status of a fundamental belief, or basic axiom, for the physicist of today.

From this point of view the displacement current of Maxwell takes on a new significance. As we have seen, the original concept was fashioned from detailed considerations of the behaviour to be expected of a real medium, the physical ether. Now, if we want any justification for its acceptance, other than that it serves correctly as a basis for the correlation of observed phenomena, we turn to the theory of relativity, and note that, if we do not accept the notion of displacement current, and the role assigned to it by Maxwell in the description of the physical situation, we offend the basic axiom of that theory, namely that the world appears essentially of the same structure to each of two observers in uniform relative motion. We can thus make our choice between a pragmatic justification based on the phenomena of electro-magnetism simply, or a similar justification based on the varied phenomena of the world as a whole; what we cannot do is to justify the concept of displacement current on the basis of a quasi-mechanical model. This outcome is paralleled in many branches of physics at the present time: the models of the last century are, one by one, losing their relevance in detail; only the mathematical symbolism remains. In respect of Maxwell's theory, and Whittaker's comment on its development (see p. 254), it appears, in the end, that much more 'scaffolding' has been removed from the whole edifice of that theory in the years since 1865 than was removed by its author in the previous decade.

However, putting subtleties aside, let us return to the theory itself, and to the other grounds, besides numerical coincidence, for Maxwell's inference (p. 266) 'that light consists in the transverse undulations of the same medium which is the cause of electric and magnetic phenomena'. That light consists of transverse undulations of some kind is required by the facts of polarisation. Maxwell's theory predicted that an electromagnetic wave must be by nature a transverse wave process. At any point traversed by such a wave, the physical quantities the magnitudes of which oscillate with the frequency of the wave are the intensities of the electric and magnetic fields at the point. The theory predicted unambiguously that in an isotropic medium these vector quantities must have directions which are at right angles to the direction of wave propagation. Moreover, of necessity, so it predicted, they must have directions which are at right angles to one another: if a set of right-handed axes is taken, having OZ along the direction of wave propagation, and if the electric vector is parallel to OX, then the magnetic vector must be parallel to OY in such a case. The fact that two vector quantities were involved rather than one, and that this necessary relation obtained between their directions and the direction of wave propagation, had the further result that the problem of the reverse wave in the theory of diffraction (see p. 183) did not arise. Finally, for Maxwell's ether, unmodified by matter—and even more obviously for empty space—there was no valid reason why the quantities ϵ and μ should depend upon the frequency of the disturbance: thus the theory predicted that, in this case, the phase velocity should be the same whatever the wavelength. There were therefore very weighty grounds, other than mere numerical coincidence, for Maxwell's inference. Yet it must not be forgotten that, at the time when the inference was made, electromagnetic waves were still merely a prediction of a speculative theory: no one had produced waves having the properties which the theory required, by means which were demonstrably electromagnetic in character.

9.2. THE SPECTRUM OF ELECTROMAGNETIC RADIATION

The interrelation of the two subjects light and electricity, through the identification of light as an electromagnetic wave process, remained speculative for more than twenty years after Maxwell's theory was published. On the other hand, the assimilation of the subjects light and heat had already been effected—some twenty years previously. At the intuitive level, the recognition of a common behaviour must have occurred at a very early stage in human evolution: the light and heat of the sun appear in permanent association. At the scientific level, however, the definitive experiments were not made until the first half of the nineteenth century. There had been speculation, it is true: indeed in 1717 Newton had written (*Optiks*, book 3, query 18): 'Is not the heat . . . conveyed through the vacuum by the vibrations of a much subtiler medium than air. . . . And is not this medium the same by which light is refracted or reflected. . . . And is it not . . . expanded through the heavens?' But it was not until 1800 that F. W. Herschel, the astronomer, having produced a spectrum of sunlight with a prism, found that a thermometer placed in the spectrum registered a higher temperature in the red than in the violet, and a higher temperature still when it was situated outside the visible spectrum, beyond the red. A new field of observation was clearly awaiting a more sensitive instrument of detection.

The necessary instrument was realised in the thermo-multiplier (thermopile) of Leopoldo Nobili (1784-1835) and Macedonio Melloni (1798-1854) in 1831. In that year, however, Melloni, having been involved in the abortive revolution of 1830, had to leave his professorship at Parma and flee to France. But he was able to continue his work, and in his country of exile he carried out the first detailed demonstration that heat radiation is reflected and refracted according to the same laws as apply to visible light. He also made an extensive study of the process of absorption. As a result, he became a convinced advocate of the view that radiant heat is essentially 'dark' or 'obscure' light, different only in respect of wavelength from such radiation. But the conclusive verification of this point of view came from the work of others in the years which followed.

In a brilliant series of investigations, accounts of which were published over the period 1835 to 1838, J. D. Forbes (see p. 246) demonstrated the polarisation of heat, by double refraction as well as by reflection: then in 1847 A. H. L. Fizeau (see p. 203) and Jean Bernard Léon Foucault (1819-1868) observed and studied its diffraction by a grating. By 1850 the statement might well have been made that light is merely visible heat. Such a statement is at least consonant with the more modern view—that energy in whatever form must ultimately degenerate into heat through inter-action with matter. Moreover, long before 1850, it was known that there was also 'obscure' light of shorter wavelength than the visible. J. W. Ritter (1776-1810) had discovered the photochemical action of this 'ultra-violet' radiation in 1801, and in 1804 Young succeeded in obtaining a 'photograph' of Newton's rings making use of it. By 1862, therefore, Maxwell's inference, that light is propagated as an electromagnetic wave process, would naturally be understood to refer not only to visible light, but also to 'obscure' light of longer and shorter wavelength—to radiations of the infra-red and ultra-violet regions of the spectrum, of altogether in-definite range. Against this background of speculation, the obvious supposition would be that if demonstrably electromagnetic radia-tion were to be produced in the laboratory it would be radiation in the extreme infra-red, rather than in the ultra-violet, radiation of wavelength measured in centimetres, not in a unit ten thousand times smaller than this.

Success in this direction was not achieved until 1887. The successful experimenter was Heinrich Rudolf Hertz (1857-1894). Hertz had gone to Munich to study engineering, but almost immediately, at the age of twenty, he abandoned his intention of entering the profession of architecture, for which that study was prescribed, and set himself to master the work of the French mathematical physicists. Then, in October 1878, he presented himself in the laboratories of Kirchhoff and Helmholtz in Berlin. He was at once accepted for research, and became assistant to Helmholtz in 1880. His experimental investigations in the field of Maxwell's theory were started in 1885, when he was appointed professor of physics at Karlsruhe Polytechnic, and they virtually ceased when he moved to the university chair at Bonn in 1889. During these four years he had provided full justification for Maxwell's speculations, in almost every particular. Hertz had been thinking about these matters since the problem was first put to him by Helmholtz in 1879, but it was in fact a chance observation that put him on the right path to their experimental demonstration. He was operating an induction coil with a spark gap, and he noticed that, when a nearly closed loop of wire was connected, by one metallic conductor only, to any point in the secondary circuit of the activated coil, 'sympathetic' sparking occurred across the small gap in the loop. Having found that he could obtain similar effects even though there was no metallic connection between the loop and the coil, he had a rudimentary detector of electrical effects at a distance ready-made in the nearly closed loop.

Hertz's oscillator (transmitter) eventually consisted of a pair of rectangular metal plates, one in connection with each knob of the spark gap of an induction coil. The connections were symmetrical and the plates were arranged to be co-planar. His 'improved' detector was a single circular loop of copper wire, closed except for an adjustable gap of small separation. With this equipment, suitably modified to suit the occasion, he was able to show that there is a radiation (as distinct from an induction) effect from such a source, and to demonstrate that, in respect of reflection, refraction and polarisation, this radiation has properties similar to those of visible light. In addition, he was able to determine the velocity of propagation, at least as to order of magnitude,

'Hertzian' waves, waves indubitably electromagnetic in character, were in this way shown to be precisely of the type that Maxwell had predicted—and the inference that light, visible and 'obscure', is propagated as an electromagnetic disturbance in an insulating medium was at last vindicated.

This brief history of vindication would not be unbiased if reference were not made to the work of David Edward Hughes (1831-1900). Born in London, by the age of nineteen Hughes was professor of music at a small college in Kentucky. He had, however, the talents of an inventor rather than a musician. He gave up his teaching post in 1854, and in the following year was granted a U.S. patent for a type-printing telegraph. He invented the carbon microphone, and, having improved on his original design, he noticed that such an instrument, when used in a receiving circuit, was sensitive to 'sudden electrical impulses, whether given out . . . through the extra current from a coil or from a frictional machine', up to a distance of 500 yards or more. This was in 1879. Here was a purely empirical discovery, not preceded by a detailed theoretical study of Maxwell's theory, or conditioned by pre-conceived notions on a grand scale. Hughes demonstrated his experiments in London, but the opinion of Stokes (see p. 256) and others (1880) was that Hughes's own idea that he was dealing with electric waves was unjustified. As a result the matter was not pursued farther, and an account of the observations was not published until 1899.

Nowadays the term 'Hertzian waves' has become old-fashioned: what was a frontier research in fundamental physics has given rise, in the field of large-scale engineering practice, to a world-wide network of 'radio' stations crowding the spectrum of wavelengths from several kilometres to a centimetre or so. Over a frequency range of almost twenty octaves, electromagnetic waves are in daily use for the peaceful—and less peaceful—activities of mankind. Another fourteen octaves, or thereabouts, bridges the gap between the centimetre waves of the special-purpose radio transmitter and visible light. Physicists have studied the properties of this infra-red radiation ('near', 'far' and 'extreme' infra-red) in sufficient detail over this whole range of frequencies to know that there is merely a continuous gradiation of effect, that there are no dis-continuities of character. The traditional nomenclature reflects differences in modes of production or detection, not differences in properties. In 1917, E. F. Nichols and J. D. Tear were able to detect, and examine spectroscopically, a constituent of heat radiation (in the extreme infra-red) with a wavelength of $4 \cdot 2 \times 10^{-2}$ cm. —and also to produce, electrically, radiation of shorter wavelength ($2 \cdot 2 \times 10^{-2}$ cm.), using a suspension of fine metallic particles in an insulating oil as a system of multiple spark gaps. In this way an 'overlap' was effected in the region of the spectrum of wavelength around $\frac{1}{3}$ mm. The overlap could equally well have been made elsewhere: it is little more than an accident of history that it was first made precisely where it was.

Visible light, having wavelengths from about $7 \cdot 7 \times 10^{-5}$ cm. (red) to $3 \cdot 9 \times 10^{-5}$ cm. (violet), accounts for almost exactly one octave of the spectrum of electromagnetic radiations. In the survey just completed, we have traversed some thirty-three octaves of lower frequency. In respect of the board features of propagation phenomena, we have been unable to record any fundamental discontinuity in behaviour over this enormous range. The modern physicist will assert that over a range of higher frequencies almost equally great—some twenty-eight octaves according to present reckoning—there is observable radiation of the same general character. He will say that from the near ultra-violet, through the spectral region of the X-rays, through that of the γ-rays, and beyond, there is no abrupt change in propagation behaviour. To make our survey complete, therefore, we must add, briefly, the history of discovery in these latter fields.

In 1895 Wilhelm Konrad Röntgen (see p. 116) discovered a 'dark' radiation, to which all bodies appeared in some degree transparent, emitted from the glass wall of a discharge tube under the particular conditions of discharge in which 'cathode rays' show faintly in the tube and produce a patch of bright phosphorescence on the glass. He named this radiation the X-radiation. In the following year the radioactivity of uranium was discovered, and was exhibited as a characteristic atomic property of the element, by Antoine Henri Becquerel (1852-1908). In 1899 Ernest Rutherford (1871-1937) made the first analysis of the radiations spontaneously emitted by uranium preparations, and recognised two components which he designated the α- and β-rays. In 1900 a third more penetrating component was found by Paul Villard. Rutherford confirmed this finding, and applied the term γ-rays to the new component.

s

From the outset it appeared that the γ-radiation from radio-active substances and the X-radiation from discharge tubes had very closely similar properties. Among the more obvious of these was the action on a photographic plate in the manner of visible (or ultra-violet) light. As early as 1896, indeed, Stokes (see pp. 173, 256) had given good reasons why X-rays should have the character of pulses of electromagnetic radiation simulating the behaviour of light of the extreme ultra-violet. But to obtain experimental confirmation of this point of view was very difficult, technically, at the time. The significant criteria, of course, are that diffraction and polarisation effects should be found under appropriate conditions of experiment. Early attempts (1899-1901) to demonstrate the diffraction of X-rays in passing through narrow slits were inconclusive. Then, in 1905, polarisation by reflection (scattering) appeared to be proved by the experiments of C. G. Barkla in Liverpool. However, at about the same time, Barkla (1877-1944), later professor at King's College, London, and at Edinburgh, was discovering other effects of an entirely different character, and the simple issue tended to become confused. We cannot discuss these other effects here; we shall have to consider some of them in the next section (p. 280). The difficulties of interpretation to which they gave rise remained largely unresolved when, in 1912, Max von Laue (1879-1960) and his pupils found incontrovertible evidence for diffraction, using the naturally ordered array of atoms in a crystal as a three-dimensional grating. After 1912, therefore, it was at least certain that the X-rays from a discharge tube exhibit the two effects of diffraction and polarisation—and that they are produced in an electrical process (the stopping of negatively charged electrons in the metal 'target' of the tube). The conclusion could no longer be avoided: whatever other properties the radiation may possess, it exhibits these three features, which enable wavelengths to be assigned, and allow the assigned wavelengths to be interpreted as those of a transverse electromagnetic wave process of the Maxwellian type. As far as these features are concerned, there is no discontinuity of behaviour as the wavelength decreases. Two years later Rutherford and E. N. da C. Andrade succeeded in observing the diffraction of certain of the less penetrating γ-rays, using a crystal 'grating' in a modified arrangement, thereby extending the range of validity of this statement.

The experiments of von Laue and Rutherford and Andrade, to which we have just referred, established the essential identity of two types of radiation to which physicists had already given distinctive names. In this respect the result was entirely analogous to that achieved by Nichols and Tear three years later (see p. 273). As in this later case, therefore, we conclude that the distinction of nomenclature is significant only in respect of the mode of origin of the radiation: X-rays are radiations produced when charged particles (in the original experiments, electrons) are suddenly accelerated or decelerated—and γ-rays are similar radiations having their origin in processes occurring in the nuclei of atoms (originally, the nuclei of atoms of the radioactive substances). Strictly, we should not use these terms with other connotations. But we note, in passing, that the spectral regions to which the terms may properly be applied now overlap very considerably.

We have stated that some twenty-eight octaves of electromagnetic radiation of frequency greater than that of visible light have been the subject of experimental investigation. This statement implies a spectrum extending, in wavelength, continuously from about 4×10^{-5} cm. to 1.5×10^{-13} cm. The X-rays with which Barkla and von Laue worked occupy roughly the middle octave or two of this range. Pedantically, we should refuse to accept a radiation as a wave radiation unless we can determine its wavelength by a direct comparison with a standard length, or its frequency, effectively, by direct counting against a standard of time. The procedure of wavelength determination for X-rays and the less penetrating γ-rays, in terms of the grating spacing of a crystal, fulfils these requirements completely, but a crystal grating spacing is the smallest comparison length that matter-in-bulk provides us with, and the crystal diffraction method reaches its natural limit of usefulness when the wavelength of the radiation is about 1.5×10^{-10} cm. Obviously, our statement that a further ten octaves of the spectrum beyond this limit have been the subject of study requires further justification. We do not withdraw the statement—but the pedant may look askance at our attempt to justify it.

The argument in justification is as follows. We have recorded the fact that 'other effects of an entirely different character' began to appear in Barkla's experiments, so that the simple fact of polarisation was overlaid with observations for which no explanation was forthcoming on the basis of a classical wave-theory interpretation. Gradually, however, these other effects were brought within the compass of a new theory in which the frequency of the wave picture was retained as a characteristic parameter descriptive of the 'quality' of the radiation (see § 9.3). It was then found that, in parallel with the continuity of behaviour in relation to wave-process phenomena, as wavelength decreased and frequency increased, there was continuity of behaviour in relation to these other effects, which became the more pronounced as the wave-process effects became difficult to demonstrate experimentally. Ultimately, for radiations of the highest frequencies, it was no longer possible to observe the wave-like properties directly (crystal gratings were too coarse), but the other effects provided an entirely acceptable basis for the calculation of frequencies—and of wavelengths, too, for the velocity of propagation is the velocity of light in all cases. It was a far-reaching extrapolation, it is true, but there is as yet no reason to suppose that in relation to empty space the idea of an electromagnetic wave of wavelength however small is a physically meaningless idea. So we do not withdraw the statement that electromagnetic radiation has been studied over the whole spectral range down to wavelengths of the order of $1 \cdot 5 \times 10^{-13}$ cm. (which is, in fact, of the order of the radius of a proton, the nucleus of the hydrogen atom)—but we have obviously reached the stage at which we should enquire more fully regarding these 'other effects' which have bulked so largely in our latest argument.

9.3. THE PARTICLE-LIKE PROPERTIES OF LIGHT

In 1887 Hertz found that small sparks could be obtained across a minute gap in an isolated circuit when an induction coil was operated so as to produce sparks across a 'primary' gap in its neighbourhood. From this observation, as we have seen (p. 271), he proceeded, by successive stages, to build up the experimental case for the validity of Maxwell's inference that light is propagated as an electromagnetic wave process. In the same series of 'preliminary' researches, he also observed that when two spark gaps are fairly close together, and sparks are passing freely across one, the breakdown voltage of the other gap is less than normal. He followed up this observation, also, and identified the incidence of ultra-violet light from the sparks of the first gap on the metal electrodes of the second as the immediate cause of the phenomenon. Unwittingly, he had made the first observation in the long series of experiments by which the particle-like properties of light have since been demonstrated and explored. In the whole history of physics, in retrospect, antithesis is nowhere so strikingly exemplified as in these preliminary researches of Hertz in 1887.

In 1888 W. L. F. Hallwachs showed that the action of the ultra-violet light in Hertz's experiments was to cause the leakage of negative electricity from the metal electrode on which it was incident. Over a number of years from 1889 J. P. L. T. Elster and H. F. K. Geitel investigated this 'photo-electric' action, showing that the material of the electrode was an important factor in the process: for the same irradiation, the more electro-positive the metal the greater the effect. A. G. Stoletow (1890) was the first to investigate the phenomenon systematically with electrodes 'in vacuum'. Under these conditions he found that the leakage of negative electricity was independent of the strength of the collecting field, within wide limits. In 1897 Joseph John Thomson (1856-1940), Rayleigh's successor as Cavendish professor at Cambridge—and others independently, though not so conclusively—discovered the negative electron as the invariable carrier of the cathode rays in the discharge tube—whatever the residual gas in the tube, and in 1899 he showed that the leakage of negative electricity in the photoelectric effect was by virtue of the emission of these same particles from the irradiated surface of the metal. But the culminating research was that of P. E. A. Lenard (1862-1947), published in 1902. Lenard, a former pupil of Hertz at Bonn, found that, though the magnitude of the leakage current was proportional to the intensity of the light incident on the surface, the kinetic energies of the individual electrons constituting that current were independent of the intensity of the light. Moreover, for the same light, the photoelectrons had in general the greater energy the more electro-positive the metal from which they were emitted. When this stage had been reached, it had clearly become evident that the photoelectric effect posed very serious difficulties for any interpretation based on the classical electromagnetic theory of light.

According to the classical theory, the rate of transport of energy, across any surface on which radiation is incident normally, is proportional to the area of the surface and to the square of the amplitude of the electric field intensity at the surface. In the photoelectric effect, according to observation, the energy incident on a metal surface, far from being uniformly effective over the surface, becomes concentrated on a very few of the very many electrons lying in the immediate surface layers of the metal. In the case of zinc, for example, there are some $6 \cdot 6 \times 10^{22}$ atoms per cm.^{3}, and if we allow only one electron per atom, as a conservative estimate, the first layer of atoms provides some $1 \cdot 6 \times 10^{15}$ electrons per cm.^{2} of surface available for photoelectric emission—or some $6 \cdot 1 \times 10^{-16}$ cm.^{2} of surface as 'catchment area' for each such electron, if all were to compete equally for the incident radiation.

In Lenard's experiments the average energy carried away by a single electron was found to be of the order of 3×10^{-12} erg. Ten years previously Stoletow had shown, in a similar arrangement, that the photoelectric current reaches its full value in less than 10^{-3} sec. from the instant of first illumination. According to a crude classical picture, therefore, 3×10^{-12} erg of energy must have been intercepted by an area of 6×10^{-16} cm.^{2} of surface in 10^{-3} sec.—and the incident flux must have been at least as great as 5×10^6 erg cm.$^{-2}$. sec.$^{-1}$. In actual fact it was probably of the order of 1 erg cm.$^{-2}$ sec.$^{-1}$ in Lenard's experiments.

This one illustrative example shows clearly that the electromagnetic theory was in real difficulties over the photoelectric effect. It is little wonder, then, that, as first Silliman Memorial lecturer at Yale University in 1903, Thomson should say 'on the view we have taken of a wave of light the wave itself must have a structure, and the front of the wave, instead of being, as it were, uniformly illuminated, will be represented by a series of bright specks on a dark ground'. Thomson, indeed, had already recognised a similar difficulty in the ionisation produced by X-rays in passing through a gas. Ionisation of gas molecules implies the liberation of electrons at the expense of the energy of the radiation, so Thomson said 'we suppose that the front of the Röntgen ray consists of specks of great intensity separated by considerable intervals where the intensity is very small'.

Thomson saw the difficulties clearly, but his attempt to circumvent them by use of classical analogies provided no real basis of solution. It was Einstein (see p. 267) in 1905, who, breaking with the old theory altogether, introduced an entirely different point of view. Five years previously, Max Planck (1858-1947), confronted with the difficulties which had then become critical for any classical theory of the equilibrium between radiant (heat) energy and matter in a constant-temperature enclosure, had originated the 'quantum' hypothesis. He had shown that, formally at least, these difficulties could be removed if it were supposed that interchange of energy between radiation and matter can occur only in finite amounts proportional to the (classically specified) frequency of the radiation. In this way a new 'universal' constant, Planck's constant h, was introduced into physics—albeit speculatively. Planck supposed that, for radiation of frequency v (v is now conventionally used, rather than f, for frequency in quantum physics), the basic unit or quantum of energy is hv. By 1905 the new hypothesis had not in fact been accorded wide acceptance, but Einstein recognised in the phenomena of the photoelectric effect just the type of behaviour that Planck had imagined—and, with the single-mindedness, and, as it later appeared, the blind wisdom, of youth (he was then twenty-six), he postulated that light is indeed not only absorbed and emitted in energy quanta but also propagated as 'photons' (a term not used by Einstein at the time, but appropriated later). In this thorough-going revision of viewpoint, the energy-content of the photon became its prime characteristic, the associated frequency no more than a convenient alternative parameter of description. The measure of the associated frequency was given, in appropriate units, by dividing the measure of the energy by the measure of h, but the classical electromagnetic connotation of frequency was tacitly abandoned.

Thus Einstein's photons replaced Thomson's 'bright specks'—and the 'dark ground' became absolutely dark. When it was first put forward, this whole idea appeared wildly paradoxical—except in the context of the photoelectric effect and the theory of 'blackbody' radiation—but as time passed it was seen to have more and more relevance to experiment. On the other hand, there was no escaping the paradoxes: they had simply to be endured. They showed up most acutely, perhaps, in Taylor's experiment on interference under weak illumination (see p. 209). This could be described in the statement that the normal interference pattern is obtained even though the time spent by a single quantum in traversing the apparatus is considerably less than the average time between the entry of one quantum and the next. Classical electromagnetic theory, as we have seen, was already in some difficulty here, though it might provide a reasonable formal basis for understanding: Einstein's hypothesis, in its original crude form, certainly provided none. Yet more and more of the discovered properties of ultra-violet light and of X-rays (see p. 274) appeared to require a photon-type explanation. In particular, the detailed experiments of O. W. Richardson (1879-1959) and K. T. Compton (1887-1954) in 1912, and of R. A. Millikan (1868-1953) in 1916, demonstrated this quite clearly. The photoelectric effect with light occurs in precise conformity with the quantitative predictions of Einstein's hypothesis: when the frequency of the incident light, classically determined, is increased from v to v', the maximum energy of the photoelectrons from a given metal increases by an amount $h(v' - v)$. Finally, in 1923, A. H. Compton (b. 1892) elucidated experimentally a mode of action of X-rays on matter which previous observers had failed to understand. In the 'Compton effect', now so called, it is a very close approximation to the truth to say that the basic action is a particle-like collision between an X-ray photon and an electron, free and at rest. In this action the electron acquires energy at the expense of the photon; after the collision the photon appears as of diminished frequency (or increased wavelength), for its energy has decreased.

Reviewing these developments in brief, we see, first, that there are certain phenomena, which attain greater importance as the classical wavelength of the radiation decreases, for which no classical electromagnetic interpretation is possible, and, secondly, that, though these phenomena may be brought within the framework of a non-classical (quantum) scheme of interpretation, yet this scheme still retains formal contact with the classical theory through the, now ambivalent, concepts of frequency and wavelength. And we add the other side of the picture—that quite obviously the phenomena of diffraction and interference (and these are in evidence at all wavelengths) are quite incomprehensible within an interpretive scheme in which wholly individualised photons are the only structural units.

Here is the essence of the duality which the observed facts force upon the theorist who surveys the whole field of the physics of 'radiation' in an attempt to formulate its laws. At the level of this book, we have to admit that the attempt ends with the fundamental paradox still basically unresolved.

9.4. THE WAVE-LIKE PROPERTIES OF MATTER IN MOTION

When a narrow beam of X-rays is incident on a not-too-thick sample of a crystalline substance in the form of a powder, most of the beam passes through the sample undeviated in direction. Because the individual micro-crystals in such a powder are randomly orientated, if any overall effects of diffraction result, they must obviously be such that the axis of the beam is an axis of rotational symmetry of the pattern which is observed. If X-rays of a single wavelength are used in such an arrangement, it is found that a pattern of circular 'fringes' is in fact obtained on a photographic plate placed normally to the beam, and at some distance from the sample, on the side of emergence. The pattern has an intense central 'spot', marking the trace of the undeviated beam. This statement of experimental fact describes, in brief, the essence of the 'powder method' of X-ray crystallography introduced in 1916 by J. W. P. Debye (b. 1884), then professor of physics at Zürich, and P. Scherrer (who later succeeded to Debye's chair).

When a narrow beam of electrons is incident on a metal foil, the electrons lose energy, producing ionisation along their path, and they suffer deflection in the process of close encounter with the atomic nuclei and the electrons in the metal. In general, even when the incident electrons all have the same energy within narrow limits, the emergent beam is not well defined, either in energy or in direction. However, if the metal foil is sufficiently thin—say of the order of only ten to a hundred atoms thick—the probability that an individual electron shall traverse the foil without significant change of direction or loss of energy is considerable, and if the experiment is performed in a good 'vacuum' it is possible to obtain a well-developed central 'spot' on a photographic plate, disposed, as in the powder-method experiment with X-rays, normally to the beam and on the side of emergence. In 1927, G. P. Thomson (b. 1892), then professor of natural philosophy at Aberdeen, and A. Reid, showed, for the first time, that in such an arrangement a pattern of circular 'fringes' is obtained with incident electrons homogeneous in respect of energy, 'just as' a pattern of such fringes is obtained, in the powder method, with X-rays homogeneous in respect of wavelength.

In discussing this result, one point must be cleared at the outset: if the pattern which Thomson and Reid found with mono-energic electrons is to be validly compared with the diffraction pattern obtained in the powder method with monochromatic X-rays, then the behaviour of the metal foil of the former experiment must have been effectively that of a powder of minute crystals. The point must be made—but it presents no essential difficulty: it is well known to metallurgists that in the solid state, as they are normally fabricated, metallic substances consist of aggregates of small crystals randomly orientated, the average size of the crystals depending upon the previous treatment of the specimen.

The observation of Thomson and Reid, surprising as it was at the time, was not made by accident. There had been speculation concerning the possibility of observing diffraction effects with electrons for some years, and the experiment had been designed to test that possibility. In fact, C. J. Davisson (1881-1958) and L. H. Germer, of the Bell Telephone Laboratories, New York, were also investigating the possibility, in another arrangement, at the same time, and were able to report positive findings somewhat earlier than their British competitors. Davisson and Germer directed a beam of mono-energic electrons normally on to one face of a single crystal of nickel, and examined the distribution of 'reflected' electrons in altitude and azimuth. For particular values of the electron energy they found marked concentration of reflection about 'preferred' directions. If priority is in question, it should certainly be conceded to this work of Davisson and Germer: that we have instead given priority of description to the work of Thomson and Reid is due to the simplicity of the comparison that can be made between their results and the corresponding results with X-rays, as we have described them. In 1937 the Nobel prize for physics was awarded to Davisson and Thomson, jointly, for these pioneering investigations.

We have stated already that for some years before 1927 there had been speculation concerning the possibility of observing diffraction effects with electrons—or, for that matter, with other sub-microscopic particles. Prince Louis Victor Pierre Raymond de Broglie (b. 1892) was the originator of these speculations. He was impressed by the seemingly irresolvable duality of character exhibited by light, and by similar 'radiations' which transmit energy through empty space with unique velocity (experimentally determined as very close to 3×10^{10} cm. sec.$^{-1}$, and conventionally denoted by c). He asked himself whether there might not be a similar duality of character exhibited in the behaviour of 'particle' radiations, which may transport energy through space with any velocity—provided that it is not greater than c. This limitation on the velocity of transport of energy (as it appears to any observer of the physical world) is a basic tenet of Einstein's theory of relativity (see p. 267), and de Broglie was impressed, also, by the seemingly universal scope of that theory. According to the theory, we distinguish between the mass of a particle observed at rest and its mass when in motion (the latter being greater than the former in the ratio $1 : \left(1 - \dfrac{v^2}{c^2}\right)^{\frac{1}{2}}$, v being the observed velocity of the particle)—and we recognise that mass is an attribute of energy, or *vice versa*, the total energy concentrated in a particle being given by the product mc^2, where m is the observed mass (at rest or in motion). When the particle is at rest, this expression gives its intrinsic energy; when the particle is in motion, the additional energy which it possesses, according to Einstein's expression, is the kinetic energy of the particle. For any particle to be capable of moving with the velocity of light, its intrinsic energy (or mass) must obviously be zero (otherwise its energy would be infinite when its velocity was c).

Against this background, de Broglie re-interpreted the duality of character exhibited by light in 1924. Energy, he said, is transmitted by photons. But, in order to calculate the distribution of intensity in a diffraction experiment with monochromatic light, it is necessary to operate in terms of a wave process having the same phase velocity (in empty space) as the photons, and a frequency determined by the energy of an individual photon (see p. 279). If E is the energy and ν the frequency, then $\nu = E/h$. The effective mass of the photon, at the velocity of light (the photon can travel through empty space with no other velocity), is E/c^2. The effective momentum, then, is E/c, or $h\nu/c$—or h/λ, if λ is the associated wavelength. (This value of the photon momentum is in fact required if a correct expression for the pressure of light is to be obtained.) The distribution of intensity in the diffraction pattern, calculated for this wave process according to classical wave theory (see § 8.6), is to be taken as giving the 'expectation value' (see p. 208) of the flux of photons from point to point over the field— but, because discrete entities are involved, the number of photons which will in fact arrive, in any specified time, in any given area, is strictly unpredictable. Prediction can be made only in relation to 'average' values: fluctuations are inevitable.

In this re-interpretation, one feature is obvious. The wave process involved in the propagation of light has been largely denuded of physical reality: to speak of it as an electromagnetic wave process is strictly gratuitous. All that we have left is a 'phase wave' (for it is differences of phase which ultimately determine intensities), or a 'probability wave', to which the normal laws of superposition apply.

De Broglie's enquiry may now be seen in its full context. From the point of view of relativity theory, a photon of light represents the limiting case of an entity (particle), of intrinsic mass zero, transporting energy with velocity c. In this phenomenon it is necessary to recognise the participation of a phase wave travelling with the particle: must it not, therefore, be necessary, de Broglie asked, to recognise a similar wave process as involved in the more general phenomenon of the transport of energy by a particle of which the intrinsic mass is finite and the velocity is (necessarily) less than c? If we were to define the frequency of this phase wave in terms of the total energy of the particle, using Planck's constant h as for the photon, and the wavelength of the phase wave in terms of the momentum of the particle, similarly, we should have the following relations

$$E = mc^2 = h\nu \qquad (198)$$
$$P = mu = h/\lambda \qquad (199)$$

and, because m is written for the mass of the particle at the velocity u, the subsidiary relation

$$m = m_0\left(1 - \frac{u^2}{c^2}\right)^{-\frac{1}{2}} \qquad (200)$$

where m_0 is the intrinsic (rest) mass of the particle. On these assumptions, v, the phase velocity of the phase waves is given by

$$v = \nu\lambda = c^2/u \qquad (201)$$

—and we see at once that the phase velocity is different from u— and that it is, in fact, greater than c. Strictly sinusoidal phase waves of wavelength λ do not travel with the velocity of the particle with which they are associated: they travel with a velocity greater than that with which energy may be transported, according to the theory.

At first sight this result appears to involve a serious difficulty which did not appear in our discussion of the relation between the photon (in empty space) and its phase wave. In that case, however, the velocity of the photon is necessarily unique: the velocity of the phase wave is unique, also, and of the same magnitude c. In the case of the particle, on the other hand, it is impossible to know its velocity with absolute precision; in consequence it is impossible to define the wavelength precisely. Moreover, on the evidence of equations (199) and (201), the phase velocity of the phase waves depends upon their wavelength. It is as if empty space were dispersive for the phase waves of particles. In summary, we conclude that for any 'real' particle the associated phase waves cannot be specified more exactly than to say that a sharply peaked spectrum of wavelengths is involved (a 'narrow line'), and we note that these waves are effectively propagated in a dispersive medium. The phase waves of a particle, then, constitute a 'group' in the nomenclature of § 7.6, and it becomes important to calculate the velocity of propagation of this group.

In general, the velocity of a group of waves, of which the representative spectrum is a narrow line of dominant wavelength λ, is given (equation (159)) by

$$U = \frac{d\nu}{d(1/\lambda)} .$$

Substituting from equations (198), (199) and (200), we have, for the phase waves of a particle,

$$U = c^2 \frac{d\gamma}{du} \bigg/ \frac{d(u\gamma)}{du}$$

where

$$\gamma = \left(1 - \frac{u^2}{c^2}\right)^{-\frac{1}{2}} .$$

Thus

$$U = c^2\left(u + \gamma \bigg/ \frac{d\gamma}{du}\right)^{-1}$$

$$= c^2\left(u + 2\gamma^2 \bigg/ \frac{d\gamma^2}{du}\right)^{-1}$$

$$= c^2\left\{u + \frac{c^2}{u}\left(1 - \frac{u^2}{c^2}\right)\right\}^{-1}$$

$$= u.$$

In this result the apparent difficulty that we noted largely disappears: the group velocity of the phase waves defined in terms of equations (198)-(200) is seen to be identical with the velocity of the particle. There is no tendency, then, for the particle and its associated phase waves to separate, and de Broglie's idea of generalising from the photon to the material particle gains greatly in plausibility.

It has been said that the experiments of Davisson and Germer and Thomson and Reid were undertaken because of the speculations that were current at the time regarding the possibility of observing diffraction effects with electrons—and that de Broglie was the originator of these speculations. This is indeed true; the original ideas were de Broglie's, and how original they were our brief description of them will have shown. But the credit for making fairly precise suggestions regarding methods of experimentation is due to W. Elsasser (1925). Clearly, the appropriate experimental technique will depend very significantly on the absolute value of the wavelength ('de Broglie wavelength') which equation (199) predicts for the sub-microscopic particles at the disposal of the experimenter. The value of Planck's constant is $6 \cdot 6 \times 10^{-27}$ erg sec., the rest mass of an electron is $9 \cdot 1 \times 10^{-28}$ g. For values of electron velocity very much less than the velocity of light, therefore, equation (199) may be written numerically (in c.g.s. units)

$$\lambda = 7 \cdot 2 / u.$$

For an electron of velocity $7 \cdot 2 \times 10^8$ cm. sec.$^{-1}$ the de Broglie wavelength is 10^{-8} cm. (1 Ångström unit), the smallest wavelength of the X-rays given out by an X-ray tube operated at some 12,400 volts. The electron itself would acquire this velocity if it moved through a difference of potential of 160 volts, in vacuum. The phase waves of electrons accelerated through potential differences of from 100 to 10,000 volts are thus comparable in wavelength with the X-rays obtained from a tube operated at 100,000 volts (such a tube produces X-rays having a continuous spectrum of wavelengths from larger values to a 'cut off' at $1 \cdot 24 \times 10^{-9}$ cm.). It is numerical considerations such as these which pointed the way to the arrangements which were used by Davisson and Thomson—arrangements in which diffraction effects similar to those obtained with X-rays were sought, and were successfully found. Once the initial experimental discovery had been made, it was not long before equation (199) was verified in detail over a considerable range of velocity: de Broglie's generalisation then became more than plausible—the predictions issuing from it were quantitatively correct.

During the years 1930 to 1932 evidence for wave-like properties began to accumulate in respect of other particles, of atomic, rather than electronic, mass. The momentum of such particles, at least if we consider the positive ions accelerated in a discharge tube, or the α-particles emitted by radioactive substances, is very much greater than the momentum of electrons such as were used in the experiments of Davisson and Thomson. De Broglie wavelengths are therefore much smaller, and a comparison length smaller than the grating spacing of a crystal is needed if a significant experiment is to be designed. Such a length is provided by the effective extent of the electrostatic field of an atomic nucleus. It is in this field that charged particles are 'scattered' in nuclear encounters (see $M L \& T$, p. 238). In 1930 J. Chadwick (b. 1891) investigated the scattering of α-particles by the nuclei of helium atoms and observed an effect which could be explained only in terms of the interference of two wave processes, the phase waves corresponding to the two 'classical' possibilities, that a particle moving in a given direction after a collision should be the original α-particle, or, alternatively, the helium nucleus set in motion in that direction. (Interference occurs in this case because these two particles as 'identical', and because, whether the observed particle is the original α-particle or the projected helium nucleus, the velocity is the same. If these conditions were not fulfilled, the two values of the de Broglie wavelength would be different, and interference would be impossible.) In 1931 C. Gerthsen observed essentially the same phenomenon with accelerated hydrogen ions scattered in hydrogen gas. Then in 1932 Otto Stern (b. 1888) succeeded in a more difficult technique. Having more experience than any other physicist at the time in the production of 'molecular beams'—unidirectional streams of molecules moving with 'thermal' velocities, he was able to demonstrate diffraction effects in the reflection, from crystal faces, of beams of hydrogen molecules and helium atoms, and to verify de Broglie's relation in this situation also. The root mean square velocity of a hydrogen molecule at $0°$ C is $1·8 \times 10^5$ cm. sec.$^{-1}$ (see $M L \& T$, p. 302); since its mass is some 3680 times the mass of the electron, its de Broglie wavelength at this velocity is $1 \cdot 1 \times 10^{-8}$ cm. Obviously, in this case, crystalline reflection provides the most likely possibility of observing marked diffraction effects, having regard to the negligible power of penetration of molecules travelling with such velocities. In his original experiments in this field, later to be extended to other molecular species. Stern in fact employed gas sources having temperatures ranging from that of liquid air to some 300° C.

It would take us too far outside the natural bounds of our subject to pursue the evidence for the wave-particle duality beyond this point. Sufficient has been said to demonstrate that the speculations of de Broglie were indeed well founded. Based upon them, a whole new theory descriptive of the motion of the ultimate entities which constitute matter and radiation has been built up over the past thirty years. This new formalism is referred to as 'Wave Mechanics'. Great successes have attended its use in atomic physics generally, but our last comment on it in this place must be that, in the limit, when the de Broglie wavelength is very small compared with the sizes of obstacles or the characteristic lengths describing fields of force, the predictions of the new theory must be in all cases the same as those of the 'old' theory of Newton, Maxwell and Einstein. For any macroscopic object, unless its velocity is minute to the point of derision, the de Broglie wavelength is smaller by many powers of ten than the diameter of the nucleus of a hydrogen atom. More realistically, we conclude that the de Broglie wavelength must be at least of the same order as a principal linear dimension of the macroscopic object itself, before the predictions of wave mechanics in relation to its motion are likely to differ appreciably from the predictions of the Newtonian mechanics of particles. And, we might add, with some confidence, as realists, this is impossible!

CHAPTER 10

MISCELLANEOUS

10.1. AIMS

In one sense this chapter is a miscellany, in that it brings together topics which are not closely interrelated, and which have no obvious place elsewhere in the book. In another sense it is a unity, for it deals with systems all of which are effectively two-dimensional systems—not strictly so, of course, any more than stretched strings or rods are strictly one-dimensional, but the broad distinction that is implied is convenient, nevertheless.

Accepting this distinction, we see that until now our concern has been, almost exclusively, with systems that are either one-dimensional or three-dimensional. We have been concerned with the vibrations of bodies, or systems of particles, which are effectively linear, and with the propagation of wave processes in extended (three-dimensional) media. As we have developed the subject, the properties of two-dimensional systems have been left over, to be relegated to an appendix. That, essentially, is the nature of the present chapter. Having confessed so much, we should, perhaps, attempt to justify the relegation.

In the main, justification is to be found in the aim which we set ourselves in the Preface: 'It was considered appropriate that [the book] should be devoted to the formulation and elaboration of the classical concept of waves.' Obviously, then, the two ingredients of our title, *Vibrations and Waves*, are not to be regarded as of equal importance for this limited aim. In truth, we have been interested in vibrations, but primarily to the extent that the characteristic features of wave motions could be elicited from their study. Our interest in the wave motions themselves has been basic. Since two of the sections of this chapter (§§ 10.2 and 10.3) deal with the vibrations of two-dimensional systems the study of which adds nothing of significance to our understanding of waves, it is not surprising that they should have been relegated. Only the last section (§ 10.4) has a different character. In one

T

aspect this section has affinities with section 10.2, in another with sections 7.4 and 7.5; in each aspect information concerning a particular type of wave motion is elicited in the discussion. On this basis, it might have been appropriate to have divided the material of section 10.4 between the other sections mentioned. The decision to bring it together at the end of the present chapter, instead, derives more from the desire to relate the two aspects of the matter in question, stressing their common features rather than their disparities, than from any other consideration. In any case, its inclusion here does not disturb the unity of the chapter, for the system involved is a two-dimensional system according to our naïve classification.

In terms of our basic aim, therefore, we are according only marginal attention to two-dimensional systems in this book. If our aim had been otherwise, the balance of treatment would, no doubt, have been different. If we had been more concerned with vibrations than with waves, and particularly if our concern had been predominantly with mathematical methods rather than with the simple realities of phenomena, we should have given more prominence than we have done to the systems discussed in this chapter. One example will suffice to illustrate this statement. The theoretical physicist finds himself involved in the use of Bessel Functions in the treatment of many problems. He first makes their acquaintance, in any systematic course of instruction, almost certainly in relation to the problem of the vibrations of a circular membrane. However, our primary aim here is not to exemplify the various methods of the theorist; it is to familiarise the student of physics with the properties of real physical systems, and with the concepts necessary for their understanding. It is hoped that the reader who has already mastered some of the more advanced mathematical techniques will find our less formal treatment profitable: it is certain that many who have not acquired those techniques will wish to acquire them later. However that may be, in the next section we embark on an elementary discussion of the vibrations of a stretched membrane, without setting up and solving the appropriate differential equation in terms of Bessel Functions explicitly. To some extent this will involve stating results rather than deriving them, but at this stage in the book we make no apology for this practice. No account of any subject can exhaust all its possibilities.

10.2. VIBRATIONS OF A STRETCHED MEMBRANE

We shall be dealing in this section with the vibrations of a membrane of finite extent and uniform thickness, held under tension in a rigid frame. We shall assume that the thickness is very small indeed compared with the other linear dimensions of the membrane, that the exposed surfaces of the membrane are plane when there is no disturbance, and that the tension is homogeneous. By the last restriction we imply that, any finite straight line being considered in an exposed surface of the undisturbed membrane, the membrane on one side of the line acts on the membrane on the other side with a force, in the median plane of the membrane and perpendicular to the line, proportional to the length of the line. We represent such a state of homogeneous strain, therefore, by a quantity T, a force per unit length, defined in this way. We shall confine attention to small displacements of the membrane in a direction at right angles to its undisturbed surface, and we shall assume that the tension in the membrane is the same whatever this displacement.

Let us take the median plane of the undisturbed membrane as the xy plane, and let z be the instantaneous value of the displacement of the membrane at the point (x, y) at time t. In general, in such circumstances, the median 'surface' of the membrane will be curved, and, considering any small element of the membrane, we see that the membrane surrounding that element will exert a resultant force on it, the line of action of this force being along the normal to the element through its mid-point. We have already considered the analogous 'one-dimensional' case in § 2.2: about any point in a stretched string, where the radius of curvature of the axis of the string is r, the resultant force on an element of string of length Δl is $T\Delta l/r$ along the normal, T being the tension in the string. In that section we did, in fact, draw the analogy in the reverse sense: we compared the expression for the force per unit length of a stretched string with that giving the force per unit area which is balanced by the excess pressure inside a spherical soap bubble in equilibrium. Here, considering the properties of the taut membrane in its own right, we should, perhaps, make the comparison with the soap film directly, rather than through the intermediary of the string. The point hardly needs making that in many respects a soop film and a membrane under homogeneous tension are similar dynamical systems (not similar in all respects, of course, as will appear in § 10.4). But we now need more than our previous result for simple spherical curvature—and, indeed, in systematic accounts of surface tension phenomena, not only the sphere, but many more complicated shapes of drop and bubble and supported film are regularly considered in the textbooks. We therefore examine the problem in its generality.

If P be an arbitrary point on a curved surface S without discontinuities, any plane N containing the normal to the surface through P will cut the surface in a curved line C. In general, if P′ be a point in this line very close to P, the normal to the surface through P′ will not lie in N—that is, it will not intersect the normal to the surface through P. Whilst, therefore, there is significance in the definition of the radius of curvature at P of the plane section of S by N (that is the radius of curvature at P of the plane curve C), there is no basis for a definition of a radius of curvature of the surface S at P in the direction defined by C. These statements should be self-evident on close consideration. What is not immediately obvious, but is proved in the standard works on three-dimensional geometry, is that for any point P on a 'smooth' curved surface there are two planes, N_1, N_2, intersecting in the normal to the surface through P and mutually at right angles, such that for neighbouring surface points, P_1', P_2', in these planes, the normals to the surface do lie in N_1 and N_2, respectively. For any point P, then, there are two directions in the surface, determined by the sections in N_1 and N_2, for which it is possible to define the radius of curvature of the surface. N_1 and N_2 are said to determine the principal normal sections of the surface through P and the radii of curvature, at P, of these sections are referred to as the principal radii of curvature of the surface at P. In what follows, we shall denote these principal radii of curvature by r_1 and r_2. If the normals to the surface through P_1' and P_2' intersect the normal through P on the same side of the surface, the latter is said to be 'synclastic' at P; alternatively, if the intersections of the normals occur on opposite sides of the surface, it is said to be 'anticlastic' at P. We shall denote by ρ the radius of curvature of a non-principal normal section. Then it is further shown, in the treatises, that, if ρ has reference to the normal section inclined at an angle θ to the principal section for which the radius of curvature is r_1,

$$\frac{1}{\rho} = \frac{\cos^2 \theta}{r_1} + \frac{\sin^2 \theta}{r_2} \qquad (202)$$

(We used this result, without elaboration, in § 3.3—see p. 60.)

Let us now accept equation (202), and consider any two normal sections of a curved surface by planes at right angles to one another. Because the principal sections are themselves in mutually perpendicular planes, we have, using an obvious notation,

$$\frac{1}{\rho_1} + \frac{1}{\rho_2} = \frac{1}{r_1} + \frac{1}{r_2} \qquad (203)$$

We conclude, in words, that, at any point on a curved surface, the sum of the curvatures of any two mutually perpendicular normal sections is a constant. This constant quantity, equal to the algebraic sum of the principal curvatures of the surface at the point, is traditionally referred to as the mean curvature of the surface at that point.

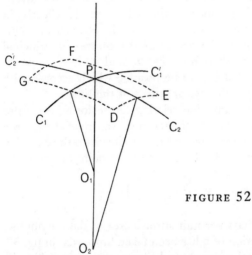

FIGURE 52

In fig. 52 a situation is illustrated in which, in the neighbourhood of P, the surface is synclastic. $C_1'PC_1$ and $C_2'PC_2$ represent the principal normal sections through P, and O_1 and O_2 the centres of principal curvature of the surface at P. Let us consider a small 'rectangular' element of the surface around P, the sides of the rectangle being parallel, respectively, to $C_1'PC_1$ and $C_2'PC_2$. Let this rectangle intercept a small length Δa of the former principal section and a length Δb of the latter. The rectangular element of surface, DEFG, is shown dotted in the figure, with $DE = \Delta a$, $GD = \Delta b$.

Now suppose that DEFG represents an element of a membrane under homogeneous tension T. Forces of magnitude $T\Delta b$ act across GD and FE, producing a resultant $T\Delta b \cdot \Delta a / r_1$ along PO_1. Similarly, the resultant of the tensions across DE and GF is $T\Delta a \cdot \Delta b / r_2$ along PO_2. These two resultants act together along the normal to the surface at P. Obviously, in total, an element of the membrane around this point is subject to a 'restoring' force, in the direction of the centres of principal curvature belonging to the point, of magnitude $T\left(\dfrac{1}{r_1} + \dfrac{1}{r_2}\right)$ per unit area of surface. This result has been derived specifically for the case in which the surface of the membrane is synclastic in the region under consideration. If the surface is anticlastic, it is not difficult to see that the same result remains valid, once the appropriate sign convention has been adopted in respect of the radii r_1 and r_2. Clearly, in this case, the overall restoring force acts on the element of membrane in the direction of the nearer of the centres of principal curvature. We assume, therefore, that r_1 and r_2 have opposite signs, and we choose that one to be positive which accords with the particular formalism that we are using at the time.

Having obtained an expression relating the restoring force per unit area of displaced surface to the mean curvature of the surface and the tension in the membrane, we may write down the equation giving the acceleration of displacement of the point (x, y) in the form

$$m \frac{\partial^2 z}{\partial t^2} = - T \left(\frac{1}{r_1} + \frac{1}{r_2}\right).$$

Here m denotes the mass per unit surface area of the membrane, and the positive direction of z has been taken 'upwards' in fig. 52. On the basis of equation (203), and always supposing that the displacement is very small (or, more precisely, that the tangent plane at any point on the displaced surface of the membrane is inclined at a very small angle to the median plane of the undisturbed membrane), we have

$$-\left(\frac{1}{r_1} + \frac{1}{r_2}\right) = \frac{\partial^2 z}{\partial x^2} + \frac{\partial^2 z}{\partial y^2},$$

whatever choice of rectangular axes (of x and y) is made in the initial plane. Then the equation of motion becomes

$$\frac{\partial^2 z}{\partial t^2} = \frac{T}{m}\left(\frac{\partial^2 z}{\partial x^2} + \frac{\partial^2 z}{\partial y^2}\right) \qquad (204)$$

This general result was obtained first by Euler in 1766, but the problem of the normal modes of membranes having boundaries of various simple shapes was not solved in detail until many years later. For our purposes, we merely note the obvious similarity in form between equation (204) and equation (110)—and other 'wave' equations that we might have obtained if we had adopted the traditional approach of the mathematical physicist (see p. 128) earlier in this book. There is an obvious similarity between the equations, and the obvious difference—that two spatial co-ordinates are involved in equation (204), as independent variables, whereas only one such independent variable is involved in equation (110). Our present equation is the two-dimensional form of the other.

In this section, as we have implied, our main concern is with the normal modes of vibration of membranes of simple shapes: we revert, therefore, to the method that we employed at the outset (see §§ 2.3, 2.6). We seek constant values of μ such that

$$\frac{\partial^2 z}{\partial t^2} = -\mu z$$

is satisfied instantaneously at all points on the membrane, then we calculate the frequencies of the normal modes by use of the standard equation

$$4\pi^2 f^2 = \mu \, .$$

In following this procedure we have to satisfy

$$\frac{\partial^2 z}{\partial x^2} + \frac{\partial^2 z}{\partial y^2} + \frac{\mu m}{T} z = 0 \qquad (205)$$

with μ constant, over the whole membrane. The situation is simplest when the membrane is rectangular, and this is the case that we shall consider first.

Let us take axes of x and y along two edges of the membrane that meet in a point. Let the 'length' of the boundary of the membrane along the x-axis be a, and the 'breadth' of the boundary along the y-axis be b. Then the boundary conditions determining the motion of the membrane are given by $z=0$ for $x=0$, $x=a$, $y=0$ and $y=b$, and it is easy to see that if k and l are positive integers, the equation

$$z = A \sin k\pi \frac{x}{a} \sin l\pi \frac{y}{b} \qquad (206)$$

satisfies these conditions, and that it is a solution of equation (205), always provided that

$$\frac{\mu m}{T} = \pi^2 \left(\frac{k^2}{a^2} + \frac{l^2}{b^2} \right) \qquad (207)$$

Equation (207) gives values of μ appropriate to our problem: the corresponding values of f are given by

$$f^2 = \frac{T}{4m} \left(\frac{k^2}{a^2} + \frac{l^2}{b^2} \right) \qquad (208)$$

Equation (206) was first derived as a solution to the problem of the normal modes of a rectangular membrane by Poisson in 1829. It may indeed be shown that it provides a complete* solution, so that equation (208), which follows from it, specifies the whole series of frequencies belonging to such modes. It will be obvious, at once, that these frequencies do not constitute a harmonic series, each being determined by two integers in any case. Furthermore, it will be clear that, when the ratio a^2/b^2 is incommensurable, it is impossible for the frequencies of any two normal modes, say the modes (k, l) and (k', l'), to be the same. It will also be clear that, for vibration in any normal mode so determined—in general, for the normal mode (k, l), there will be $k-1$ nodal lines parallel to the breadth, and $l-1$ nodal lines parallel to the length, of the membrane, dividing the membrane into kl equal rectangular areas of disturbance.

In § 2.11, for the case of the stretched string, we used Fourier's theorem to establish the result that the most general type of

---

* We have apparently limited the solution by the restriction that k and l shall be positive integers, but a little consideration will show that precisely the same normal mode is involved if in equation (206) we insert in turn the pairs of integral numbers (k, l) $(-k, l)$, $(k, -l)$ and $(-k, -l)$. The restriction in question does not, therefore, limit the generality of our treatment.

sustained motion of which a finite length of string is capable is that which would result if the normal modes of the string were superposed with arbitrary amplitudes and phases. In subsequent chapters, particularly in chapter 3, we took for granted the general validity of this result. We follow that course now, making use, in particular, of a less comprehensive proposition, namely, that any combination of two or more normal modes, the amplitudes and relative phases being specified, is a possible type of sustained motion of a vibratory system.

In the case of the rectangular membrane, when the ratio a^2/b^2 is incommensurable, the exercise of superposing normal modes adds little of interest to our understanding of the situation, for the frequencies are all different. However, when a^2/b^2 is an integral fraction, it is always possible to find two sets of integers, (k, l) and (k', l'), such that

$$\frac{k^2}{a^2} + \frac{l^2}{b^2} = \frac{k'^2}{a^2} + \frac{l'^2}{b^2} \tag{209}$$

In that case the frequencies of the normal modes (k, l) and (k', l') are the same—and indeed, in general, the frequencies of the two modes (nk, nl) and (nk', nl') will then be identical, whatever the value of the integer n. When two or more normal modes of a system have the same frequency, we say that sustained motion of the system with that frequency is 'degenerate'. As we shall see (p. 300), the 'displacement profile' corresponding to such motion is not of uniquely determined form.

In the last paragraph we have made a statement without proof which merits further consideration. We have stated that if a^2/b^2 is an integral fraction then equation (209) can always be satisfied using integral values of k, l, k', l'. Let us write

$$\frac{a^2}{b^2} = \frac{p}{q},$$

where p and q are positive integers having no common factor. Then equation (209) may be rewritten

$$\frac{k^2 - k'^2}{l'^2 - l^2} = \frac{p}{q},$$

or

$$\frac{(k - k')(k + k')}{(l' - l)(l' + l)} = \frac{jp}{jq} \tag{210}$$

where j is itself an arbitrary integer. On the basis of equation (210), obviously one solution of equation (209) which satisfies the conditions that we have imposed is implicit in the four equations

$$k - k' = l' - l = j,$$
$$k + k' = p,$$
$$l' + l = q.$$

This solution is given explicitly by

$$
\begin{aligned}
k &= (p+j)/2, & l &= (q-j)/2 \\
k' &= (p-j)/2, & l' &= (q+j)/2
\end{aligned}
\tag{211}
$$

It will be noted that, when p and q are given, not every choice of j leads to integral values of k, l, k', l' according to equations (211). Indeed, when p is odd and q is even (they cannot both be even, according to our definition), or *vice versa*, every choice of j results in values for two of these quantities which are of the form $(2r+1)/2$, where r is integral. In each case, however, formally at least, equation (210) is satisfied, and it is merely necessary to multiply all the values of k, l, k', l' concerned (two of them 'half-integral' at this stage of the calculation) by the factor 2 in order to obtain a set of integral values which satisfy equation (209).

Again, since we have specified (p. 296) that k, l, k', l' should be positive integers, it might appear that the integer j should be limited to such positive values as are smaller than the smaller of the integers p and q. This limitation, also, is illusory. We have stated (footnote, p. 296) that the four sets of integers which result from taking all possible combinations out of the bracket $(\pm k, \pm l)$ specify the same normal mode. We should more properly write $l = |q-j|/2$, $k' = |p-j|/2$ in equations (211), therefore, and accept any positive value of j as relevant to our problem. We could, indeed, go farther and accept negative values of j, but this would add nothing to our solution. Clearly, to change the sign of j in equations (211) is merely to interchange the values of (k, l) and (k', l'). Aside, then, from the negative values, which are redundant, the only values of j which are irrelevant in the present context are $j = 0$, $j = p$ and $j = q$.

We have now established the truth of the proposition which

previously (p. 297) we asserted without formal justification. Although we have not derived a tidy formula enumerating the frequencies, it will be abundantly evident from what we have done that, when a^2/b^2 is commensurable, there are many frequencies (strictly, an unlimited number) corresponding to each of which the solution giving the normal mode of the membrane is a degenerate solution. Let us take a very simple example. Let $p=5$, $q=3$. In the table below we have calculated, strictly according to equations (211), the values of k, l, k', l' for $1 \leqslant j \leqslant 6$. The figures in brackets are the 'effective' values obtained by multiplying the original values by two, or neglecting the negative sign, or both, as appropriate according to our previous discussion. Following these adjustments, in the final column of the table we have inserted, where relevant, the values of $3k^2+5l^2$ ($\equiv 3k'^2+5l'^2$), which quantity, according to equations (208) and (209), is proportional, in this case, to the square of the frequency of the degenerate vibration. Clearly the table might be extended in-

TABLE

j	k	l	k'	l'	$3k^2+5l^2$
1	3	1	2	2	32
2	$3\frac{1}{2}$ (7)	$\frac{1}{2}$ (1)	$1\frac{1}{2}$ (3)	$2\frac{1}{2}$ (5)	152
3	4	0	1	3	*
4	$4\frac{1}{2}$ (9)	$-\frac{1}{2}$ (1)	$\frac{1}{2}$ (1)	$3\frac{1}{2}$ (7)	248
5	5	-1 (1)	0	4	*
6	$5\frac{1}{2}$ (11)	$-1\frac{1}{2}$ (3)	$-\frac{1}{2}$ (1)	$4\frac{1}{2}$ (9)	408

* Irrelevant solutions.

definitely; moreover, it is not exhaustive. We have already stated, generally, that if any set of values k, l, k', l' satisfies equation (209) then the set nk, nl, nk', nl' also satisfies the equation. Within the range of frequencies covered by the table, therefore, we have to consider the sets 6, 2, 4, 4 and 9, 3, 6, 6, which would not otherwise arise, and for which the appropriate values of $3k^2+5l^2$ are 128 and 288, respectively. The first six frequencies for which the motion is degenerate, in this case, are thus in the ratios of the square roots of the numbers 4, 16, 19, 31, 36 and 51, that is in the ratios $1 : 2 : 2 \cdot 180 : 2 \cdot 784 : 3 : 3 \cdot 571$.

Having considered the frequencies of the possible degenerate vibrations, we should next consider further our general statement that for any such frequency the two-dimensional displacement profile characteristic of the motion of the membrane is not of uniquely determined form (p. 297). It requires no elaborate proof to justify this statement. Assuming that the normal modes (k, l), (k', l') have the same frequency f, as before, the motion of the membrane when these modes are superposed with arbitrary amplitudes and phases is described, in terms of the expression for the instantaneous displacement of a representative point on the membrane, by the equation (compare equation (209))

$$z = A \sin k\pi \frac{x}{a} \sin l\pi \frac{y}{b} \cos 2\pi f t + B \sin k'\pi \frac{x}{a} \sin l'\pi \frac{y}{b} \cos (2\pi f t + \delta).$$

The two-dimensional displacement profile of this motion is given by

$$z = (z_0{}^2 + z_0'{}^2 + 2 z_0 z_0' \cos \delta)^{\frac{1}{2}} \tag{212}$$

where

$$z_0 = A \sin k\pi \frac{x}{a} \sin l\pi \frac{y}{b},$$

$$z_0' = B \sin k'\pi \frac{x}{a} \sin l'\pi \frac{y}{b}.$$

Obviously, the form which equation (212) defines is not uniquely determined: its details depend significantly on the values of A, B and δ concerned. Here we shall not follow this aspect of the matter farther, except to show, by a simple illustration, that in the case of degenerate vibrations it is possible to obtain patterns of nodal lines on a rectangular membrane quite different from the rectangular patterns characteristic of the single normal modes which equation (206) describes.

Let us simplify the issue, to begin with, by considering only the situation in which, in relation to equation (212), $A = B$, $\delta = \pi$. In this case,

$$z = A \left(\sin k\pi \frac{x}{a} \sin l\pi \frac{y}{b} - \sin k'\pi \frac{x}{a} \sin l'\pi \frac{y}{b} \right).$$

By a two-stage transformation, we obtain as an alternative form

$$z = A\left[\sin\frac{\pi}{2}\left\{(k+k')\frac{x}{a}+(l+l')\frac{y}{b}\right\} \sin\frac{\pi}{2}\left\{(k-k')\frac{x}{a}-(l'-l)\frac{y}{b}\right\}\right.$$

$$\left.-\sin\frac{\pi}{2}\left\{(k+k')\frac{x}{a}-(l+l')\frac{y}{b}\right\} \sin\frac{\pi}{2}\left\{(k-k')\frac{x}{a}+(l'-l)\frac{y}{b}\right\}\right],$$

then, substituting for $k+k'$, $l+l'$, $k-k'$ and $l'-l$ (see p. 298), and noting that $pb/a=qa/b=\sqrt{pq}$, we have

$$z = A\left[\sin\frac{\pi}{2}\sqrt{pq}\left(\frac{x}{b}+\frac{y}{a}\right) \sin\frac{\pi}{2}j\left(\frac{x}{a}-\frac{y}{b}\right)\right.$$

$$\left.-\sin\frac{\pi}{2}\sqrt{pq}\left(\frac{x}{b}-\frac{y}{a}\right) \sin\frac{\pi}{2}j\left(\frac{x}{a}+\frac{y}{b}\right)\right]$$

(213)

The nodal condition $z=0$, taken in conjunction with equation (213), defines such nodal lines as there may be in this particular case, but we see that, although the situation has already been severely simplified, no explicit solutions emerge. For a square membrane, however, one result may be established, of restricted generality. We now write $a=b$, and $p=q=1$. Then it is clear that the diagonal $x=y$ is a nodal line, under the conditions that we have assumed, for all degenerate vibrations which are specified in terms of equations (211)—that is whatever the value of j. For, making the appropriate substitutions in equation (213), we obtain

$$z = A\left[\sin\frac{\pi}{2a}(x+y) \sin\frac{\pi}{2a}j(x-y)-\sin\frac{\pi}{2a}(x-y) \sin\frac{\pi}{2a}j(x+y)\right]$$

$$= 0.$$

Let us repeat our conclusion in words. If the two normal modes involved in a degenerate vibration of a square membrane according to any of the specifications of equations (211) are superposed with a phase difference of 180° and with equal amplitudes, then one diagonal of the square is a nodal line in every such case. We note that the diagonals are never nodal lines when the motion is not degenerate and only a single normal mode is involved.

We have now discussed the vibrations of a rectangular membrane in some detail. The corresponding vibrations of a circular membrane are more complicated, and we shall do little more than state certain results valid in respect of them. Indeed, we shall confine attention almost exclusively to the symmetrical modes of vibration, in which the question of degenerate solutions does not arise. A 'symmetrical' mode, in this connection, is one in which the displacement amplitude of an arbitrary point on the membrane is a function of the radial distance alone, or, in the notation which we have previously used, if r is the distance of the point from the centre of the membrane, then, in a symmetrical normal mode, $z = \phi(r)$, simply.

To define the problem precisely, let us suppose that a uniform membrane, of mass m per unit area of surface, is held in a state of homogeneous tension T in a circular frame of radius a. Then it is clear that the boundary condition is given by $\phi(a) = 0$: the circular boundary is a vibration node for all modes. It should also be clear that the centre of the membrane is an anti-node: it cannot be a node, for it is characteristic of a nodal point, or line, that the sign of the displacement changes from one 'side' of the nodal point (or line) to the other. It would be inconsistent with our assumption of circular symmetry to admit this possibility in respect of the central point of the membrane in the present context. There may be other nodal and anti-nodal circles, in the symmetrical modes, but the centre is an anti-nodal point for all such modes.

For our present purposes, we shall be content to quote the results giving the radii of the nodal circles, and the corresponding frequencies of vibration, for the symmetrical normal modes of the circular membrane of radius a. Basically what is required for this specification is a table of solutions of the equation

$$\mathcal{J}_0\left(k\pi\frac{r}{a}\right) = 0,$$

where
$$\mathcal{J}_0(x) = 1 - \frac{x^2}{2^2} + \frac{x^4}{2^2 4^2} - \dots$$

$\mathcal{J}_0(x)$ is referred to as the zero-order Bessel Function of the first kind. If $x_1, x_2, \dots$ are the values of x for which $\mathcal{J}_0(x) = 0$, then $_n r_1, _n r_2, \dots, _n r_i, \dots _n r_n$, the radii of the nodal circles for the normal mode of order n, are given by the equations

$$k\pi = x_n$$

$$k\pi \frac{n^{r_i}}{a} = x_i \tag{214}$$

The first four values of x_n/π are 0·7655, 1·7571, 2·7546 and 3·7534. It will be noticed that, to a very rough approximation for small values of n (and to a much better approximation for very large value of n), $x_n/\pi = n - \frac{1}{4}$.

The frequency of the nth normal mode is given by

$$f_n = \frac{k}{2a}\sqrt{\frac{T}{m}} \tag{215}$$

(which may be compared with equation (208) for the rectangular membrane), that is by

$$f_n = \frac{x_n}{2\pi a}\sqrt{\frac{T}{m}} \tag{216}$$

or, even more significantly, by

$$f_n = \frac{0·383}{n^{r_1}}\sqrt{\frac{T}{m}} \tag{217}$$

It will be realised that equation (216) has been obtained by substituting for k, in equation (215), the value given by the first of equations (214), and that equation (217) has been similarly derived by substituting for k/a from the second of equations (214) and inserting the numerical value of the constant x_i/π appropriate when $i = 1$. We say that equation (217) is even more significant, for our purposes, than equation (216), because it illustrates the result that the frequency of vibration, in the nth normal mode, is the same as that which the membrane would have, in its first normal mode, if its radius were reduced to that of the first nodal circle of the nth mode. In the nth mode, the membrane within the first nodal circle (or, indeed, between any two nodal circles) vibrates as it might vibrate if its area were limited to the region within that circle (or to the annular region between two such circles) and it were held at the same tension as before.

It will be seen that the series of frequencies specified by equations (215)-(217) is not a harmonic series; on the other hand substitution of the approximate relation $x_n/\pi = n - \frac{1}{4}$ in equation (216) shows that the series possesses a near-regularity of another type—it is a series in which the difference of frequency between successive terms is roughly constant, namely, $(T/m)^{\frac{1}{2}}/2a$.

Reference has already been made, in passing, to the other normal modes of vibration of a circular membrane which do not exhibit circular symmetry. Here, nothing further will be said about these normal modes except that they are characterised by nodal lines which are diameters of the membrane. In general, both nodal circles and nodal diameters are in evidence: because in every such mode there is at least one nodal line which is a diameter, clearly, the central point of the membrane is a nodal point for all of them. Obviously, also, in the specification of these normal modes, two integers are involved—the numbers of circular and diametral nodal lines, respectively, in the two-dimensional pattern of displacement.

10.3. ELASTIC VIBRATIONS OF PLATES

In the last section we described the vibrations of a uniformly stretched membrane as the two-dimensional analogue of the vibrations of a flexible string maintained under constant tension. We noted that the complexity of the situation is considerably greater for this two-dimensional system than for the one-dimensional. Not only is there the limitless choice, for two-dimensional systems generally, of the shape of the boundary, but even with the simplest boundary shapes the problem of the membrane appeared as one of some subtlety.

In this section our subject is the two-dimensional analogue of the transverse elastic vibrations of a rod. When we considered that problem, in section 4.3, we were unable to treat it, in full, systematically: we were compelled to quote certain basic results rather than to derive them. Here, therefore, in respect of the corresponding two-dimensional system, we shall be even more restricted than we were in section 10.2; there will be little that we shall be able to follow through consecutively to the end—and it will not be as profitable as it was then merely to quote results for the intrinsic interest that attaches to them. Yet, from the practical side, it should not be forgotten that the telephone is a more widely-used instrument than the kettledrum: in the realm of daily life the properties of the circular plate clamped around the circumference are more 'important' than those of the circular membrane held under homogeneous tension. It is merely an unfortunate fact that the former system is one degree more complicated, physically, than the latter.

Let us, first of all, then, discuss our present problem in entirely general terms. In earlier chapters of this book, when we have been dealing with the problem of normal modes of continuous systems, we have invariably obtained an expression for the frequencies in which are multiplied together a pure number, different for the different modes, a physical quantity—or a combination of such quantities—of the dimensions L^{-1}, and a second composite quantity of the dimensions L^1T^{-1}, a velocity. In the simplest cases this velocity has been identifiable as the velocity of propagation of a sinusoidal disturbance (of whatever wavelength) in an infinite system conformable with the finite system under consideration. In less simple cases—and that of the transverse vibrations of a cantilever was one of these (see p. 90)—it was not possible to make such an identification, but our generalisation concerning the form of the expression for the frequencies was exemplified, nevertheless. The same generalisation covers the cases dealt with in the last section (see equations (208) and (215)), and we should expect it to remain valid here. On the other hand, our present system being, in one of its possible forms, the two-dimensional analogue of the cantilever, it is unlikely that we shall be able to identify the velocity which should appear in the frequency formula. We are dealing now with elastic vibrations, and, in conformity with the results previously obtained in similar situations, we should expect the velocity term to be of the form $(E/\rho)^{\frac{1}{2}}$, ρ denoting the density of the material of the plate and E the modulus of elasticity appropriate to the type of strain involved. Let us, then, follow these various leads, in turn, in an attempt to build up a 'reasonable' expression for the frequencies—even if we are able to make that expression explicit only for the very simplest case.

First, let us consider with which elastic modulus we are concerned. This is not a question which can be dealt with summarily. The stress in the vibrating plate arises because of the instantaneous curvature of its originally flat surface. In the case of the rod (p. 85) we decided that the appropriate modulus, relating the bending moment to the curvature, is Young's modulus. But in that case,

U

from point to point along the rod, the axis of the bending moment was assumed to be unidirectional—perpendicular to the axis of the rod, and horizontal, when bending was produced by an external load. At any point in the plate, the situation will not be as simple as this, whatever we assume to be the boundary conditions.

In discussing our present problem, our initial assumption is that, at any point in the plate, the three components of stress (the normal stress and the two components of tangential stress) over any section parallel to the free surface of the plate are zero. We shall be concerned to evaluate the 'restoring' force acting from the rest of the plate on a small portion of the plate around an arbitrary point. In general, then, we may have to do with six non-zero components of stress. With reference to a set of rectangular axes (of x and y), arbitrarily oriented in a plane parallel to the tangent plane to the median surface of the plate at the point in question, we define four of these stress components as follows: we denote by p_x and p_y the magnitudes of the components of tensile stress acting (normally) across the normal sections of the plate which are perpendicular, respectively, to OX and OY, and by p_{yx} and p_{xy} the magnitudes of the components of shearing stress acting (tangentially) over these same sections and parallel to the xy plane. We note that, when the plate is vibrating, the instantaneous values of p_x, p_y, p_{yx} and p_{xy} will necessarily vary from point to point, along any normal to the median surface, through the plate— changing sign through that surface, over which all these components of stress vanish. To begin with, therefore, we confine attention to the state of stress of a very thin element of the plate lying parallel to the median surface.

In fig. 53 such an element is shown in 'plan', together with the arbitrary axes of x and y, and arrows indicating the convention of sign which we shall adopt in relation to the stress components. In general, an element such as ABCD will be curved, in conformity with the curvature of the portion of the median surface to which it corresponds. Let us suppose that $X_0'OX_0$ and $Y_0'OY_0$ are the directions of the lines of principal curvature through O, the midpoint of the element which we are considering, and let θ denote the measure of the angle between OX_0 and OX. It is a property of the rectangular axes $X_0'OX_0$, $Y_0'OY$, which the lines of principal curvature uniquely determine, that the state of stress of the element may be described, in relation to this set of axes (and no

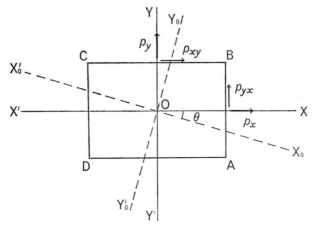

FIGURE 53

other), by the two components of tensile stress p_{x_0} and p_{y_0} alone: these components are finite, but $p_{y_0 x_0}$ and $p_{x_0 y_0}$ are zero. In fig. 54 is illustrated a very small portion of the whole plate, rectangular with respect to the lines of principal curvature through the central point O. Across the facets $A_0 B_0'$ and $B_0 C_0'$ (and across the facets opposite to them) the distributions of tensile force described by p_{x_0} and p_{y_0}, constitute couples (the principal bending moments— compare p. 84), simply, the axes of these couples being parallel, respectively, to $Y_0' OY$ and $X_0' OX$.

Since it is of the essence of the problem with which we are concerned to be able to take count of the change of curvature, in respect of both magnitude and direction, from point to point over the plate as a whole, our main investigation must be made with reference to arbitrary axes. We return, therefore, to fig. 53, and to the relations that exist between the two specifications of the state of stress at any point in a thin element of the plate—the relation, that is, between the stress components p_x, p_y, p_{yx}, p_{xy} and the equivalent set of components p_{x_0}, p_{y_0}, which we have now defined. Following the method adopted in relating the two specifications of a simple shearing stress in $M L \,\&\, T$, § 16.1, we obtain, in this case,

$$p_x = p_{x_0} \cos^2 \theta + p_{y_0} \sin^2 \theta$$
$$p_y = p_{x_0} \sin^2 \theta + p_{y_0} \cos^2 \theta$$

(218)

$$-p_{yx} = -p_{xy} = (p_{x_0} - p_{y_0}) \sin \theta \cos \theta$$

(219)

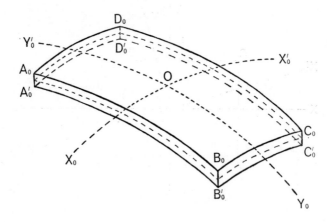

FIGURE 54

To obtain our next set of equations, we must consider once more a thin element of the plate rectangular with respect to the lines of principal curvature through its centre. Let us assume that the element is situated at a distance ζ 'above' the median surface (shown dotted in fig. 54). Let the principal radii of curvature of that surface at O be r_1 and r_2, and the principal components of elongation (extensive strain) of the element be e_{x_0} and e_{y_0}. Then, if Y denotes the measure of Young's modulus and σ is Poisson's ratio for the material of the plate, we have

$$e_{x_0} = \frac{1}{Y}(p_{x_0} - \sigma p_{y_0}) = \frac{\zeta}{r_1},$$

$$e_{y_0} = \frac{1}{Y}(-\sigma p_{x_0} + p_{y_0}) = \frac{\zeta}{r_2}.$$

Hence
$$p_{x_0} = \frac{Y\zeta}{1-\sigma^2}\left(\frac{1}{r_1} + \frac{\sigma}{r_2}\right)$$

$$p_{y_0} = \frac{Y\zeta}{1-\sigma^2}\left(\frac{\sigma}{r_1} + \frac{1}{r_2}\right)$$

(220)

In terms of equations (218), (219) and (220), we are now in a position to derive expressions for the components of stress at any

point in the plate, in respect of an arbitrary set of axes, the same
for the whole plate,* the independent parameters in these expressions being the magnitudes and directions of the principal
curvatures of the median surface of the plate, defined, from point
to point, by the quantities r_1, r_2 and θ of the equations in question.
We have, in fact,

$$p_x = \frac{Y\zeta}{1-\sigma^2}\left\{\left(\frac{\cos^2\theta}{r_1}+\frac{\sin^2\theta}{r_2}\right)+\sigma\left(\frac{\cos^2\theta}{r_2}+\frac{\sin^2\theta}{r_1}\right)\right\}$$

$$p_y = \frac{Y\zeta}{1-\sigma^2}\left\{\sigma\left(\frac{\cos^2\theta}{r_1}+\frac{\sin^2\theta}{r_2}\right)+\left(\frac{\cos^2\theta}{r_2}+\frac{\sin^2\theta}{r_1}\right)\right\}$$
(221)

$$-p_{yx} = -p_{xy} = \frac{Y\zeta}{1-\sigma^2}(1-\sigma)\left(\frac{1}{r_1}-\frac{1}{r_2}\right)\sin\theta\cos\theta \quad (222)$$

We next replace the independent parameters r_1, r_2 and θ in equations (221) and (222) by the appropriate partial derivatives, with
respect to x and y, of z the instantaneous displacement of the
point (x, y) in the median plane of the undisturbed plate. We are
assuming that positive values of r_1 and r_2 correspond to lines of
principal curvature which are convex towards the positive direction of z. We then have (see equation (202) and p. 306)

$$\frac{\cos^2\theta}{r_1}+\frac{\sin^2\theta}{r_2} = -\frac{\partial^2 z}{\partial x^2}$$

$$\frac{\sin^2\theta}{r_1}+\frac{\cos^2\theta}{r_2} = -\frac{\partial^2 z}{\partial y^2},$$

and a further result, which we have not previously quoted,

$$\left(\frac{1}{r_1}-\frac{1}{r_2}\right)\sin\theta\cos\theta = \frac{\partial^2 z}{\partial x\,\partial y}.$$

* There is only one proviso, here. Hitherto, our 'arbitrary' axes
X'OX, Y'OY have been taken 'in a plane parallel to the tangent plane
to the median surface of the plate at the point in question'. Provided
always that the median surface is nowhere inclined to its initial undisturbed plane configuration at more than a very small angle, we can
obviously take arbitrary axes in that initial plane as effective for the plate
as a whole. We make the necessary assumption, therefore, and adopt
arbitrary axes accordingly.

In consequence we may write, more neatly than before,

$$-p_x = \frac{Y\zeta}{1-\sigma^2}\left(\frac{\partial^2 z}{\partial x^2} + \sigma\frac{\partial^2 z}{\partial y^2}\right)$$

$$-p_y = \frac{Y\zeta}{1-\sigma^2}\left(\sigma\frac{\partial^2 z}{\partial x^2} + \frac{\partial^2 z}{\partial y^2}\right)$$

(223)

$$-p_{yx} = -p_{xy} = \frac{Y\zeta}{1-\sigma^2}(1-\sigma)\frac{\partial^2 z}{\partial x\,\partial y} \qquad (224)$$

In respect of equations (223) and (224), ζ varies, along any normal through the plate, between the limits $d/2$ and $-d/2$, d being the thickness of the plate.

Let us now consider any small rectangular element of a normal section of the plate, stretching from its upper to its lower surface. It is clear that the forces parallel to the median surface acting over this element reduce to two couples, simply: because of the symmetry across this surface which equations (223) and (224) reveal, the elementary tensile and shearing forces cancel completely, except for the torques to which, separately, they give rise. To give precision to our statement, let us assume that the rectangular element of normal section is perpendicular to OX, and that its breadth is Δy. Then the tensile forces specified by p_x (equation (223)) reduce to a couple $M_x\Delta y$, acting from the material to the positive side of the section on the material to the negative side (in respect of x), where

$$M_x = \int_{-\frac{d}{2}}^{\frac{d}{2}} p_x\zeta d\zeta.$$

Here we adopt for p_x the sign convention of fig. 53, and for M_x the right-handed screw convention (see $M L \,\&\, T$, p. 81). Similarly, the shearing forces specified by p_{yx} reduce to a couple $T_x\Delta y$, where

$$T_x = -\int_{-\frac{d}{2}}^{\frac{d}{2}} p_{yx}\zeta d\zeta.$$

We therefore have, explicitly,

$$M_x = -\frac{Yd^3}{12(1-\sigma^2)}\left(\frac{\partial^2 z}{\partial x^2} + \sigma\frac{\partial^2 z}{\partial y^2}\right) \qquad (225)$$

$$T_x = \frac{Yd^3}{12(1-\sigma^2)}(1-\sigma)\frac{\partial^2 z}{\partial x\,\partial y} \qquad (226)$$

Over the element of normal section that we have considered the couple of which $M_x \Delta y$ is the measure is a bending moment having Y'OY as axis; the couple of which $T_x \Delta y$ is the measure is a twisting torque effective about X'OX.

By a calculation similar to that which we have just carried out, we obtain, analogously, for the bending moment per unit length, and the twisting torque per unit length, across a rectangular element of normal section perpendicular to OY,

$$M_y = \frac{Yd^3}{12(1-\sigma^2)}\left(\sigma\frac{\partial^2 z}{\partial x^2}+\frac{\partial^2 z}{\partial y^2}\right) \qquad (227)$$

$$T_y = -\frac{Yd^3}{12(1-\sigma^2)}(1-\sigma)\frac{\partial^2 z}{\partial x\,\partial y} \qquad (228)$$

The axis appropriate to M_y is X'OX; that appropriate to T_y is Y'OY.

Our aim, as already indicated, is to evaluate the 'restoring' force acting from the rest of the plate on a small portion of the plate around an arbitrary point (p. 306). In fig. 54, according to its original description, is illustrated such an elementary portion of the plate, rectangular with respect to the lines of principal curvature at its mid-point O. Let us use this same figure to represent an elementary portion of the plate, rectangular with respect to the 'arbitrary' axes of x and y which we are now employing, disregarding the subscripts in the figure for this purpose. Let $CB = \Delta x$ and $AB = \Delta y$, and let equations (225)-(228) refer to conditions at the mid-point O. Then, in general, the bending moment over the facet AB' will not be precisely the same as that over CD', and, as a result, an 'unbalanced' couple of amount

$$\frac{\partial M_x}{\partial x}\Delta y\Delta x$$

will act about Y'OY. About the same axis there will also be an unbalanced couple

$$\frac{\partial T_y}{\partial y}\Delta x\,\Delta y$$

representing the difference between the twisting torques over BC' and AD′. In the same way, about X′OX, the elementary rectangular portion of the plate under consideration will be subject to unbalanced couples of total amount

$$\left(\frac{\partial M_y}{\partial y}+\frac{\partial T_x}{\partial x}\right)\varDelta x\varDelta y.$$

We are assuming that the motion of every point in the plate, in the course of its vibration, is normal to the initial plane. Provided that the vibration is of small amplitude, this is a sufficiently good approximation to the truth. Accepting it, we have to conclude that the so-called 'unbalanced' couples that we have just identified must, in fact, be balanced by the action of forces of which we have not as yet taken count. The only stress components that we have not hitherto considered are the possible components of shearing stress parallel to OZ. If, over a rectangular element of normal section of the plate through O and perpendicular to OX, the total shearing force per unit area in the direction OZ is denoted by F_{zx}/d, and if F_{zy}/d denotes the corresponding quantity when a normal section perpendicular to OY is in question, the operation of these shearing forces over the pairs of facets AB′ and CD′, and BC′ and AD′, respectively, will equilibrate the 'unbalanced' couples if

$$-F_{zx}\varDelta y\varDelta x+\left(\frac{\partial M_x}{\partial x}+\frac{\partial T_y}{\partial y}\right)\varDelta x\varDelta y = 0,$$

that is, if
$$F_{zx} = \left(\frac{\partial M_x}{\partial x}+\frac{\partial T_y}{\partial y}\right) \tag{229}$$

and
$$F_{zy} = -\left(\frac{\partial M_y}{\partial y}+\frac{\partial T_x}{\partial x}\right) \tag{230}$$

We have introduced the quantities F_{zx} and F_{zy} as characteristic of the state of stress at the mid-point O, and for the purposes of equations (229) and (230) we have effectively assumed that the same values apply over the whole of the elementary rectangular portion of the plate under consideration. In general, this will not be so: the portion of plate AC′ (fig. 54) will be subject to an unbalanced force, in the direction OZ, given by

$$\frac{\partial F_{zx}}{\partial x}\varDelta y\,\varDelta x+\frac{\partial F_{zy}}{\partial y}\varDelta x\,\varDelta y.$$

If we denote this quantity by $F_z\,\varDelta x\,\varDelta y$, we have

$$F_z = \frac{\partial^2 M_x}{\partial x^2} - \frac{\partial^2 M_y}{\partial y^2} + \frac{\partial}{\partial x\,\partial y}(T_y - T_x).$$

Here we have substituted for F_{zx} and F_{zy} from equations (229) and (230). If we now substitute for M_x, M_y, T_x and T_y from equations (225)-(228), we have, finally,

$$-F_z = \frac{Yd^3}{12(1-\sigma^2)}\left\{\frac{\partial^4 z}{\partial x^4} + \sigma\frac{\partial^4 z}{\partial x^2\,\partial y^2} + \sigma\frac{\partial^4 z}{\partial x^2\,\partial y^2} + \frac{\partial^4 z}{\partial y^4}\right.$$
$$\left. + 2(1-\sigma)\frac{\partial^4 z}{\partial x^2\,\partial y^2}\right\},$$

$$\text{or} \quad -F_z = \frac{Yd^3}{12(1-\sigma^2)}\left(\frac{\partial^4 z}{\partial x^4} + \frac{\partial^4 z}{\partial y^4} + 2\frac{\partial^4 z}{\partial x^2\,\partial y^2}\right) \tag{231}$$

This is the expression for the restoring force (per unit area of plate) that we have been seeking. The instantaneous acceleration of the mid-point of the elementary portion AC' is now given by

$$F_z = \rho d\frac{\partial^2 z}{\partial t^2} \tag{232}$$

where ρ is the measure of the density of the material of the plate, as already defined.

Taking equations (231) and (232) together, we see that when the variation of curvature over the median surface of the plate is completely specified, the acceleration at any point in that surface is proportional to $Yd^2/(1-\sigma^2)\rho$. Our original aim was to identify the modulus E, which we expected would appear in a term $(E/\rho)^{\frac{1}{2}}$ in the expression for the frequencies of the normal modes, once the boundary conditions were given. The present result not only allows this identification to be made—the modulus in question is clearly $Y/(1-\sigma^2)$, but it also shows that, if $\{Y/(1-\sigma^2)\rho\}^{\frac{1}{2}}$ occurs in the formula, then it does so with d as a multiplier. Having established this conclusion, we shall confine our further discussion to the special case of the telephone diaphragm—that is, the circular plate clamped around the circumference.

As we stated previously, if the expression for the frequencies contains a term of the dimensions of a velocity, then this term must be multiplied by another of the dimensions of a wave number

(L^{-1}). Arguing from equations (231) and (232), we have now identified, for the circular plate, the composite term $d\{Y/(1-\sigma^2)\rho\}^{\frac{1}{2}}$,
rather than a single velocity term. Obviously the additional multi-
plier, in this case, must be of the dimensions L^{-2}, in order that a
frequency shall be specified. But, d, the thickness of the plate,
having already been incorporated in the expression, the only linear
quantity remaining is the radius, a. The most 'reasonable' expression for the frequencies of the normal modes is, therefore,

$$f = c\frac{d}{a^2}\sqrt{\frac{Y}{(1-\sigma^2)\rho}} \qquad (233)$$

where c is a pure number, different for the different modes.

In the case of the circular plate, as for the circular membrane,
we distinguish between symmetrical and unsymmetrical modes.
In the symmetrical modes the nodal lines are concentric circles,
simply; in the unsymmetrical modes there is always at least one
nodal line which is a diameter. When the plate is clamped around
the circumference there are $(n-1)$ nodal circles, other than the
boundary, in the nth symmetrical mode. The radius of the single
nodal circle, when $n=2$, is $0.381a$. The value of the constant c in
equation (233) for this normal mode is 1.82, and, for the first
symmetrical normal mode, when there is no nodal circle other
than the boundary, $c=0.471$.

10.4. VIBRATIONS AND WAVES ON LIQUID FILMS

A soap film, supported on a rigid wire frame in such a way that in
its undisturbed state it has no curvature, is in many ways equivalent to a plane membrane under homogeneous tension. The
magnitude of this tension, 2γ (γ being the surface tension) is characteristic of the material of the film: it cannot be changed by
altering the configuration of the wire frame, or by any application
of force across the boundary of the film. In this last respect, of
course, the soap film differs from a solid membrane, but otherwise
the dynamical properties of the two systems are very closely the
same. This fact was demonstrated experimentally by N. W. Robin-
son and R. W. B. Stephens in 1934. Soap films were formed across
a circular opening in a flat plate closing one end of a resonance tube
of variable volume, and, under suitable conditions, when the air
in the tube was maintained in vibration, the film also was set in

vibration in one of its normal modes, and the pattern of nodal lines could be revealed by 'instantaneous' photography. Equation (205) applies in general to this type of motion, and equations (215)-(217) to the specification of the frequencies of those normal modes which involve nodal circles only.

Now let us suppose that we have an 'infinite' soap film formed between parallel wires of indefinite length separated by a distance a. The frequencies of the normal modes in this case are given by

$$f = \frac{n}{2a}\sqrt{\frac{2\gamma}{m}} \qquad (234)$$

where n is any positive integer and m represents the mass per unit surface area of the film. We obtain this result, in the limit, from equation (208), writing $T = 2\gamma$, $a = a$, $b \rightarrow \infty$. Clearly, the normal mode vibrations of such a film may be described as standing plane waves, of wavelength λ given by $\lambda = 2a/n$. We therefore conclude that, for the type of film vibration that we are considering—the membrane-type vibration, plane waves are propagated over the film with phase velocity $\sqrt{2\gamma/m}$. The phase velocity being independent of the wavelength, there is no dispersion for plane waves of this type. Indeed, the two-dimensional wave equation (204) is characterised by the more general solution, that, for distances from a point source significantly greater than λ, a membrane will transmit a disturbance of any wave-form, equally in all directions over the surface, with velocity $\sqrt{T/m}$.

In the last paragraph we emphasised the fact that the conclusions there reached refer specifically to the 'membrane-type' vibrations of the film. The implication was that there are vibrations of other types to which the same conclusions are strictly irrelevant. Let us consider this implication further. We have described certain normal mode vibrations of an infinite film between parallel supporting wires as standing plane waves of wavelength $2a/n$. Fig. 55 represents a section through the film, by a plane at right angles to its length, exhibiting the standing wave profile when $n = 2$—and grossly exaggerating the thickness of the film in the interest of clarity. The previous description, and the figure itself, draw attention to the motion of the film as a whole. In fact, the vibration being defined as membrane-like, it is tacitly assumed that the motion of any individual particle of the liquid film is perpendicular to its

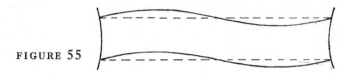

FIGURE 55

undisturbed surface. We may, however, describe this normal mode vibration in an alternative—and more detailed—manner, regarding the film as a volume of liquid 'enclosed' between parallel surfaces. Over each of these surfaces we may consider progressive waves to travel back and forth, being reflected without loss by the supports, thereby constituting separate standing wave patterns on the two 'enclosing' surfaces individually. It is necessary only to stipulate that the wavelengths and amplitudes shall be the same for the two progressive wave trains in question, and to adjust their relative phases appropriately, in order that the resultant wave profile for the film as a whole shall be as illustrated in fig. 55. Thus, if, to begin with, only one of the surfaces of the film were disturbed in this way, and if the film were very thick, individual particle motions in and near the disturbed surface would vary across the breadth of the film in the manner indicated in fig. 56 (*a*). This figure is a reproduction of fig. 31 (see p. 157). Suppose now that the other surface of the film, also, is disturbed, and that the wavelength is the same for the two disturbances. We reflect fig. 56 (*a*) in AB, to take account of the fact that the liquid is 'below' the one surface and 'above' the other, and adjusting the relative phases of the disturbances to suit our purposes, we move the reflected pattern to the right (or the left) through a distance equal to LN ($= \lambda/2$). In this way we have fig. 56 (*b*), and we take this pattern to represent individual particle motions in and near the 'other' surface. Finally, we imagine the thickness of the film to be reduced to the very small value characteristic of the actual situation. Then individual particle motion throughout the whole film is given, to a very good approximation, by the superposition of the motions represented by figs. 56 (*a*) and 56 (*b*), respectively. To this approximation, particle motion is unidirectional throughout, being perpendicular to the surface of the film, and of zero amplitude at L, N and P. To be academically precise (as can be argued on the basis of equations (135)), there will be motion of very small amplitude parallel to the surface of the film, except over its median section, this motion

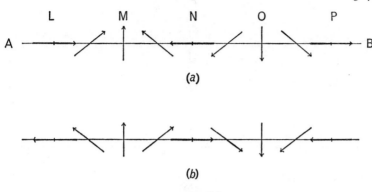

(a)

(b)

FIGURE 56

changing phase through that section, but the essential features of the vibration will be given in terms of the transverse motion, exclusively. Clearly, we have here established the alternative description of the normal mode vibration illustrated in fig. 55—as we set out to do—and in the process we have increased our understanding of the physical phenomenon for which the description has been devised.

The chief merits of the alternative description, however, lie elsewhere. Adopting this point of view, we can envisage another type of normal mode vibration of the liquid film—a type of motion which is not membrane-like, but which involves, rather, the specifically fluid properties of the matter of which the film is constituted.

In fig. 57 (a) the individual particle motions represented in fig. 56 (a) are re-represented, only the whole pattern is moved to the left through a distance equal to LM ($=\lambda/4$). Fig. 57 (b) is obtained by simple reflection of this pattern in AB, without further displacement. Let us proceed, with figs. 57 (a) and 57 (b), as we did previously with figs. 56 (a) and 56 (b): let us combine the two patterns to give the individual particle motion throughout a very thin film vibrating according to a new specification. Strictly, over the median section of such a film—and to a very good approximation elsewhere—particle motion will now be unidirectional and parallel to the surface of the film; it will be of zero amplitude at M, O and Q. Above and below the median section there will be transverse components of motion, of opposite phase (or in opposite

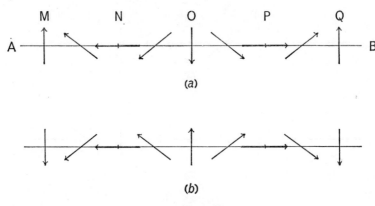

FIGURE 57

sense) on the two sides of that section, but these components will be of very small amplitude, in comparison with the others. Obviously, we have specified a 'new' type of normal mode vibration of a liquid film, and, because in fig. 57 we have a single intermediate node (of longitudinal motion) at O, we are here dealing specifically with the second-order mode, $n = 2$, as in our previous example.

Our next requirement is to construct from fig. 57 the corresponding diagram exhibiting the standing wave profile of the vibrating film, for this mode. In order to do this we have clearly to take account of the transverse components of particle motion (it was unnecessary to take account of the small longitudinal components, in relation to the membrane-type vibrations, when figs. 56 and 55 were in question). A little consideration will show that the displacement profile is in fact as illustrated in fig. 58. We have emphasised the condition that the displacement amplitude is very small indeed (compared with the wavelength) and we should not be surprised to find that there are antinodes of transverse displacement at the supports. As we have already decided, the longitudinal components of motion are of much greater amplitude than the transverse components, and the supports are nodes in respect of the longitudinal motion.

Let us now consider the relation between wavelength and frequency for this new type of vibration, following the method of § 7.4 for that purpose. Fig. 32, on which the argument of the previous section was based, can be taken over without change, as

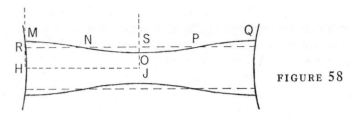

FIGURE 58

referring to one quarter of the complete film illustrated in fig. 58. This reference is made clear by the transference of lettering from the former to the latter figure. The median plane of the vibrating film now has the properties of the bottom, in the problem of the infinite channel. Fig. 58, lettered in this way, is also, at the same time, lettered so as to correspond with fig. 57, from which it was originally derived.

The method of § 7.4 consists in equating two expressions for the energy of vibration—one the straightforward expression for the additional potential energy at the instant of maximum displacement, this instant being taken to be the same for all particles, and the other the expression giving the energy in terms of the frequency and the amplitude. Clearly, in relation to our present problem, we lose nothing in generality if, in this calculation, we confine attention to one quarter of the film as indicated by the section MHJOM of fig. 58. Before we restrict ourselves in this way, however, we have to note that if the displacement pattern is symmetrical across the median plane, as we are supposing it to be, then there is no gravitational term in the expression for the additional potential energy of the whole film. In our previous notation (p. 158), and in respect of a length L of the film, $V_g = 0$. In respect of the additional potential energy 'due to surface tension', we may take over the previous result (equation (138)) without change. We have

$$V_s = \frac{\pi^2}{2} \gamma \frac{LB^2}{\lambda}.$$

In order to calculate the total energy of vibration, we make the justifiable assumptions (see above) that individual particle motion is essentially longitudinal throughout the film as a whole, and that along any normal to the median plane the amplitude of this motion is constant. These are precisely the assumptions that we made (p. 163) when making the corresponding calculation in respect of gravity waves on shallow water. Indeed, we can adopt the result of that calculation (equation (146)), also, noting only that we must substitute $d/2$ for h, if d is to represent the thickness of the film in our present case. We have, therefore,

$$E+V = \frac{\pi^2}{4}f^2L\lambda d\rho A^2.$$

In the two expressions for the energy, λ represents the wavelength and f the frequency of the standing waves, ρ denotes the density and γ the surface tension of the liquid of the film, and A and B are the maximum amplitudes of the longitudinal and transverse components of individual particle motion in the surface of the film. As, before, the ratio B/A is given in terms of equation (145), with $2h=d$. Thus

$$\frac{B}{A} = \frac{\pi d}{\lambda}.$$

Equating the two expressions for the energy, and eliminating the ratio of the amplitudes, we have, finally,

$$f^2 = \frac{2\gamma}{d\rho}\left(\frac{\pi d}{\lambda^2}\right)^2,$$

or, writing $d\rho=m$, where m is the mass per unit area of the film, as in our earlier discussion (p. 315),

$$f = \frac{\pi d}{\lambda^2}\sqrt{\frac{2\gamma}{m}} \tag{235}$$

Let us refer to the type of vibrations with which we are now dealing as 'pulsation-type' vibrations of the film. Then, if we write $2a/n=\lambda$ in equation (234), which refers to the membrane-like vibrations, and so obtain

$$f = \frac{1}{\lambda}\sqrt{\frac{2\gamma}{m}} \tag{236}$$

we may compare the two types of vibration directly in terms of equations (235) and (236).

We note, first of all, that, in all practical situations, $\lambda \gg \pi d$. Thus, for a given wavelength, $f_p \ll f_m$: for an infinite film between parallel supports, and comparing normal modes of the same order, the frequency of pulsation-type vibration is very much smaller than the frequency of membrane-like vibration. Secondly, considering the progressive waves out of which the normal mode vibrations may be regarded as constituted, we have, for the appropriate velocities of phase propagation,

$$v_m = f_m \lambda = \sqrt{\frac{2\gamma}{m}} \tag{237}$$

$$v_p = f_p \lambda = \frac{\pi d}{\lambda} \sqrt{\frac{2\gamma}{m}} \tag{238}$$

As we have previously noted (p. 315), the propagation of membrane-like waves is non-dispersive: equation (238) shows that that of pulsation-type waves is dispersive to a high degree. The group velocity (see § 7.6) of waves of the latter type is twice as great as the phase velocity. On the other hand, in relation to absolute values, the velocity of propagation of pulsation-type waves is very small, in all practical situations. If $\gamma = 25$ dyne cm.$^{-1}$, $m = 5 \times 10^{-3}$ g. cm.$^{-2}$, $d = 5 \times 10^{-3}$ cm., $\lambda = 3 \cdot 14$ cm., then $v_p = 0 \cdot 5$ cm. sec.$^{-1}$.

The possibility of the occurrence of pulsation-type waves on a thin liquid film was pointed out first by G. I. Taylor (see p. 209), in 1959. Taylor also obtained a series of photographs showing clearly that his theoretical predictions were fully vindicated by experiment.

INDEX OF NAMES

x*

INDEX OF SUBJECTS